WHEN ARE WE EVER GOING TO USE THIS STUFF?

COLLEGE MATHEMATICS FOR THE LIBERAL ARTS MAJOR

EIGHTH EDITION

By Jim Matovina and Ronald Yates
COLLEGE OF SOUTHERN NEVADA

cognella®
SAN DIEGO

ACTIVE LEARNING

This book has interactive activities available to complement your reading.

Your instructor may have customized the selection of activities available for your unique course. Please check with your professor to verify whether your class will access this content through the Cognella Active Learning portal (http://active. cognella.com) or through your home learning management system.

Bassim Hamadeh, CEO and Publisher
Kristina Stolte, Senior Field Acquisitions Editor
Carrie Montoya, Manager, Revisions and Author Care
Kaela Martin, Project Editor
Alia Bales, Production Editor
Jess Estrella, Senior Graphic Designer
Alexa Lucido, Licensing Manager
Kenneth Whitney, Interior Designer
Natalie Piccotti, Director of Marketing
Kassie Graves, Vice President of Editorial
Jamie Giganti, Director of Academic Publishing

Cover images:
Copyright © 2016 Depositphotos/toonsteb.
Copyright © 2017 Depositphotos/toonsteb.
Copyright © 2017 Depositphotos/toonsteb.

Printed in the United States of America.

3970 Sorrento Valley Blvd., Ste. 500, San Diego, CA 92121

What students are saying about the textbook and its Cognella Active Learning supplements:

"I'm more of a visual learner, so the video lessons were very helpful."

"The Check Yourself games were good practice. If I did ok in the game I knew I was understanding the concepts."

"The instructional videos this professor made were truly amazing! I loved them!"

"The Check Yourself games provide a fun interactive opportunity to test your knowledge."

"The worksheets and the Check Yourself game exercises kept learning fun and allowed for more practice."

"Each video was helpful, answered my questions, and overall helped me succeed in the class."

"The book breaks down the information in a way that helped me learn."

"Everything was applicable to daily life."

"I found it interesting to see the way the US votes and how different voting results can be calculated."

"I enjoyed reading the history material at the beginning of each chapter."

"The videos were very helpful. All online classes should have videos just like the ones in this course."

"I liked the chapters in the book; they all related to real-life math scenarios."

"The textbook was amazing."

"I liked the interactive games that allowed us to understand the material better."

"I really enjoyed the games that you could play to help you practice the material."

"The Check Yourself games were a great way to test for uncertainties before taking the daily quiz."

"I enjoyed the material on home loans and monthly payments."

"The videos helped me better understand certain topics, and the worksheets prepared me for each quiz."

"I learned more math in this semester than I ever did in high school. I mean I actually learned the type of math that I will be able to use in the future."

"Literally all the assignments contributing to my learning especially the ones that had to do with when you buy a house and the APR on credit cards and compounding interest which is something we use in everyday life and also when we look into buying a home."

"The video lessons always matched the concepts in the book, and they were clear and helpful for me to learn the lessons."

"Math has never been easy for me. This is my second time taking this course. The class this time was so much better because every video lesson matched the book and then the quiz was actually the stuff that we learned. I liked also that a lot of what we learned does apply to real life. This made class more interesting and easier to learn for me."

"The textbook is very user friendly."

"Makes math fun!"

"The videos were simple and clear, very easily understood, particularly when used in conjunction with the textbook."

"The book helped me a lot, was interesting, and was one of the first times in my entire college career that I was glad I bought it."

"There are many ways to practice problems and learn the information. The videos are very helpful."

"The videos were a great accompaniment to the textbook online."

"The videos were extremely helpful when it came to solidifying my understanding of the textbook."

"The way the concepts were presented through videos and the book made it much easier for me to understand math."

"I have never learned math so quickly and efficiently, to the extent where I actually remember."

"The videos were to the point and explained in a way the average person can understand, unlike many other courses I have taken in the past."

"I actually learned a lot about math. I can now really see just how much math is used on just about an everyday basis."

"The PowerPoints and games are very helpful."

"We actually learn how to apply this math, when this math will be applied, and why it is used in real life. Therefore, instead of just memorizing formulas we actually know what each variable in a formula means and why it is arranged a certain way."

"The book is written in an easy to understand language and is filled with helpful examples. As someone who is not very good at math, having so many opportunities to practice examples really helped me understand the material."

"The book was well written and did not overwhelm me with things I did not need to know. It was short and to the point, which helped me stay on task."

"This is the best textbook I've ever used. I appreciated the easy and informal language used to explain things in a way that was very easy to understand. Teaches you about concepts related to life."

"The instructional videos were an awesome way to learn. As a visual learner, I enjoyed the ability to go back and re-watch the videos if I felt like I wasn't grasping the concept of a particular item well enough."

"The videos presented are very clear and concise."

"I really liked the videos in the modules. Everything was explained really well, and I didn't feel bored listening to them."

"The textbook was amazing!"

"The video lessons were great and the games we got to play to practice were always fun."

"The videos and PowerPoints really help reinforce the information."

"The PowerPoints and the games were really helpful and fun."

"Each module had a teaching portion where the instructor gave lectures of each chapter and comprehensive activities to make sure that you understand the material."

"The video lessons thoroughly go over everything in great detail."

"The video lectures are very thorough and easily understandable."

"I greatly benefitted from the practice worksheets, the games, and the videos."

"The textbook is clearly written and helpful, the online exercises reinforce what's learned, and it's presented in a way that makes it accessible and applicable to the 'real world.' I learned something from EVERY exercise in this class."

"The study tools definitely made a difference for me. I am a hands-on learner, so I was initially worried about taking online classes but the videos, PowerPoints, and games gave better understanding to me after I read the book."

"The videos, Check Yourself games, and the PowerPoint presentations were all incredibly helpful to my understanding of the material."

"The book tells you exactly what you need to know and lays it out in an easy to understand manner. The video lessons laid a foundation for what we were learning."

"I really enjoyed playing the games when practicing the lessons. I found them very helpful."

"The book is great. It makes math easier to understand."

"The online components that matched the book were excellent."

"The textbook and activities online were a great help because I was actually able to understand the material and get it."

"The book was great and much easier to understand than other math classes I have taken in the past."

"The textbook was clear and concise, speaking in language that I, an amateur at math, could understand easily. The video lessons were helpful with the subjects I felt unsure about."

"The book was easy to follow and made learning easy."

"The videos, PowerPoints, and exercises in conjunction with the text made information a lot easier to understand and grasp."

"The videos were great, and further detail was given in the PowerPoint presentations. In conjunction with the text it made even the most difficult concepts understandable."

"The videos were great. The book helped reinforce all the information and the games were really fun and a great learning tool."

"I really liked the Check Yourself games! Those were extremely helpful and fun in practicing different math problems."

"The interactive games actually make the math easy to learn."

"The lecture videos and the review games helped me to understand the material."

"The textbook is well thought out especially for those not pursuing a degree in mathematics."

"The section videos were extremely helpful in understanding the material."

"I really enjoyed the videos and the games."

"I really liked the video lessons. They were always very helpful, to the point, and easy to understand."

"All the assignments cohesively applied to the chapters we covered in the textbook and I felt more than prepared for my quizzes and exams."

"I think the book is phenomenal. Really helps teach you when and where to use mathematics in the real world."

"The video lessons gave an easy and clear understanding of what needed to be learned."

"The games and videos for the class helped substantially, along with the practice worksheets."

"I learned a lot from every single lesson. I liked that in every chapter we had a small history lesson that related to or was the founding story on the subject we were going to learn."

"The book made learning easy and actually fun."

"The book is clear and understandable."

"The book was amazing in that all the material was so easy to understand. It's as if they took a survey of all the things people wished were different about their previous math books and applied them to this book."

"The video lessons were clearly explained and made the material accessible. Having review games available before each quiz provided a good way to review relevant information and let me know what sort of things to expect on the quizzes."

"Math is a tough subject for me, and I found all of the learning material to be extremely useful in my learning process."

"The short video lessons are very helpful with the comprehension of new concepts."

"I really enjoyed the videos that were included. They made a subject that I struggle in easy to learn and really enjoyable."

"The how-to videos made it feel like I was being taught step-by-step. The book was interesting because it gave examples on how the lessons being taught were applied to real-life scenarios."

"The PowerPoints and lesson videos are amazing! They perfectly explain everything in crystal clear detail."

"The online videos were awesome. They really reinforced what the book was about."

"The textbook is very well organized and easy to understand."

"The textbook was really well done, and all of the material online made learning very easy."

"The person in the videos has a way about them that makes the math problems easy to learn and not seem so intimidating."

"In the videos, not only would the teacher provide information/directions for that module, but he would also work out the problems to show you exactly how to do it. It was really easy to understand, and made the work much more enjoyable."

"The book is very easy to read and understand."

"The videos and check yourself games were enormously helpful."

"The PowerPoints, videos, and book all played a significant role in my learning. It allowed you to understand the concepts from a variety of sources."

"The brief history sections were wonderful to help get some background information about what we were going to learn. I really liked how the text would use layman's terms to better explain things. The book explained even the more complex things in an understandable way."

CONTENTS

PREFACE

This book represents material that has been compiled over a couple of decades. At the College of Southern Nevada, Professors Jim Matovina and Ronnie Yates have been teaching liberal arts math classes, both online and in the classroom, regularly since 1996. They have written and shared their materials with each other and their colleagues over the years, and those collaborations ultimately led to the creation of this book.

Changes to the Eighth Edition

With the emerging national trend of colleges reducing or eliminating prerequisite courses, instructors are now tasked with finding the best way to help students who may be underprepared. With that in mind, we have woven in a significant number of "Review" passages throughout the new edition. Students who are adept in that material should feel free to skip those passages, while those who can benefit from a review may find them helpfully placed.

That said, also ...

- We added a handful of new historical topics into a few of the chapters, so that there are now four of these readings in each chapter. We hope those are as much fun for you to read as they were for us to write.

- We renamed a couple of sections and updated the material to be more current in nature. For example, we added passages on payday loans and leases in the Consumer Math chapter, while eliminating the material on buying points on a mortgage and changing the three "Mortgage Guidelines" into two "Housing Recommendations." In the Statistics chapter we stressed the proper construction and uses of graphs.

- We added a few alternate perspectives on some of the material. These are referred to as, "From a Different Point of View." Some students may prefer the alternate approaches instead of the original presentations.

- We significantly rearranged the material in the Geometry chapter. This included moving the material on polygons to Section 5.2 from 5.3, pushing the material on similar triangles from Section 5.2 to 5.3, and grouping it with the material on circles, which was previously in Section 5.5. Section 5.5 now deals exclusively with trigonometry, which was previously in Section 5.2. The new order seems a bit more logical.

- As the material evolved over two decades, different images were made at different times by different people using different software. Then, as edits were made, those old images were stretched and shrunk to fit the various pages. Understandably, that led to some inconsistencies and distortions in those images. In this edition, all of the graphs, figures, and illustrations throughout the book were remade so they are also consistent in size and style and are no longer pixilated.

- In that same vein, all of the equations were remade so they are now consistent in font and size.

- Nearly all of the photo images appearing in the book were updated or replaced with stock photos found at Deposit Photos.

- Last, but certainly not least, we went through the material line by line, improving our grammar and eliminating a handful of typos that somehow remained. That was a bit embarrassing.

To the Instructor

This work was originally created as a textbook for MATH 120 at the College of Southern Nevada, which is commonly referred to as "Liberal Arts Math." It is fun to teach, and as a terminal course, it is typically taken by students who will fulfill the math requirement for their degree with this class. Since it does not serve as a prerequisite to other courses, instructors are typically given a fair amount of flexibility regarding content and methodology, and that is reflected in the survey nature of the course.

When working through the material covered in this book, practical applications should be stressed over symbolic manipulations, but that does not mean you should totally discount the algebra. Instead, make every effort to help the students learn where, when, why, and how each facet of the mathematics involved will help them in their lives.

To the Student

Some time ago, a class was presented with the following problem:

> A farmer looks across his field and sees pigs and chickens. If he counts 42 heads and 106 feet, how many pigs are in the field?

One student, instead of answering the question, sent an e-mail to their instructor stating, "I feel this question is unfair and misleading because pigs do not have feet. They have hooves."

While we still find that story to be hilarious, there is an important point to be made from it.

In this class, and in all math classes for that matter, your instructor is not trying to trick you. Although you will undoubtedly be presented with some challenging questions, be assured they are there to make you apply and extend both your knowledge and your thought processes. Please don't waste time and effort looking for technicalities that might invalidate a question. Instead, take each question at face value, and spend your time trying to solve it.

We completely understand that students taking this course are often Liberal Arts majors or are students who need only this math class in order to graduate. We also recognize that in many cases, students wonder why they need to take this class in the first place. All of us—yes, even your instructor—have sat in a math class at one time or another and thought, "When are we ever going to use this stuff?" Well, this is the class where we tell you.

Acknowledgments

We would like to thank the following individuals for their diligent efforts in reviewing and contributing to the material that is included in the book:

Denny Burzynski, Dennis Donohue, Billy Duke, Bill Frost, Dr. Michael Greenwich, Eric Hutchinson, Dr. Joel Johnson, Garry Knight, Andrzej Lenard, James Lee, Alok Pandey, Jonathan Pearsall, Kala Sathappan, Dr. Ingrid Stewart, Patrick Villa, Dr. Tityik Wong, and all the WONDERFUL people at Cognella.

Special gratitude is extended to all the students and instructors who reported errors in previous editions and made suggestions for improvement. Without a doubt, many people were instrumental in the development of this textbook, and we very much appreciate all of their input.

Jim and Ronnie

CONSUMER

MATH

Money. It controls nearly everything in the world. Those who have it are often seen as more powerful and influential than those who do not. So, having a basic understanding of how money grows and is (or should be) spent is essential.

Understanding percentages is key to understanding how money works. Budgets are based on different percents of available money being allocated in specific ways. Sale discounts and taxes are based on the percent of cost of the items at hand. Credit cards and loans operate on interest rates, which—you guessed it—are given in percents.

The single largest purchase most people will make in a lifetime is a home. A basic understanding of mortgages and finance charges will make you a much wiser homebuyer and could easily save you tens of thousands of dollars over a 20- to 30-year period.

We could go on, but you get the picture.

Image 1.0.1

1.1 On the Shoulders of Giants: Biographies and Historical References

Historical References in This Book

One of the most prolific mathematicians in history, **Sir Isaac Newton** is often credited with the quotation, "If I have seen further than others, it is by standing on the shoulders of giants." Throughout this book, you will find many historical references. These fascinating glimpses into the past are there to add a bit of a human element to the material. Essentially, if you can appreciate some of the people and aspects that led to the development of the mathematics at hand, you can better understand the reasoning behind its existence.

For Consumer Math ...

As a signer of both the Declaration of Independence and the Constitution, **Benjamin Franklin** is considered one of the Founding Fathers of the United States of America. His pervasive influence in the early history of the US has led to his being jocularly called "the only President of the United States who was never President of the United States." Franklin's likeness is ubiquitous, and, primarily due to his profound understanding of the power of compound interest and constant advocacy for paper currency, has adorned all the variations of American $100 bills since 1928.

Created by nineteenth-century *Wall Street Journal* editor **Charles Dow**, the **Dow Jones Industrial Average (DJIA)** is one of several stock market indices. It is an index that shows how certain stocks have traded. Dow compiled the index to gauge the performance of the industrial sector of the American stock market and, thus, the nation's economy.

On December 10, 2008, **Bernard "Bernie" Madoff**, a former chairman of the NASDAQ Stock Market, allegedly told his sons the asset management arm of his firm was a massive **Ponzi scheme**—as he put it, "one big lie." The following day, he was arrested and charged with a single count of securities fraud, but one that accused him of milking his investors out of $50 billion. The 71-year-old Madoff was eventually sentenced to 150 years in prison.

A Brief History of Money

Compensating others for goods and services is not a new concept, but the types of compensation have changed dramatically since the dawn of time. Thousands of years before the use of paper currency, trading farm animals for vegetables and grains was part of the bartering process needed for everyday life. As people explored and moved around the Earth, the need for portable, consistent, and stable currencies became a necessity. And, as currencies evolved, so did fraud.

Early forms of nonperishable currencies included things like beads, shells, and fur. Even though metal currencies can be traced to the ancient Babylonian and Chinese empires, they were wildly inconsistent in appearance and, more importantly, value. Certified and standardized coins made of precious metals began appearing in Europe and Asia in the seventh century BC, but, unfortunately, many people would accept the metal coins without checking their weight. This commonly led to unscrupulous individuals **clipping** the coins by shaving off small bits from the edges and passing them off for face value. This was eventually combatted by **milling** the coins, which involves making small grooves around the outer edge of the coins, much like what we see with today's quarters.

Image 1.1.1

Since coins in large quantities are heavy and impractical for travelers to carry, banks and governments began to store gold and issue paper banknotes at varying amounts against the value of their gold, and even on their own credibility. After the American Revolutionary War, the leaders of the new country saw the need for a monetary system and passed the **Coinage Act of 1792**, which named the dollar the official currency of the United States. In the 1860s, **President Lincoln** authorized the printing of **greenbacks**—paper notes printed with green ink on the back—by the US Treasury to help finance the Civil War. The original $1 greenback included the portrait of then Secretary of the Treasury, **Salmon P. Chase**, while President Lincoln adorned the $10 note. **Alexander Hamilton**, who was the nation's first Secretary of the Treasury, appeared on the $2, $5 and $50 greenbacks. In 1929, in an effort to reduce **counterfeiting**, the US started using standardized designs for all of its banknotes, and in the 1990s, security threads and microprinting made it difficult for copiers and printers to reproduce bills. Since 2003, redesigns of the bills in circulation have included threads that glow when exposed to UV light, two-sided watermarks of the portraits, and color-shifting numbers in the corners of the bills.

Modern cryptocurrencies, such as **Bitcoin**, are not backed by gold or any other commodity; they are managed by complex codes of encrypted data called **blockchain**. Basically, blockchain is a digital public ledger that stores identical logistical information in millions of blocks housed on tens of thousands of computers all over the world. Those blocks are then chained together, and since it is not possible to alter the same information in millions of independent blocks, the possibility of fraud is virtually eliminated. To prevent the overflooding and devaluing of the cryptocurrency market, the underlying source code limits the number of currency units that can exist. For example, the total number of bitcoin units is limited to 21 million. Cryptocurrencies only have value because someone is willing to accept them as currency, and as more people and businesses accept them, each unit becomes more desirable and, hence, more valuable.

Image 1.1.2

Benjamin Franklin

Throughout his career, **Benjamin Franklin** was an advocate for paper money. He published *A Modest Enquiry into the Nature and Necessity of a Paper Currency* in 1729, and even printed money using his own press. In 1736, he printed a new currency for New Jersey based on innovative anti-counterfeiting techniques, which he had devised. Franklin was also influential in the more restrained and thus successful monetary experiments in the Middle Colonies, which stopped deflation without causing excessive inflation.

Image 1.1.3: Benjamin Franklin

In 1785, French mathematician Charles-Joseph Mathon de la Cour wrote a parody of Franklin's **Poor Richard's Almanack** called *Fortunate Richard*. Mocking the unbearable spirit of American optimism represented by Franklin, Mathon de la Cour wrote that Fortunate Richard would bequeath a small sum of money, but stipulate it had to mature over 500 years. Franklin thanked the Frenchman for the great idea and, in his 1789 will, bequeathed £1,000 (about $4,400 at the time) to the inhabitants of Boston and Philadelphia by placing the monies in the respective city trusts and directing that it be allowed to accumulate interest for at least 100 years. By 1940, more than $2,000,000 had accumulated in Franklin's Philadelphia trust, and by 1990, the money had been used for many mortgage loans for local residents and scholarships for Philadelphia-area high school students. Franklin's Boston trust grew to $5,000,000 and was used to establish a trade school that became the Franklin Institute of Boston.

The Dow Jones Industrial Average (DJIA)

Charles Dow compiled his **DJIA** index to gauge the performance of the industrial sector of the American stock market. It is the second-oldest US market index, after the Dow Jones Transportation Average, which Dow also created. When it was first published on May 26, 1896, the DJIA index stood at 40.94. It was computed as a direct average by adding up stock prices of its components and dividing by the number of stocks in the index. The index hit its all-time low of 28.48 during the summer of 1896. Then, the DJIA averaged a gain of 5.3% compounded annually for the twentieth century; a period **Warren Buffett** called "a wonderful century" when he calculated that to achieve that return again, the index would need to reach nearly 2,000,000 by 2100. Many of the biggest percentage price moves in the DJIA occurred early in its history, as the blossoming industrial economy matured.

The original DJIA was just that—the average of the prices of the stocks in the index. The current average is computed from the stock prices of 30 of the largest and most widely held public companies in the United States, but the divisor in the average is no longer the number of components in the index. Instead, the divisor, called the DJIA divisor, gets adjusted in case of splits, spinoffs, or similar structural changes to ensure that such events do not in themselves alter the numerical value of the DJIA. Since the initial divisor was the number of component companies, the DJIA was, at first, a simple arithmetic average. The present divisor, after many adjustments, is much less than 1, which means the DJIA, itself, is actually larger than the sum of the prices of the components. At the end of June 2018, the value of the DJIA Divisor was 0.1474807199, and the updated value is regularly published in the **Wall Street Journal.**

Charles Ponzi and His Scheme

A **Ponzi scheme** is a fraudulent investment operation that pays returns to investors from their own money or money paid by subsequent investors, rather than from profit. Without significant information about the investment, only a few investors are initially tempted, and usually for small sums. After a short period (typically around 30 days), the investor receives the original capital plus a large return (usually 20% or more). At this point, the investor will have more incentive to put in additional money and as word begins to spread, other investors grab the "opportunity" to participate, with the promise of extraordinary returns. The catch is that, at some point, the promoters will likely vanish, taking all the remaining investment money with them.

This type of scheme is named after **Charles Ponzi**, who became notorious for using the technique after emigrating from Italy to the United States in 1903. Ponzi did not invent the scheme, but his operation took in so much money that it was the first to become known throughout the United States. In 1920, Ponzi went from anonymity to a well-known Boston millionaire in just six months. He canvassed friends and associates to back his scheme, offering a 50% return on investment in 45 days. About 40,000 people invested roughly $15 million

Image 1.1.4: Charles Ponzi

altogether; in the end, only a third of that money was returned to them. People were mortgaging their homes and investing their life savings, and most chose to reinvest, rather than take their profits. Ponzi was bringing in cash at a fantastic rate, but the simplest financial analysis would have shown that the operation was running at a large loss. As long as money kept flowing in, existing investors could be paid with the new money. In fact, new money was the only source Ponzi had to pay off those investors, as he made no effort to generate legitimate profits.

Ponzi lived luxuriously. He bought a mansion in Lexington, Massachusetts, with air conditioning and a heated swimming pool (remember, this was the 1920s), and brought his mother from Italy in a first-class stateroom on an ocean liner. As newspaper stories began to cause a panic run on his Securities Exchange Company, Ponzi paid out $2 million in three days to a wild crowd that had gathered outside his office. He would even canvass the crowd, passing out coffee and donuts, all while cheerfully telling them they had nothing to worry about. Many people actually changed their minds and left their money with him.

On November 1, 1920, Ponzi pleaded guilty to a single count of mail fraud before Judge Clarence Hale, who declared before sentencing, "Here was a man with all the duties of seeking large money. He concocted a scheme, which, on his counsel's admission, did defraud men and women. It will not do to have the world understand that such a scheme as that can be carried out ... without receiving substantial punishment." Ponzi was sentenced to five years in federal prison, and after three and a half years, he was released to face 22 Massachusetts State charges of larceny. He was eventually released in 1934 following other indictments and, since he hadn't gained American citizenship, was deported back to Italy. His charismatic confidence had faded, and when he left the prison gates, an angry crowd met him. He told reporters before he left, "I went looking for trouble, and I found it."

References

Benjamin Franklin Institute of Technology. "Benjamin Franklin's Legacy." http://www.bfit.edu/the-college/benjamin-franklin-s-living-legacy-/benjamin-franklin-s-legacy.

Buffet, W. "Letter to Shareholders." 2007. http://www.berkshirehathaway.com/letters/2007ltr.pdf.

Darby, M. "In Ponzi We Trust." *Smithsonian Magazine*, December 1998. http://www.smithsonianmag.com/people-places/in-ponzi-we-trust-64016168/?no-ist=&page=1.

DeLeon, C. "Divvying Up Ben: Let's Try for 200 More." *Philadelphia Enquirer*, February 7, 1993.

Dow Jones Indexes. http://www.djindexes.com.

Encyclopedia Britannica, Money. https://www.britannica.com/topic/money

Investopedia, *Blockchain, Explained.* https://www.investopedia.com/terms/b/blockchain.asp

Investopedia, *Bitcoin.* https://www.investopedia.com/terms/b/bitcoin.asp

Nash, J. R. *Bloodletters and Badmen: A Narrative Encyclopedia of American Criminals from the Pilgrims to the Present.* New York, NY: M. Evans & Company, 1995.

NOVA | PBS. *The History of Money.* https://www.pbs.org/wgbh/nova/article/history-money/

"Ponzi Arrested." *New York Times*, August 13, 1920.

State of Wisconsin Department of Financial Institutions. *History of Money.* https://www.wdfi.org/ymm/kids/history/

Sullivan, A. and S. Sheffrin. *Economics: Principles in Action.* Upper Saddle River, NJ: Prentice Hall, 2003.

US Currency Education Program. https://www.uscurrency.gov/history

World Book Encyclopedia, 1978 ed., s.v. "Dow Jones Averages."

World Book Encyclopedia, 1978 ed., s.v. "Franklin, Benjamin."

Zuckoff, M. "What Madoff Could Learn from Ponzi." *Fortune*, January 13, 2009. http://archive.fortune.com/2009/01/13/news/newsmakers/ponzi.jail.fortune/index.htm?postversion=2009011312

1.2 For Sale: Percents, Markup, and Markdown

When finding a percent of an amount or an amount that is a percent of a quantity, most people know they either need to multiply or divide by the decimal value of the percent. Unfortunately, most people can't quite remember *when* to multiply and *when* to divide. Fortunately, we can reduce all of those problems to the same equation and allow our algebra skills to tell us what to do.

Review: Place Values and Rounding

Before we dive into the material for this course, let's take a few minutes to review **place value**, and the correct way to round numbers.

When writing a number that includes a decimal, there are three distinct parts: The whole number part, the decimal point, and the decimal part.

Place values extend forever in both directions, but we will concentrate on the places close to the decimal point. A place-value chart can be helpful when determining the proper decimal name.

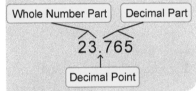

Figure 1.2.1   Number Parts

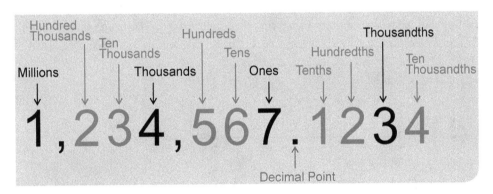

Figure 1.2.2   Place Values

Rounding always involves a specified place value, and we *must* have a place value to round to. Without a specified place value, it is incorrect to assume one out of convenience.

> If there is no directive to round to a specified place value, it is incorrect to do so. If no place value is mentioned, we cannot assume one out of convenience.

The formal procedure for the traditional rounding of a number is as follows.

1. First, determine the round-off digit, which is the digit in the specified place value column.

2. If the first digit to the right of the round-off digit is less than 5, do not change the round-off digit, but delete all the remaining digits to its right. If you are rounding to a whole number, such

as tens or hundreds, all the digits between the round-off digit and the decimal point should become zeros, and no digits will appear after the decimal point.

3. If the first digit to the right of the round-off digit is 5 or more, increase the round-off digit by 1, and delete all the remaining digits to its right. Again, if you are rounding to a non-decimal number, such as tens or hundreds, all the digits between the round-off digit and the decimal point should become zeros, and no digits will appear after the decimal point.

4. For decimals, double-check to make sure the right-most digit of the decimal falls in the place value column to which you were directed to round, and that there are no other digits to its right.

Don't Get Trapped Memorizing Instructions

We cannot let ourselves get trapped in a process of trying to memorize a set of instructions. Yes, if followed correctly, instructions can be quite valuable, but when we blindly try to stick to a formal, rigid process, we often lose sight of logic and reason. For many students, rounding numbers is a classic example of this.

If, for a second, we set aside the traditional process outlined on the previous page and understand that "rounding a number to the tenth" can be thought of as "identifying the number ending in the tenths place that is closest to the given number," we can gain a better understanding of what it means to round.

For example, if we are tasked with rounding 14.68 to the nearest tenth, we could begin by identifying the consecutive numbers ending in the tenths place (remember, for decimals, the right-most digit of the answer must fall in the stated place value) that are immediately less than and immediately greater than 14.68. Those two numbers are 14.6 and 14.7. Then, we can simply ask ourselves, "Is 14.68 closer to 14.6 or 14.7?"

Looking at a number line ...

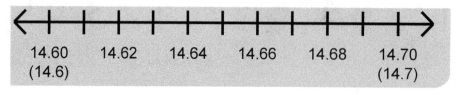

14.60   14.62   14.64   14.66   14.68   14.70
(14.6)   (14.7)

Figure 1.2.3   Number Line

Treating 14.6 and 14.7 as 14.60 and 14.70, respectively, makes it easy to see 14.68 is closer to 14.7, than it is to 14.6. The important point to remember is the last digit of our rounded answer *must* fall in the place value to which we are rounding. In other words, the answer needs to be 14.7 and not 14.70.

When rounding a decimal, the last digit of the rounded value *must* fall in the place value to which we are rounding.

EXAMPLE 1:

Round 103.4736999 to the nearest tenth, hundredth, and then hundred.

SOLUTIONS: For the tenth, begin by recognizing the four is in the tenths place. The seven immediately to its right indicates we are to change the four to a five and remove the rest of the digits. Thus, rounded to the tenth, the value is 103.5.

For the hundredth, begin by recognizing the seven is in the hundredths place. The three immediately to its right indicates we are not to change the seven and remove the rest of the digits. Thus, rounded to the hundredth, the value is 103.47.

For the hundred, begin by recognizing the one is in the hundreds place. The zero immediately to its right indicates we are not to change the one, and all the digits between the one and the decimal point are to become zeros. Thus, rounded to the hundred, the value is 100.

When to Round and When *Not* to Round

Throughout this book and, for that matter, all of mathematics, we will see many directives to "round to the nearest hundredth (or other place value), when necessary." A very important part of that directive is the "when necessary" part. How are we supposed to know when rounding is necessary and when it isn't?

First, if we are given the absolute directive, "round to the nearest hundredth" (or a different place value) we *must* round to that specified place value. Keep in mind, when we are working with money, the underlying—but often unstated—directive is to round to the nearest cent (hundredth).

Then we run into the "when necessary" scenario. This only applies to **non-terminating decimals**. If the decimal terminates, there usually is no need to round it. In fact, if we round it, our answer is less accurate than it could be. In other words, $1/32 = 0.03125$, exactly. If we round that decimal to the hundredth, to 0.03, the value is no longer equal to $1/32$. Sure, it's close, but it is *not* equal to $1/32$. 0.03 is actually $3/100$.

Non-terminating decimals are the ones to which we need to pay attention. If we dismiss the use of the "..." (called an **ellipsis**), it is impossible to write $1/3$ as a decimal. $0.33 = 33/100$, but $1/3 = 33/99$. $0.33333 = 33333/100000$, but $1/3 = 33333/99999$. 0.333333333333333 is closer, but as soon as we stop writing 3s, we no longer have exactly $1/3$. Thus, in order to save us from writing 3s indefinitely, it is necessary to round it to a specified place value.

Keep in mind; a calculator does not display an ellipsis. If you change $5/9$ to a decimal, the calculator may display the "final" digit as a 6: 0.555555556. This is because a calculator will typically round to the number of digits it can display on its screen. Some calculators may just truncate the decimal to the screen size, and others may actually hold an extra three to five digits of the decimal in memory without displaying them—this is the smarter version, since a greater amount of precision leads to a greater degree of accuracy.

If the decimal terminates within three or four decimal places, there may be no need to round. If it extends past four decimal places and we have a specified place value to which to round, then go ahead and do so. Remember, though, there must be a designated place value.

One of the few exceptions to this rule involves money. As mentioned earlier, if money is involved, we should always round to the nearest cent (hundredth) unless we are specifically told to round to a less precise value, such as the nearest dollar.

Review: Converting Between Decimals and Percents

To begin with, let's consider the meaning of the word **percent**. In mathematics, the prefix "per" means "divide by." For example, when computing miles per hour, we would take the miles and divide by the hours. The term "cent" corresponds to the value "one hundred." There are 100 years in a century, and 100 cents in a dollar. Thus, the term "percent" literally means "divide by 100." So, 11% means "11 divided by 100," which can be written as 0.11. Here we can see that converting a percent to a decimal is done by dividing by 100. Going the other direction, converting a decimal to a percent, we need to *multiply* by 100.

When converting between decimals and percents, students quickly learn the shortcut of moving the decimal point two places. This method can certainly work, but it is important to remember the correct *direction* in which to move that decimal point. To help with this, pause for a second and consider a simple example, like the fact that 75% = 0.75. Keeping an example like this in mind will make it much easier to remember the direction the decimal point must move when converting percents to decimals, and vice versa.

EXAMPLE 2:

Write each of the following as a decimal:

    a. 55%

    b. 5%

    c. 555%

SOLUTIONS:

    a. 0.55

    b. 0.05

    c. 5.55

EXAMPLE 3:

Write each of the following as a percent:

    a. 0.77

    b. 0.07

    c. 77.7

SOLUTIONS:

    a. 77%

    b. 7%

    c. 7770%

Identifying the Parts in a Percent Problem

In simple percent problems, there is a percent, a base, and an amount. The numeric value of the **percent, p,** is easy to spot—it has a % immediately after it, and for calculation purposes, the percent must be changed to its decimal equivalent. The **base, b,** is the initial quantity and is associated with the word "of." The **amount, a,** is the part being compared with the initial quantity and is associated with the word "is."

EXAMPLE 4:

Identify the amount, base, and percent in each of the following statements. If a specific value is unknown, use the variable **p, b,** and **a** for the percent, base, and amount, respectively. Do not solve the statements; just identify the parts.

   a. 65% of 820 is 533

   b. What is 35% of 95?

   c. 50 is what percent of 250?

SOLUTIONS:

   a. Percent = 65%, Base = 820, Amount = 533

   b. Percent = 35%, Base = 95, Amount = a

   c. Percent = p, Base = 250, Amount = 50

Solving Percent Problems Using an Equation

Always begin by identifying the percent, base, and amount in the problem, and remember that, usually, one of them is unknown. If we are given a percent in the problem, make sure to change it to a decimal for the calculation. If we are finding a percent, the calculation will result in a decimal, and we must change it to a percent for our answer.

Once we have identified the parts, we then need to recognize the basic form of the **percent equation.** An amount, **a,** is some percent, **p,** of a base, **b.** In other words, $a = pb$, where **p** is the decimal form of the percent.

After the equation is set up, if the **a** is the only unknown, find its value by simplifying the other side of the equation (by multiplying the values of **p** and **b**). If the unknown quantity is **b,** divide both sides of the equation by the value of **p.** Likewise, if the unknown quantity is **p,** divide both sides of the equation by the value of **b.**

EXAMPLE 5:

What is 9% of 65?

SOLUTION: The percent is 9%, so we will use $p = 0.09$. 65 is the base, so $b = 65$. Thus, the unknown quantity is a.

   $a = 0.09(65) = 5.85$

EXAMPLE 6:

72 is what percent of 900?

SOLUTION: 900 is the base, and 72 is the amount. So, b = 900, and a = 72. The unknown quantity is the percent.

72 = p(900)
72/900 = p
So, p = 0.08, which is 8%.

From a Different Point of View: What, Is, and Of

Another approach for solving a percent problem involves translating the information we are given into the terms within an equation. A percent problem will typically involve three parts, of which we will know two. The piece we are looking for, the "what," will be the unknown in our equation, which we can represent with "x." The term "is" will be written as the equals sign, and the term "of" represents multiplication. If we are given a percent in the problem, change it to a decimal for the calculation. If the problem asks us to find a percent, the calculation will result in a decimal, and we must change it to a percent for our answer. In short, translate the given information into an equation, and then solve for the missing piece.

EXAMPLE 7:

What is 9% of 65?

SOLUTION: The term "what" will be our x. The term "is" will be our equals sign, and the term "of" represents multiplication. Translating into an equation, this gives us:

x = 0.09(65)
x = 5.85

EXAMPLE 8:

72 is what percent of 900?

SOLUTION: Using the same approach for translating, we have:

72 = x(900)
72/900 = x

So, x = 0.08, and since this problem asks us to find the percent, we must remember to write our answer as 8%.

General Applied Problems Involving Percents

To solve any application problem involving a percent, a good strategy is to rewrite the problem into the form "**a** is **p**% of **b**." Remember, we should begin by clearly identifying the amount, base, and percent. Also, if we are directed to round the answer, we should not do so until the very end.

EXAMPLE 9:

Of the 130 flights at Orange County Airport yesterday, only 105 of them were on time. What percent of the flights were on time? Round to the nearest tenth of a percent.

Image 1.2.1

SOLUTION: First, identify the base is 130 flights, and 105 is the amount we are comparing to the base. The percent is the unknown.

Then, we should recognize the simplified form of this question is "105 is what percent of 130?" This gives us the equation: $105 = p(130)$.

$$105 = p(130)$$
$$105/130 = p = 0.8076923\ldots = 80.76923\ldots\%$$

Rounding to the tenth of a percent, we state, "80.8% of the flights were on time.

Sales Tax and Discounts

Sales tax is computed as a percent of the cost of a taxable item. Then, when we find the dollar amount of the tax, we add it to the cost. **Discounts** are also computed as a percent of the original price of an item. For discounts, however, when we find the dollar amount of the discount, we deduct it from the original price. If both a discount and sales tax are involved in the same computation, we need to know which one gets applied first. In most cases, the sales tax gets computed on the discounted price. However, in some cases, we may get a discount, but will still be responsible for the taxes based on the original price—it all depends on the wording used in the situation. The latter of those two situations is usually referred to as a **rebate**. Often, rebates are given as dollar amounts, instead of percents.

We also need to make sure we answer the question being asked. If the question asks for the tax, we should *only* give the tax as our answer. Likewise, if the question asks for the discount, we should *only* give the amount of the discount as our answer. If the question asks for a sales price, then we need to be sure to subtract the discount from the posted price. If the question asks for the total cost of an object, we need to be sure to add the tax to the item's price.

Finally, when working with money, unless directed otherwise, we should always round to the nearest cent (hundredth). Think about it. When we fill our gas tank and the total is $23.01, we have to pay that penny. Likewise, if your paycheck is for $543.13, you don't just get $543.

Unless specifically directed to do otherwise, always round answers involving money to the nearest cent (hundredth).

EXAMPLE 10:

Find the total cost of a $125 TV if the sales tax rate is 7.25%.

SOLUTION: The base cost of the TV is $125, so b = 125. As a decimal, p = 0.0725.

a = 0.0725(125) = 9.0625. So, to the cent, the sales tax is $9.06.

That makes the total cost of the TV $125 + $9.06 = $134.06.

EXAMPLE 11:

A pair of shoes is on sale for 20% off. If the original price of the shoes was $65, what is the sale price?

SOLUTION: The base cost of the shoes is $65, so b = 65. p = 0.20.

a = 0.2(65) = 13. So, the discount is $13.

This makes the sale price of the shoes

$65 − $13 = $52.

Image 1.2.2

By the way, in the above example, 20% is a nice number to work with. We can quickly see 10% of $65 is $6.50. Twenty percent is twice as much, so by a quick inspection, 20% of $65 is 2 × $6.50, or $13. If we spot a quick inspection calculation like the one above, we definitely have a better understanding of the material at hand. If we cannot spot something like this, we can just resort to the computation shown in the example.

Percent Increase or Decrease

Another type of percent calculation we often see involves the change in percent. When studying information, it is often valuable to examine absolute changes in amounts over a period of time, as well as relative changes with respect to those amounts. The total amount something changes may be obvious, but examining the **change in percent** can often give a better overall picture of a situation or set of data.

Absolute change is simply the difference between the beginning and ending amounts.

Percent change, indicated with the notation Δ%, is found by the formula:

$$\Delta\% = \left(\frac{\text{Ending Amount} - \text{Beginning Amount}}{\text{Beginning Amount}} \right) \times 100$$

Keep in mind, if an amount is increasing, the Δ% will be positive. If the amount is decreasing, the Δ% will be negative.

EXAMPLE 12:

Smith's Shoe Store has two salesmen, Al and Bob. Al sold 250 pairs of shoes in April and 322 pairs in May. Bob, who did not work as many hours as Al, sold 150 pairs of shoes in April and 198 pairs in May. Find the amount of increase in shoe sales for each salesman, and then find the percentage by which each salesman increased his sales, to the tenth of a percent.

SOLUTION: For the change in the amounts, Al increased his sales by 72 pairs of shoes, and Bob increased his sales by 48 pairs.

For the percent of increase in their sales ...

- For Al, $\Delta\% = (322 - 250)/250 \times 100 = 28.8\%$.

- For Bob, $\Delta\% = (198 - 150)/150 \times 100 = 32\%$.

In other words, even though he sold fewer pairs of shoes, Bob increased his rate of sales by a higher percent than Al.

EXAMPLE 13:

At the beginning of Ronald Reagan's first term as President, the US national debt was $0.9 trillion. By the end of his first term it had increased to $1.6 trillion, and by the end of his second term the debt was $2.6 trillion. By the end of George H. W. Bush's single-term presidency, the national debt increased to $4.0 trillion. During Bill Clinton's first term the national debt increased to $5.3 trillion.

During which of the four listed presidential terms did the national debt increase the greatest amount? During which term did the national debt increase at the greatest rate?

SOLUTIONS: During Bush's single term, the debt increased by $1.4 trillion, which is the largest increase of the listed terms.

Finding the percent changes to the nearest tenth of a percent ...

For Reagan's first term, $\Delta\% = (1.6 - 0.9)/0.9 \times 100 = 77.8\%$.

For Reagan's second term, $\Delta\% = (2.6 - 1.6)/1.6 \times 100 = 62.5\%$.

For Bush's single term, $\Delta\% = (4.0 - 2.6)/2.6 \times 100 = 53.8\%$.

For Clinton's first term, $\Delta\% = (5.3 - 4.0)/4.0 \times 100 = 32.5\%$.

Thus, the national debt increased at the greatest rate in Reagan's first term.

image 1.2.3

SECTION 1.2 EXERCISES

For Exercises #1 through #23, round bases and amounts to the nearest hundredth, and percents to the nearest tenth of a percent, as necessary.

1. What is 10% of 58?

2. What is 140% of 35?

3. 90 is what percent of 120?

4. 120 is what percent of 90?

5. 0.13 is what percent of 5?

6. 72 is 37% of what?

7. 45 is 112% of what?

8. 16 is 0.24% of what?

9. A student correctly answered 23 out of 30 questions on a quiz. What percent is this?

10. A basketball player made 13 out of 18 free throw attempts. What percent is this?

11. A recent survey showed 48% of people thought the President was doing a good job. If 5,000 people were surveyed, how many people in the survey approved of the President's job performance?

12. A bowl of cereal contains 43 grams of carbohydrates, which is 20% of the recommended daily value of a 2,000-calorie diet. What is the total number of grams of carbohydrates in that diet?

image 1.2.4

13. A bowl of cereal contains 190 milligrams of sodium, which is 8% of the recommended daily value in a 2,000-calorie diet. What is the total number of milligrams of sodium in that diet?

14. John's monthly net salary is $3,500, and his rent payment is $805. What percent of his net monthly salary goes toward rent?

15. Jane budgets 8% of her net salary for groceries. If she spent $300 on groceries last month, what is her monthly net salary?

16. Wade wants to buy a new computer priced at $1,200. If the sales tax rate in his area is 5.75%, what will be the amount of sales tax and total cost for this computer?

17. In the bookstore, a book is listed at $24.95. If the sales tax rate is 6.5%, what will be the amount of sales tax and the total cost of the book?

18. Mike has breakfast at a local restaurant and notices the subtotal for his food and coffee is $8.98. If the sales tax is 67¢, what is the sales tax rate?

19. Nancy wants to buy a sweater that is priced at $45. If the store is running a 40% off sale, what will be the amount of the discount and the sale price of the sweater?

Image 1.2.5

20. Sue finds a clock she likes that normally costs $19.99. If this clock is labeled 75% off, and the sales tax rate is 5.5% (of the sale price), what will be the total cost of the clock?

21. To deal with slumping sales, Eric's boss cut his salary by 15%. If Eric was making $52,000 per year, what will be his new annual salary?

22. Last year, Ms. Rose had 24 students in her six-grade math class. This year she has 30 students. What is the percent change of her class size?

23. A new printer costs $40, and last year's model cost $45. What is the percent change in the cost of this printer?

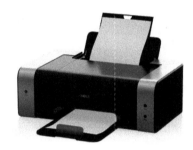

24. Is it possible for one person to be 200% taller than another person? Why or why not?

25. Is it possible for one person to be 200% shorter than another person? Why or why not?

Image 1.2.6

26. Because of losses by your employer, you agree to accept a temporary 10% pay cut, with the promise of getting a 10% raise in 6 months. Will the pay raise restore your original salary?

ANSWERS TO SECTION 1.2 EXERCISES

1. 5.8

2. 49

3. 75%

4. 133.3%

5.   2.6%

6.   194.59

7.   40.18

8.   6666.67

9.   The student answered 76.7% of the questions correctly.

10.   The player made 72.2% of his free throws.

11.   2,400 of the people surveyed approved of the President's job performance.

12.   215 carbohydrates are recommended in that diet.

13.   2,375 milligrams of sodium are recommended in that diet.

14.   23% of John's net salary goes toward his rent.

15.   Jane's monthly net salary is $3,750.

16.   The sales tax is $69, and the total cost of the computer is $1,269.

17.   The sales tax is $1.62, and the total cost is $26.57.

18.   The sales tax rate is 7.5%.

19.   The discount is $18, and the sale price is $27.

20.   The total cost of the clock is $5.28.

21.   Eric's new annual salary will be $44,200.

22.   Ms. Rose had a 25% increase in her class size.

23.   The new printer costs 11.1% less than last year's model.

24.   Sure. If a child is 2 feet tall, 200% of that is 4 feet. There are plenty of 2 feet tall children and 6 feet tall adults in the world.

25.   No. Given the previous answer, it is tempting to say yes. However, 200% of 6 feet is 12 feet. Thus, to be 200% shorter than 6 feet, you would need to be -6 feet tall ($6 - 12 = -6$).

26.   No. If your original salary was $100 per week, a 10% pay cut would make your salary $90 week. Then, a 10% raise would be 10% of the $90, not the $100. That means your new salary would be $99 per week.

1.3 The Most Powerful Force in the Universe: Simple and Compound Interest

Review: Exponents

Mathematical shorthand for repeated multiplication uses a small number written as a superscript, known as an **exponent**. For example, if the number 4 is to be multiplied by itself three times, we could write:

$$4^3 = 4 \times 4 \times 4 = 64$$

- 4^3 is the exponential notation

- $4 \times 4 \times 4$ is the expanded notation

- 64 is the value

> ### common mistake:
> 4^3 is NOT 4×3. If we were asked to compute 4×3, the expression would not include any exponents.

A few more examples would be:

$$7^2 = 7 \times 7 = 49$$
$$2^5 = 2 \times 2 \times 2 \times 2 \times 2 = 32$$
$$10^3 = 10 \times 10 \times 10 = 1000$$

Review: Order of Operations

If several people are asked to simplify the same multi-step arithmetic **expression**, a standard set of rules must be established for the order in which the operations are performed. Otherwise, different people may get different answers. For example, let's say Bill and Ted are asked to simplify the expression $3 + 4 \times 5$. Bill adds the $3 + 4$, and then multiplies that result by 5 to get a total of 35. Ted performs the multiplication first, and then adds 3 to get a total of 23. Who is right? In case you aren't sure yet ... it is Ted.

Arithmetic started with addition (and subtraction). Repeated addition led to multiplication (and division), and repeated multiplication led to the use of exponents. In addition to those procedures, parentheses or other grouping symbols can also be used in an expression. Let's consolidate all of these processes into a single list, known as the "order of operations."

Arithmetic **Order of Operations:**

1. All operations contained within parentheses ( ) or other grouping symbols, such as brackets [ ], or braces { }, should be done first.

2. Secondly, simplify all expressions containing exponents.

3. Multiplication and division are done next, as we come to them going from left to right.

4. Addition and subtraction are done last, again, as we come to them going from left to right.

To help remember this order, many students like to memorize the acronym **PEMDAS** (Parentheses, Exponents, Multiplication, Division, Addition, Subtraction). This can be really helpful, but be careful!

If you do not realize multiplication and division are done as we come to them going from the left to the right, you may fall into the trap of thinking multiplication always precedes division—it does not. The same holds true for addition and subtraction.

EXAMPLE 1:

Simplify: $5 + 6 \times 3$

SOLUTION: Since multiplication is performed before addition, start by multiplying 6×3. Then, add 5 to that result.

$5 + 6 \times 3$
$= 5 + 18$
$= 23$

EXAMPLE 2:

Simplify: $13 - 5 + 6$

SOLUTION: Remember, perform addition and subtraction as we come to them going from left to right. Here, that means the subtraction must be done first.

$13 - 5 + 6$
$= 8 + 6$
$= 14$

EXAMPLE 3:

Simplify: $13 - (5 + 6)$

SOLUTION: Since $(5 + 6)$ is inside parentheses, that operation is performed first.

$13 - (5 + 6)$
$= 13 - 11$
$= 2$

EXAMPLE 4:

Simplify: $42 \div 3(2)$

SOLUTION: There are parentheses in this expression, but take note that there is no operation to perform inside these parentheses. We have division and multiplication to perform here, and those are done going from left to right.

$42 \div 3(2)$
$= 14(2)$
$= 28$

EXAMPLE 5:

Simplify: $5 \times (2 + 3)^2 - (6 - 4) + 1$

Solution: Here, we start with the operations that are inside the parentheses. Then, perform the operation using the exponent. After that, the multiplication is done. Finally, we have addition and subtraction, which are performed as we come to them going from left to right.

$$5 \times (2 + 3)^2 - (6 - 4) + 1$$
$$= 5 \times (5)^2 - 2 + 1$$
$$= 5 \times 25 - 2 + 1$$
$$= 125 - 2 + 1$$
$$= 123 + 1$$
$$= 124$$

Review: Solving Equations

An **equation** is a mathematical statement indicating that two expressions are equal. A **solution** is a value of the variable that makes the equation true. When **solving an equation,** steps are taken to determine all the values of the variable that will make the equation a true statement.

One of the steps available for use is known as the **addition property of equality**. This property states, "if the same quantity is added to both sides of an equation, the solution remains the same." Since any quantity can be added to both sides of an equation, a quantity is chosen that will isolate the variable.

EXAMPLE 6:

Solve: $x - 8 = 24$

Solution: To solve this equation, we want to isolate the variable (x). To do that here, we will add 8 to both sides of the equation. This will cause the (-8) and the $(+8)$ on the left side of the equation to cancel each other out. We also simplify the right side of the equation, giving us our solution.

$$x - 8 = 24$$
$$x - 8 + 8 = 24 + 8$$
$$x = 32$$

As you might expect, we can add either positive numbers (like we did in Example 6), or negative numbers to both sides of an equation.

EXAMPLE 7:

Solve: $x + 7 = -8$

Solution: Here, we will add (-7) to both sides of the equation.

$$x + 7 = -8$$
$$x + 7 + (-7) = -8 + (-7)$$
$$x = -15$$

Note: It is perfectly fine to think of the process as "subtracting 7 from both sides."

Another approach that may be used when solving an equation involves the **multiplication property of equality**, which states that "if both sides of an equation are multiplied (or divided) by the same non-zero quantity, the solution remains the same." Just as it is with the addition property of equality, since any quantity can be used, a quantity is chosen that will isolate the variable.

EXAMPLE 8:

Solve: $6x = 24$

SOLUTION: To solve this equation, we want to isolate the variable (x). To do that here, we will divide both sides of the equation by 6.

$6x = 24$
$6x/6 = 24/6$
$x = 4$

You may be thinking, "if we *divide* by a number, why is this called the "multiplication" property of equality?" Instead of dividing by 6, we could have multiplied by (1/6) and had the same outcome. In the same way that the addition property of equality applies to both addition and subtraction, the multiplication property of equality applies to both multiplication and division. This streamlines our processes into just two properties that we use when trying to isolate a variable.

Some of the equations we solve will make use of *both* the addition and multiplication properties of equality. In some equations, we will use the distributive property to remove any parentheses, and some equations will require us to simplify each side of the equation as much as possible by combining like terms. That being the case, some equations will require several steps in the solving process.

common mistake:

When faced with $6x = 24$, some students attempt to isolate the x by subtracting 6 from both sides of the equation. Remember, the 6 and x are linked by multiplication, and multiplication is undone by division, not subtraction.

If the variable exists on both sides of the equation, use the addition principle to remove it from one side. Try not to think of moving terms from one side of an equation to the other. Instead, focus on removing unwanted terms by adding their opposite. Then, remember, whatever we have done to one side of the equation, we must also do the same thing to the other side to keep the equation balanced. Once the term containing the variable has been isolated, then apply the multiplication property to remove any unwanted multiplication—just be sure to do it to both sides of the equation.

EXAMPLE 9:

Solve: $5x + 13 = 38$

SOLUTION: To solve this equation, we want to isolate the variable (x). Here, we first need to isolate the term containing the variable. To do so, we begin by subtracting 13 from both sides of the equation. Then, we will divide both sides of the equation by 5.

$5x + 13 = 38$
$5x + 13 - 13 = 38 - 13$
$5x = 25$
$x = 5$

EXAMPLE 10:

Solve: $8(x - 3) + 5x = 15(x - 2)$

SOLUTION: In this problem, we first need to use the distributive property to remove the parentheses. Next, we need to simplify as much as possible by combining like terms. Then, to make sure the variable exists on only one side of the equation, we can subtract 13x from both sides. From here we follow the process shown in Example 9 to isolate the variable.

$$8(x - 3) + 5x = 15(x - 2)$$
$$8x - 24 + 5x = 15x - 30$$
$$13x - 24 = 15x - 30$$
$$13x - 24 - 13x = 15x - 30 - 13x$$
$$-24 = 2x - 30$$
$$-24 + 30 = 2x - 30 + 30$$
$$6 = 2x$$
$$3 = x$$

Simple vs. Compound Interest

If an investment is made (or money is borrowed) and the new total is collected at the end of a designated period, the **Future Amount, A,** is the original amount invested *plus* any earned interest. Keep that in mind. If we invest $500 for a few years and our money earns us $75 in interest, the future amount returned to is our original $500 + $75 = $575. It would be a pretty bad investment if the amount returned to us was only the $75 in interest. In fact, giving up $500 to get $75 back is actually *losing* money!

As for the interest, there are two ways to calculate it. **Simple interest** is just that: simple. It is calculated once during the investment period and is only computed upon the principal (money invested or borrowed) of the loan or the investment. **Compound interest**, on the other hand, is compounded more than once throughout the investment period. Furthermore, each time the interest is compounded, it is then added to the existing balance for the next compounding. That means we are actually earning (or paying) interest on interest!

Keeping It Simple

Interest is a percentage of a principal amount calculated for a specified period, usually a stated number of years. Thus, the formula for simple interest is **i = prt**.

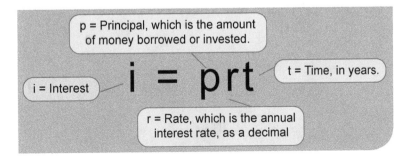

Figure 1.3.1   Simple Interest Formula

- **i**, in this formula, represents the amount of **simple interest** that is earned or is to be paid.

- **p** stands for the **principal**, which is the original amount invested.

- **r** is the annual interest **rate**. Be sure to convert the rate to its decimal form for use in the formula.

- The **time**, **t**, represents the term of the loan or investment, and is usually stated in terms of years.

Typically, rates are stated in annual amounts, which is usually indicated with the acronym APR (Annual Percentage Rate). It is possible, however, to have the rate stated in terms of a time period other than years. If that is the case, make sure the rate and time are in agreement. That is, if we are working with a monthly rate, we need to state the time period in months, as well.

> **IMPORTANT**
>
> The rate and time must be in agreement.

Also, remember, this formula gives us the amount of interest earned, so to find the **future amount**, **A**, of the loan or investment, we have to add that interest to the original principal, $A = p + i$.

> The simple interest formula returns the amount of interest for the investment. If we want to find the future amount of the investment, A, we need to add the original amount, $A = p + i$.

EXAMPLE 11:

Find the future amount for a 5-year investment of $2,000 with 8% simple interest.

SOLUTION: First, find the interest. $i = \$2,000(0.08)(5) = \$800$. The future amount, A, returned to us is found by adding that interest to the original investment.

$A = \$2,000 + \$800 = \$2,800$

The future amount at the end of the 5-year period will be $2,800.

When working with simple interest calculations, we need to pay attention to the directives. Sometimes we are asked to find the future amount of an investment. Alternatively, we may be asked to find just the amount of interest earned, the rate, or even the amount of time in question.

EXAMPLE 12:

A $2,500 investment earned $395 in simple interest over a 5-year period. What was the interest rate of this investment? State your answer as a percent.

SOLUTION: $i = prt$, so, substituting the known values:

$\$395 = \$2,500(r)(5)$

Simplifying the right side of the equation gives us:
$395 = $12,500(r)

Dividing both sides by $12,500 leads us to:
r = $395/$12,500 = 0.0316

This is the decimal form of the rate. As a percent, r is 3.16%.

EXAMPLE 13:

How much principal must be invested at 4% simple interest for 5 years to earn $500?

SOLUTION: i = prt, so:

$500 = p(0.04)(5)

Solving for p, we have:
$500 = p(0.2)
p = $500/0.2 = $2,500

$2,500 should be invested at 4% for 5 years in order to earn $500 in interest.

EXAMPLE 14:

How long would it take for an investment of $2000 to earn $240 in interest, if it is invested at 6% simple interest?

SOLUTION: i = prt, so:

240 = 2000(0.06)(t)

Solving for t, we have:
240 = 120(t)
240/120 = t
2 = t

It would take 2 years for this investment to earn $240 in interest.

Compounding the Situation

Legend has it, a Chinese emperor was so enamored with the inventor of the game of **chess**, he offered the guy one wish. The inventor asked for something along the lines of one grain of rice for the first square on the chessboard, two for the second square, four for the third, eight for the fourth, and so on—doubling for each of the 64 squares on the board. Thinking it was a modest request, the emperor agreed. Of course, upon finding out the inventor would receive $2^{64} - 1 = 18,446,744,073,709,551,615$ grains of rice (more than enough to cover the surface of the earth), he had the guy beheaded. Perhaps that story is what inspired **Albert Einstein** to refer to compound interest as the "most powerful force in the universe."

The compounded amount formula is $A = p(1 + r/n)^{nt}$.

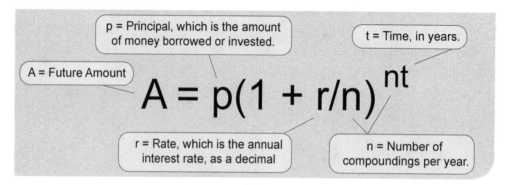

Figure 1.3.2   Compounded Amount Formula

Don't fall into the trap of trying to memorize that formula. When we attempt to memorize something, we ultimately forget it or, even worse, recall it incorrectly. If we want to be able to recall a formula correctly, we need to understand the various components of it.

Next, notice how we have referred to that formula as the compounded "amount" formula and NOT the compound "interest" formula. For the **compounded amount formula**, one of the most important things to realize is, unlike the formula for simple interest, the compounded amount formula returns the **future amount** of the investment, instead of just the **interest, i**.

> The compounded amount formula returns the future amount of the investment, A. If we want to find only the interest, we need to subtract the original amount,
>
> $$i = A - p.$$

Just like in the simple interest formula, **p** stands for the **principal**, which is the original amount invested, and **t** stands for the **time** of the loan or investment stated in terms of years.

In the compounded amount formula, the interest rate, **r**, is also referred to as the **annual percentage rate** (APR). Be sure to convert the APR to its decimal form for use in the formula.

Next, pay special attention to **n**, the **number of compoundings per year**. In most instances, this is described by using terms like monthly, annually, or quarterly. Make sure you know what each of those terms means.

- Monthly means 12 times per year

- Quarterly means 4 times per year

- Semiannually means two times per year

- Annually means once a year

- Biannually means once every two years

Since **n** refers to the number of compoundings per year, **r/n** is the rate for each period. For example, if the APR is 15%, and the amount is compounded monthly, the monthly rate is 15%/12 = 1.25%. Do keep in mind, though, the **r** in the formula represents the APR.

We add **1** to the monthly rate to account for the interest being added to the original amount. This is similar to a sales tax computation. If an item sells for $10, and the tax rate is 7%, the amount of the tax is $10(0.07) = $0.70, which would then be added to the original $10 to get a total cost of $10.70. Alternatively, we could compute it all in one step by multiplying $10(1+0.07) = $10(1.07) = $10.70. In other words, the **(1+r/n)** in the compound amount formula is exactly like the (1+0.07) in that tax calculation we did earlier.

The exponent in the formula, **nt**, is the total number of compoundings throughout the life of the investment. For example, if the amount is compounded monthly for 5 years, there will be a total of 12(5) = 60 compoundings.

Image 1.3.1

EXAMPLE 15:

Find the future amount due for $2,000 borrowed at 6% Annual Percentage Rate (APR) compounded quarterly for 3 years.

Solution: First, since quarterly implies four compoundings per year, **r/n** = 0.06/4 = 0.015. Then, add **1**, and raise that sum to the power that corresponds to the number of compoundings. In this case, 4 times a year for 3 years is 12. Finally, multiply by the amount borrowed, which is the principal.

$A = \$2{,}000 \times (1 + 0.06/4)^{4 \cdot 3} = \$2{,}000 \times (1.015)^{12} = \$2{,}000 \times 1.195618 = \$2{,}391.24$

The future amount at the end of 3 years will be $2,391.24.

Using Your Calculator

In the previous example, we were faced with a multi-step calculation. Using a scientific calculator effectively can greatly expedite the process. For the exponentiation, $(1.015)^{12}$, we could literally multiply $(1.015)(1.015)(1.015) \ldots (1.015)$ twelve times, but it is much faster to use the exponentiation key on our calculator. Depending on the calculator, the exponentiation key may look like $\boxed{x^y}$ or $\boxed{\wedge}$. Thus, $(1.015)^{12}$ would be done on a scientific calculator as $1.015 \boxed{x^y} 12$, and then, hit the $\boxed{=}$ key. For more involved computations, we can use the parentheses keys. In all, we should never have to hit the $\boxed{=}$ key more than once.

EXAMPLE 16:

Use a calculator to compute $\$1{,}000(1 + 0.14/12)^{24}$.

Solution: Literally type: 1000 $\boxed{\times}$ $\boxed{(}$ 1 $\boxed{+}$ 0.14 $\boxed{\div}$ 12 $\boxed{)}$ $\boxed{x^y}$ 24 $\boxed{=}$

You should get 1,320.9871, which you will manually round to $1,320.99.

As with questions involving simple interest, when we are working with compounded amounts, we need to pay attention to the directives. Some questions may ask for the future amount returned, **A**, while others may just ask us to find the amount of interest, **i**.

EXAMPLE 17:

On the day her son was born, Tricia invested $2,000 for him at a guaranteed APR of 8%, compounded monthly. How much will that investment be worth when he turns 50? How much will it be worth if he leaves it alone until he turns 65?

SOLUTION: On his 50th birthday, the investment is worth:

$$A = \$2,000 \times (1 + 0.08/12)^{12 \cdot 50} = \$2,000 \times (1.00666667)^{600}$$
$$A = \$2,000 \times 53.878183179 = \$107,756.37$$

On his 65th birthday, the investment is worth:

$$A = \$2,000 \times (1 + 0.08/12)^{12 \cdot 65} = \$2,000 \times (1.00666667)^{780} = \$356,341.84$$

EXAMPLE 18:

If $1,500 is invested at 5% APR compounded annually for 10 years, how much interest is earned?

SOLUTION: The future amount, $A = \$1,500 \times (1 + 0.05/1)^{1 \cdot 10} = \$2,443.34$. Thus, the interest earned is found by subtracting the value of the original investment: $2,443.34 − $1,500 = $943.34.

SECTION 1.3 EXERCISES

Unless specifically directed to do otherwise, always round answers involving money to the nearest cent (hundredth).

1. Find the simple interest on $12,000 for 2 years at a rate of 6% per year.

2. Find the simple interest on $25,000 for 6 months at a rate of 8.5% per year.

3. How much time is needed for $1,800 to accumulate $360 in simple interest at a rate of 10%?

4. How much time is needed for $600 to accumulate $72 in simple interest at a rate of 4%?

5. If $4,300 earns $1,290 in simple interest over 6 years, what is the annual rate?

6. If $200 earns $45 in simple interest over 3 years, what is the annual rate?

7. How much principal is needed to accumulate $354.60 in simple interest at 9% for 4 years?

8. How much principal is needed to accumulate $65,625 in simple interest at 15% for 7 years?

9. If $500 earns $40 in simple interest over 2.5 years, what is the annual rate?

10. $800 was invested at a simple annual interest rate for 10 years and was worth a total of $975 at the end of that period. What was the interest rate? Round your answer to the nearest hundredth of a percent.

11. How much time is needed for $1,250 to accumulate $375 in simple interest at a rate of 5%?

12. Find the simple interest on $900 for 18 months at a rate of 9.5% per year.

13. If $420 earns $31 in simple interest over 30 months, what is the annual rate?

14. How much time is needed for $660 to accumulate $514.80 in simple interest at a rate of 12%?

15. Find the simple interest on $1,975 for 3 1/2 years at a rate of 7.2% per year.

16. Find the interest, i, and the future amount, A, for $825 invested for 10 years at 4% APR, compounded annually.

17. Find the interest, i, and the future amount, A, for $3,250 invested for 5 years at 2% APR, compounded annually.

18. Find the interest, i, and the future amount, A, for $75 invested for 6 years at 3% APR, compounded semiannually.

19. Find the interest, i, and the future amount, A, for $1,550 invested for 7 years at 5% APR, compounded semiannually.

20. Find the interest, i, and the future amount, A, for $625 invested for 12 years at 8% APR, compounded quarterly.

21. Find the interest, i, and the future amount, A, for $2,575 invested for 2 years at 4% APR, compounded quarterly.

22. Find the interest, i, and the future amount, A, for $1,995 invested for 6 years at 5% APR, compounded semiannually.

23. Find the interest, i, and the future amount, A, for $460 invested for 7 years at 6% APR, compounded quarterly.

24. To purchase a refrigerated showcase, Jamestown Florists borrowed $8,000 for 6 years. The simple interest was $4,046.40. What was the rate?

Image 1.3.2

25. To purchase new equipment, Williams Brake Repair borrowed $4,500 at 9.5%. The company paid $1,282.50 in simple interest. What was the term of the loan?

26. John Doe earned $216 simple interest on a savings account at 8% over 2 years. How much principal was originally invested in the account?

27. Michelle is 25 and wants to retire at the age of 50. If she invests a $60,000 inheritance at 7% compounded semiannually, how much will she have when she turns 50?

28. In order to pay for college, Brooke's parents invest $20,000 in a bond that pays 8% interest compounded semiannually. How much money will there be in 18 years?

29. A couple sets aside $5,000 into a savings account that is compounded quarterly for 10 years at 9%. How much will the investment be worth at the end of 10 years?

ANSWERS TO SECTION 1.3 EXERCISES

1. $1,440

2. $1,062.50

3. 2 years

4. 3 years

5. 5%

6. 7.5%

7. $985

8. $62,500

9. 3.2%

10. 2.19%

11. 6 years

12. $128.25

13. 2.95%

14. 6.5 years (or 78 months)

15. $497.70

16. $i = \$396.20, A = \$1,221.20$

17. $i = \$338.26, A = \$3,588.26$

18. $i = \$14.67, A = \$89.67$

19. $i = \$640.11, A = \$2,190.11$

20. $i = \$991.92, A = \$1,616.92$

21. $i = \$213.36, A = \$2,788.36$

22. $i = \$688.05, A = \$2,683.05$

23. $i = \$237.92, A = \$697.92$

24. 8.43%

25. 3 years

26. $1,350

27. $335,095.61

28. $82,078.65

29. $12,175.94

1.4 Spending Money You Don't Have: Installment Buying and Credit Cards

What Is Installment Buying?

Installment buying is the process of purchasing something and paying for it later. Do not confuse this with **layaway buying**, in which a customer makes monthly payments and then obtains the product after it is paid for in full. For the convenience of paying later, the consumer normally must pay a finance charge. Also, the terms of any such agreement must, by law, be disclosed in writing at the beginning of the process. This law is the **Truth-in-Lending Act (TILA)**. More information about the TILA can be found online in the Wikipedia entry at http://en.wikipedia.org/wiki/Truth_in_Lending_Act.

To simplify the calculations we will encounter in this section, we will not consider any applicable taxes that would normally be imposed on the indicated purchases. Conceptually, the calculations are the same with or without those taxes.

Simple Finance Charges

Normally, borrowing money or having the privilege of making regular payments is not free. The **finance charge** is the amount of the purchase in excess of the selling price. Sometimes the finance charge is a straight fee, and other times it is a percentage of the purchase price. In all cases, however, it is the amount in excess of the selling price.

EXAMPLE 1:

Joel wants to purchase a TV for $1,075. Since he does not have the cash up front, he enters into an agreement to pay $35 a month for 36 months. Find the total cost and the finance charge for this purchase.

Solution: The total amount he will pay is $35 × 36 = $1,260. Therefore, the finance charge would then be $1,260 − $1,075, or $185.

As mentioned in the previous section, we need to pay close attention to the agreement between the rate and the time period. Typically, the rates will be stated in annual amounts, so, if the time period for the installment loan is stated in months, we either need to convert the time to years or the rate to a monthly rate.

common mistake:

6 months is not 0.6 years; it is 1/2 year, which is 0.5 years.

Monthly Payments

A critical component of installment buying is the calculation of the monthly payment. The tricky part of determining a monthly payment is realizing the last payment will usually be slightly more or slightly less than all the other monthly payments.

EXAMPLE 2:

A recliner is for sale at a price of $450, but it may be purchased on an installment plan by paying $100 down, and then paying the balance plus 18% simple interest in 12 monthly payments. What would be the amount of each payment?

Solution: Using the simple interest formula, we will calculate the amount of interest that is to be paid: $i =$ prt, or $i = (\$350)(0.18)(1) = \$63$. Remember, the interest rate has to be in decimal form and the time is stated in years.

Adding that $63 to the balance of $350, the total amount of the payments will be $413. Since there will be 12 payments, each one should be $413/12 = $34.416666 ..., which is $34.42 when rounded to the nearest cent.

It is worth mentioning that the last payment may not be exactly $34.42; it would be the remaining balance to get to a total of $413. To keep things simple, we will only concern ourselves with the regular payment amount.

The total cost of the recliner would be the price of $450 plus the finance charge of $63, or $513 total.

EXAMPLE 3:

Sarah buys a new mountain bike for $375 and pays for it over 2 years with 13.5% simple interest. What is her monthly payment?

Solution: To find the amount of interest she will pay, use the simple interest formula.

i = ($375)(0.135)(2) = $101.25

This brings the total cost for the bike up to $476.25. Since she will be making 24 payments, $476.25/24 = $19.84375. That means the monthly payments will be $19.84 (with the last one being $19.93).

In the two previous examples, the assumption is that no additional money is paid on top of the monthly payment. That is, if the payment happens to be $19.84, we are assuming the amount paid is exactly $19.84 and not a convenient $20.

Credit Card Finance Charges

If we pay off a credit card balance each month, we are not charged any finance charges. If, however, we carry a balance to the next month, the **finance charge** on a credit card is the simple interest on the average daily balance using a daily interest rate. In such a calculation, we also need to know how many days are in the billing cycle.

The **billing cycle** is the number of days between credit card statements, and usually corresponds to the number of days in a specific month, which will be 28 (29 in a leap year!), 30 or 31 days. We could pull out a calendar and count the days, but a faster way is to simply recognize the month that we are considering and look to see if there are 30 or 31 days in it.

Image 1.4.1

EXAMPLE 4:

How many days are in the billing cycle that runs from June 15 through July 14?

Solution: This billing cycle crosses over the end of June. Since there are 30 days in June, there are 30 days in this billing cycle.

The **Average Daily Balance (ADB)** is just that—the average of the daily balances for all the days in the billing cycle. We could find the ADB by finding the balance for every day in the billing cycle, adding them all together, and then dividing that sum by the number of days in the billing cycle. If, however, we are lucky enough to see the balance remain unchanged for stretches of several days at a time, the calculation can be a little quicker.

EXAMPLE 5:

If a credit card has a balance of $20 for 21 days and then a balance of $40 for 9 days, what is the average daily balance for that 30-day period?

Solution: Rather than adding together $20 + $20 + $20 + $20 + ... + $20 + $20 (21 times), we can simply multiply $20 × 21 to get $420. Likewise, for the 9-day stretch, the sum of those daily balances will be $40 × 9, or $360. Then, for the entire 30-day period, the sum of all 30 individual balances will be $780. Thus, the ADB for that 30-day period will be $780/30, which is $26.

The final piece of the credit card interest puzzle is the **daily percentage rate.** The interest rate stated with a credit card is always an **annual percentage rate** (APR). Since there are 365 days in a year (366 in a leap year!), the daily interest rate is the APR/365.

Putting it all together, the monthly finance charge on the credit card is,

Monthly Finance Charge = (ADB) × (APR/365) × (# of Days in Billing Cycle)

EXAMPLE 6:

Let's say we have an average daily balance of $183.65 on a credit card with an APR of 16.9%, over a billing period of 31 days. What would the finance charge be?

Solution: Remember, we need to change the APR to decimal form ...

$$\$183.65 \times (0.169/365) \times (31) = \$2.64 \text{ (to the nearest cent)}$$

Further Credit Card Calculations

EXAMPLE 7:

The balance on Amy's credit card on April 4, the billing date, was $1,953.64. She sent in a $1,000 payment, which was posted on April 12, and made no other transactions in the billing cycle. Assuming the APR on the card is 7.94%, answer the following:

a. What is the average daily balance, ADB, during the billing cycle?

b. How much is the finance charge, FC, during the billing cycle?

c. What will be the new balance when she receives her May 4 statement?

Solutions: For the ADB, first note that the billing cycle crosses over the end of April, which has 30 days. That means the billing cycle has 30 days. It starts on April 4, and the balance changes when the payment gets posted on April 12, which is a span of 8 days. For the first 8 days, the balance was $1,953.64, and for the 22 days remaining in the cycle, the balance was $953.64. Thus,

a. ADB = ($1,953.64 × 8 + $953.64 × 22)/30
ADB = $36,609.20/30 = $1,220.31 (rounded to the cent)

b. For the FC, multiply the ADB by the daily percentage rate, DPR, and the number of days in the cycle.

FC = ADB × DPR × Days
FC = $1,220.31 × (0.0794/365) × 30 = $7.96 (to the cent)

c. Finally, for the new balance, add the FC to the last daily balance.

Bal = $953.64 + $7.96 = $961.60

EXAMPLE 8:

The balance on the Does' credit card on May 12, their billing date, was $378.50. For the period ending June 11, they made the following transactions.

- May 13, Charge: Toys, $129.79

- May 15, Payment, $50.00

- May 18, Charge: Clothing, $135.85

- May 29, Charge: Gasoline, $37.63

a. Find the average daily balance for the billing period.

b. Find the finance charge that is due on June 12. Assume an APR of 15.6%.

c. Find the balance that is due on June 12.

SOLUTIONS: To answer these questions, or, for that matter, any question, our chances are greatly improved if we are organized and neat. First determine what it is we are trying to find. For question a) we are trying to find the average daily balance. Before we try to calculate it, can you define it?

Question 1:   What is an average daily balance?

Answer: The average daily balance is the average of all the daily balances throughout the billing cycle. It is found by adding together the outstanding balance for each day and, then, dividing by the number of days in the cycle.

So, to do the calculation, we must begin by finding the balance for each day in the month. Fortunately, for a couple of long stretches, the balance remains unchanged. What about the billing date? Should it be included in the calculation?

Question 2:   Should the billing date be included in the calculation?

Answer: The billing date signifies the beginning of the next billing cycle. In other words, for this problem, the issuance of the monthly statement (and, thus, the billing date) occurs on June 12. So, do not include June 12 in the calculations for this billing cycle—it will be the first day of the next billing cycle.

Here are the necessary calculations for this problem:

TABLE 1.4.1

Dates	# of Days	Debits (Charges)	Credits (Payments)	Balance Due	# of Days × Balance
May 12	1			$378.50	$ 378.50
May 13–14	2	$129.79		$508.29	$ 1,016.58
May 15–17	3		$50.00	$458.29	$ 1,374.87
May 18–28	11	$135.85		$594.14	$ 6,535.54
May 29–June 11	14	$ 37.63		$631.77	$ 8,844.78
Totals:	31				$18,150.27

Question 3: How were the numbers in the "Balance Due" column calculated?

Answer: The Balance Due numbers are found by adjusting the outstanding balance by the indicated transaction—add purchases (Debits) and subtract payments (Credits). For example, going into May 18, the balance was $458.29. Then, add in the purchase of $135.85 to get the Balance Due of $594.14.

Question 4: How do we determine the number of days with the same balance?

Answer: The number of days can be determined two ways. We can make a list for the entire month, or we can simply subtract. Be sure to subtract the dates on which the balance changes. For example, the balance remained unchanged on the three days from the 15th to the 17th, but 17 - 15 is only 2. Since the balance changed on the 18, we should subtract 18 - 15. Be careful when the billing cycle crosses into the next month. Since there is a May 31, the last stretch of days is 14 days. If this were April's bill, that last stretch would only contain 13 days.

Question 5: At the end of the row beginning with May 15, how was the amount of $1,374.87 determined?

Answer: 3 days at a balance of $458.29. This gives us 3 × $458.29 = $1,374.87.

Question 6: What are the numbers in the last row (31 and $18,150.27)?

Answer: The 31 is the number of days in the billing cycle. The $18,150.27 is the sum of the outstanding balances for every day in the billing cycle. Both numbers are found by adding together the numbers directly above them.

By the way, a nice little check in the middle of the calculations is to verify that the sum of the days in the "# of Days" column is, indeed, the correct number of days in the billing cycle. For this problem, as we noted earlier, since we cross over May 31, there are 31 days in this billing cycle. Since the sum of the days in the "# of Days" column is 31, we have accounted for every day in the cycle.

And, thus, to answer the three original questions ...

a. The average daily balance is $18,150.27/31 = $585.49

b. The finance charge is ($585.49) × (0.156/365) × (31) = $7.76

c. The balance due on June 12 is $631.77 + $7.76 = $639.53

One More Question ...

Question 7: Why was the finance charge added to the $631.77 and not $585.49?

Answer: The finance charge gets added to the final outstanding balance, not the average daily balance.

How about another?

EXAMPLE 9:

The balance on the Smiths' credit card on November 8, their billing date, was $812.96. For the period ending December 7, they made the following transactions.

- November 13, Charge: Toys, $231.10

- November 15, Payment, $500

- November 29, Charge: Clothing, $87.19

a. Find the average daily balance for the billing period.

b. Find the finance charge that is due on June 12. Assume an APR of 15.6%.

c. Find the balance that is due on June 12.

SOLUTIONS: Assuming they have an APR of 5.9%, find the balance that is due on December 8.

Here are the necessary calculations for this problem:

TABLE 1.4.2

DATES	# OF DAYS	DEBITS (CHARGES)	CREDITS (PAYMENTS)	BALANCE DUE	# OF DAYS × BALANCE
Nov. 8–12	5			$ 812.96	$ 4,064.80
Nov. 13–14	2	$231.10		$1,044.06	$ 2,088.12
Nov. 15–28	14		$500.00	$ 544.06	$ 7,616.84
Nov. 29–Dec. 7	9	$ 87.19		$ 631.25	$ 5,681.25
Totals	30				$19,451.01

a. The average daily balance is $19,451.01/30 = $648.37.

b. That makes the finance charge $648.37 × 0.059/365 × 30 = $3.14.

c. Then, the balance forwarded is $631.25 + $3.14 = $634.39.

Using Your Calculator

You may have picked up on that fact that many of the calculations in this section have a lot of steps. As with any multi-step calculation, there are a lot of opportunities for simple mistakes, and it only takes one simple mistake to throw off the final answer. One of the most common simple mistakes is rounding at an intermediate step.

One way to combat this is to make effective use of our calculator. If the APR for a credit card is 16.9%, the daily percentage rate is 0.169/365. If we did that calculation by itself as 0.000463013 ... and used a rounded version, such as 0.00046,

common mistake:

A very common mistake is rounding at an intermediate step. Our answers will be the most accurate if we only round once, and at the very end of the problem.

in the next step, we may get an answer of $2.62 instead of $2.64. Sure, the difference is just a couple pennies, but it is still incorrect.

Instead of doing the calculation piecemeal, we should take full advantage of the features of the scientific calculator and do the entire calculation in one long computation, using the maximum number of digits at each intermediate step, and hitting the equals key only once. Then, since the answer is money, we round to the nearest cent at the very end.

Credit Cards in General

Credit cards can be very useful. Unfortunately, they are also very dangerous. In the late 1980s, credit card companies would target unsuspecting college students who were just a year or two away from their parents' watchful eyes. Many times, those students did not even have jobs or a regular income; the companies were issuing the credit cards to the students based solely on *potential* income. In turn, many college students would rack up thousands of dollars of debt without even realizing the consequences. New credit card laws that went in to effect in February of 2010 specifically attempt to limit this practice with a few restrictions. Credit card companies are now banned from issuing cards to anyone under 21, unless they have adult co-signers on the accounts, or can show proof they have enough income to repay the card debt. The companies must also stay at least 1,000 feet from college campuses if they are offering free pizza or other gifts to entice students to apply for credit cards.

Image 1.4.2

Other highlights from the **Credit CARD Act of 2009** (**CARD** stands for **C**ard **A**ccountability **R**esponsibility and **D**isclosure) include limits on interest rate hikes and fees, allowing card holders at least 21 days to pay monthly bills, mandates on due dates and times, and clear information on the consequences of making only minimum payments each month. For that last one, the credit card companies must identify how long it would take to pay off the entire balance if users only made the minimum monthly payment.

Payday Loans

A typical credit card for an individual with average credit scores will have annual interest rate (APR) ranging from 15–20%. People with poor credit who can qualify for a credit card may be subjected to a high APR of 25–30%.

Sadly, as an alternative, payday lenders will charge $15–$20 per two-week period for every $100 borrowed. It's easy to see that $20 is 20% of $100, but keep in mind, that is a *bi-weekly* rate. If that rate was extended to a full year, the APR would be 20% × 26 = 520%. That's right. 520%.

To make things worse, depending on the loan agreement that is signed, if you fail to repay the loan in the agreed upon period (again, typically two weeks), the APR could increase by another 200–300%. If someone is unable (or unwilling) to repay a loan in the agreed upon period, charging additional fees compounds the problem. Often, this **debt rollover** traps borrowers in a cycle that is difficult to escape. For that reason, in many of the states where payday lending is legal, rollovers are not allowed, meaning the individual is not allowed to borrow funds again and/or subjected to criminal charges, jail time and fines.

The federal **Truth-in-Lending Act** requires payday loan companies to disclose the cost of a loan, including the APR and any finance charge. Even with that disclosure, these loans are very popular, with approximately 20,000 payday lenders in the US, which is more than the number of McDonald's restaurants. To make that comparison even more dramatic, payday loan companies are not even allowed in 14 states!

If you are just starting out on your own, it is common to be turned down by banks and credit card companies. That said, as enticing as they may be, it is critically important to avoid payday loans. If you do not have the money, give a second thought to the purchase. Above all, don't spend money you do not have.

SECTION 1.4 EXERCISES

Be sure to round all money answer to the nearest cent. Be aware that some of the following exercises have multiple parts. Be sure to answer all the questions that are asked.

1. Mary bought a used car for $3,500, which was financed for $160 a month for 24 months.

   a. What is the total cost for the car?

   b. How much is the finance charge?

2. Jose borrowed $800 from his local credit union for 8 months at 6% simple interest. He agreed to repay the loan by making eight equal monthly payments.

   a. How much is the finance charge?

   b. What is the total amount to be repaid?

   c. How much is the monthly payment?

3. Pam purchased a new laptop, which was advertised for $750. She bought it on the installment plan by paying $50 at the time of purchase and agreeing to pay the balance, plus 18% simple interest on the balance in 24 monthly payments.

   a. How much is the finance charge?

   b. How much will each payment be?

   c. What is the total cost of the laptop?

4. Joe buys a new stereo for $875 and pays for it over 2 years with 6.5% simple interest. What is his monthly payment?

5. How many days are in a credit card billing cycle that runs from July 17 through August 16?

6. How many days are in a credit card billing cycle that ends on December 12?

7. How many days are in a credit card billing cycle that ends on September 22?

8. If a credit card has a balance of $30 for 11 days and then a balance of $50 for 20 days, what is the average daily balance for that 31-day period?

9. If a credit card has a balance of $120 for 10 days, a balance of $150 for the next 12 days, and a balance of $90 for 8 days, what is the average daily balance for that 30-day period?

10. If the APR on a credit card is 6.57%, what is the daily interest rate? Round your answer to the nearest thousandth of a percent.

11. If the APR on a credit card is 8.75%, what is the daily interest rate? Round your answer to the nearest thousandth of a percent.

12. The average daily balance is $210.39 on a credit card with an APR of 13.4% over a billing period of 30 days. What will the finance charge be?

13. The average daily balance is $90.15 on a credit card with an APR of 5.4% over a billing period of 30 days. What will the finance charge be?

14. The balance on Maria's credit card on May 10, the billing date, was $3,198.23. She sent in a $1,000 payment, which was posted on May 13, and made no other transactions during the billing cycle. Assuming the APR on the card is 7.9%, answer the following.

    a. What is the average daily balance for the billing period?

    b. How much is the finance charge for the billing period?

    c. What will be the new balance when she receives her June 10 statement?

15. The balance on Jim's credit card on April 17, the billing date, was $78.30. For the period ending May 16, he made the following transactions. Assume an APR of 5.2%.

    - April 20, Payment, $50.00

    - May 1, Charge: Gas, $29.20

    a. Find the average daily balance for the billing period.

    b. Find the finance charge that is due on May 17.

    c. Find the balance that is due on May 17.

16. The balance on Carrie's credit card on November 19, the billing date, was $238.50. For the period ending December 18, she made the following transactions. Assume an APR of 2.9%.

    - November 23, Payment, $150.00

    - December 1, Charge: Clothing, $129.19

    - December 10, Charge: Dinner, 37.43

a. Find the average daily balance for the billing period.

b. Find the finance charge that is due on December 19.

c. Find the balance that is due on December 19.

17. The balance on Ted's credit card on August 9, the billing date, was $1,298.51. For the period ending September 8, he made the following transactions. Assume an APR of 3.9%.

   - August 14, Payment, $350.00

   - August 22, Charge: Gasoline, $39.92

   - August 29, Charge: Groceries, $87.17

   a. Find the average daily balance for the billing period.

   b. Find the finance charge that is due on September 9.

   c. Find the balance that is due on September 9.

18. The balance on Melissa's credit card on August 4, the billing date, was $2,913.34. She sent in a $1,500 payment, which was posted on August 16, and made no other transactions in the billing cycle. Assuming the APR on the card is 6.34%, answer the following:

   a. What is the average daily balance during the billing cycle?

   b. How much is the finance charge during the billing cycle?

   c. What will be the new balance when she receives her September 4 statement?

19. Quick Loans will loan you $200 with the understanding that you will repay them $235 in two weeks. What is the APR for this loan?

20. Cheatem Loans will lend you $500 with the understanding that you will repay them $600 in one month. What is the APR for this loan?

21. Dollar Loans advertises a $500 loan will cost you $2.75 per day in interest. What is the APR for this loan?

ANSWERS TO SECTION 1.4 EXERCISES

1. a. $3840   b. $340

2. a. $32 (use $T = 8/12$)   b. $832   c. $104

3. a. $252   b. $39.67 ($39.59 for the last one)   c. $1002

4. $41.20 for the first 23 months, $41.15 for the last payment.

5. 31

6. 30

7.   31

8. $42.90

9. $124.00

10.   0.018%

11.   0.024%

12. $2.32

13. $0.40

14.   **a.** $2295.00   **b.** $15.40   **c.** $2213.63

15.   **a.** $48.87   **b.** $0.21   **c.** $57.71

16.   **a.** $197.24   **b.** $0.47   **c.** $255.59

17.   **a.** $1059.07   **b.** $3.51   **c.** $1079.11

18.   **a.** $1,993.99   **b.** $10.74   **c.** $1,424.08

19.   455%

20.   240%

21.   201.75%

1.5   Living Out of Your Car: Leasing vs Buying

General Lease Information

A **lease** is a contract that allows for one party to use the property of another party, for an extended period of time. Leases can be written for just about anything, but generally include cars, heavy equipment, general office equipment, housing or office space.

The **lessee** is the party or individual wanting to utilize the property, and the **lessor** is owner of the property. A lease involving tangible property, such as a car or real estate, is also referred to as a **rental agreement**, and leases involving non-tangible property, such as cell phone airtime, are usually referred to as **contracts**. Whether a rental agreement or a contract, the lessee will pay the lessor a monthly fee for the property's usage. A lease indicates legal conditions and responsibilities of both the lessee and lessor.

Leasing vs Buying Cars

Driving a new vehicle with the latest technology, having lower monthly payments, and minimizing maintenance costs are just a few reasons **leasing a car** is an attractive option for many people. Before we blindly dive into a lease, however, we should carefully consider four basic things:

1. The Up-Front Payment

2. The Monthly Payment

3. The Length of the Lease

4. Possible Additional Charges at the End of the Lease

EXAMPLE 1:

Mike leases a new pickup by paying $3000 up-front and $249 a month over three years. The lease also stipulates he will be charged $0.15 per mile for every mile over 36,000. If he puts 40,196 miles on the truck, what will be the total cost of the lease?

SOLUTION: Noting the excess mileage is $40{,}196 - 36{,}000 = 4196$ miles ...

Total Cost = $\$3000 + 36(\$249) + 4196(\$0.15) = \$12{,}593.40$

Image 1.5.1

EXAMPLE 2:

Deanna wants to lease a new Toyota Camry, and she is presented with the following three options. Compute the total cost of each option and determine which one is best for her. Provided the vehicle has less than 30,000 miles on it by the end of the lease, there will not be any additional charges.

- Option 1: $0 up-front, with a payment of $209/month for 36 months.

- Option 2: $999 up-front, with a payment of $189/month for 36 months.

- Option 3: $2999 up-front, with a payment of $149/month for 36 months.

SOLUTION: - Option 1: $\$0 + \$209(36) = \$7524$

- Option 2: $\$999 + \$189(36) = \$7803$

- Option 3: $\$2999 + \$149(36) = \$8363$

With all other things being equal, the option Deanna chooses will be based on her financial situation and cash reserves at the time of the lease. If she really wants the smallest monthly payment and has the $2999 to pay up-front, Option 3 may be her best choice. If, however, she can afford the larger monthly payment, she would save over $800 by choosing Option 1.

Some people greatly prefer buying vehicles instead of leasing them. Well-built and well-maintained vehicles may last for many years, and having no monthly payment frees up hundreds of dollars that can be used in other ways. If we wish to buy a car instead of leasing, we should compare the cost associated with leasing, and the costs associated with buying—and then selling—the same item over the same period.

EXAMPLE 3:

The new Camry Deanna is considering leasing can be purchased for a down payment of $4000 and 36 monthly payments of $550. After 3 years, she will own the car and, based on projections, she will be able to sell it for $16,000. If she follows this plan, what will be the total net cost for the car?

Image 1.5.2

SOLUTION: The total net cost will be the amount paid less the amount recovered.

The amount paid will be $4000 + $550(36) = $23,800.

Thus, $23,800 − $16,000 = $7800.

Taking another look at the previous examples, Lease Option 1 offers a lower total net cost, no up-front or down payment costs, monthly payments that are less than half of the purchase payments, and no re-sale headaches at the end of three years. Thus, if Deanna wants to get a new car in three years, leasing is the much better option. If, however, she wishes to keep her Camry for 5-6 years, having it paid off in three years means she will no longer have a monthly car payment expense.

Be aware, since we would pay tax, title, license and other documentation fees whether we leased or bought a car, they are not factored into our calculations. We would also need to check with our insurance company to see if they offered different rates for leasing and buying the same vehicle.

When taking out a loan to purchase a car, the term of the loan is typically 5 years (60 months). The Camry in above examples could be purchased over 60 months with a smaller payment (around $350), but a longer term also means more interest paid on the loan and, hence, a higher total net cost. The additional costs associated with a 60-month loan do not mean they are not worth it. In fact, if the vehicle maintains a higher resale value, the average annual cost associated with the longer-term plan may actually make it a better option.

Be very careful with leases. Even though the allure and peace of mind that comes with driving a new car every few years may make the extra expenses worth considering, we need to realize the company leasing the vehicle is looking to make money. Many leases may be advertised as having "no down payment," but may include other up-front costs. Also, be prepared to pay substantial penalties if a specified mileage is exceeded, or another term is violated in the agreement. Due to complex and clever language, it is not uncommon for the total cost of a lease to be much, much more than anticipated.

Some leases also give us the option of buying the vehicle at the end of the contract. Thus, if we really like the car, we may be able to keep it. Unfortunately, this usually leads to a higher total cost than buying it outright. According to LeaseTrader.com, if we are planning on keeping the car for more than 4 years, buying it outright might be the better choice. However, if we do not want to keep the car for more than 4 years, we should give serious and careful consideration to a lease.

Leasing a Home

Probably the most common type of **lease** is a real estate rental agreement for residential or business use, with the lessor being referred to as a **landlord** and lessee being called the **tenant**. **Rent** payments on the property are usually made on a monthly basis.

In a **fixed-term tenancy**, either the landlord or the tenant may terminate a rental agreement when the specified term is nearing completion, but neither party may terminate the lease early without a penalty based on the remaining period of the lease.

An **at-will tenancy** is a tenancy in which either the landlord or the tenant may terminate at any time by giving reasonable notice. Either the lessor or the lessee can for any reason, or for no reason at all, end it at any time.

The **security deposit** is an initial payment paid by the tenant and held by the landlord until the property is returned or vacated. Normal wear and tear are expected and a list of pre-existing damage to the property is provided before the tenancy begins. Upon the termination of the rental agreement, if the property is returned in good condition, all or part of the security deposit is returned to the tenant. Depending on the language in the rental agreement, charges for cleaning or other fees may be deducted before the deposit is returned.

EXAMPLE 4:

A property owner is asking for a $1000 security deposit and $850/month rent. If half of the security deposit is forfeited, what will be the total cost for a two-year lease?

Solution: Total Cost = 0.5($1000) + 24($850) = $20,900

So, how much can you afford for monthly housing expenses? According to the **US Census Bureau** (https://www.census.gov/housing/census/publications/who-can-afford.pdf), the amount a family should devote to housing expenses should not exceed 30% of their monthly gross income.

Housing Recommendation #1:

The amount a family should devote to monthly housing expenses should not exceed 30% of their monthly gross income.

EXAMPLE 5:

Ben and Jeri have a combined monthly income of $8,500. According to Housing Recommendation #1, how much can they afford for a monthly rent payment?

Solution: 0.3($8500) = $2550

Keep in mind, if you are going to pay for renter's insurance, you should add that monthly cost to your rent when considering your monthly housing expenses.

'Til Death Do Us Part

If you wish to purchase a home, you will likely need to secure a mortgage from a lending institution to do so. In French, the word *mort* means death and the word *gage* means pledge. Thus, the literal meaning of the word **mortgage** is "death pledge." Now that's something to think about ...

Amortization is a situation in which the borrower agrees to make regular payments on the principal and interest until a loan is paid off. There are a lot of variables involved in obtaining a loan to purchase a home, and each should be weighed carefully before one enters into such a major commitment.

Amortization Tables

Somewhere, someone once sat down and, hopefully using a computer, calculated the monthly payments for loans using different amounts, interest rates, and time periods. Extensive **amortization tables** are rarely seen, but they are pretty large and fairly organized. Succinct versions of these tables are a nice way to quickly compare calculations for different time periods. If you use a table computed on a fixed amount of $1,000, you can scale the amount to match any principal, being sure to round the calculated amount to the nearest cent.

Here is a partial amortization table.

TABLE 1.5.1

	MONTHLY MORTGAGE PAYMENT PER $1,000		
RATE (%)	15 YEARS	20 YEARS	30 YEARS
4.50	7.6499	6.3265	5.0669
4.75	7.7783	6.4622	5.2165
5.00	7.9079	6.5996	5.3682
5.25	8.0388	6.7384	5.5220
5.50	8.1708	6.8789	5.6779
5.75	8.3041	7.0208	5.8357
6.00	8.4386	7.1643	5.9955
6.25	8.5742	7.3093	6.1572
6.50	8.7111	7.4557	6.3207
6.75	8.8491	7.6036	6.4860
7.00	8.9883	7.7530	6.6530
7.25	9.1286	7.9038	6.8218
7.50	9.2701	8.0559	6.9921
7.75	9.4128	8.2095	7.1641

Using the table to find the monthly payment for a 7% loan for 30 years, we see the payment factor per $1,000 is 6.6530. Then, since the numbers in the table are given as per $1,000, to determine the monthly payment for a $120,000 loan, we multiply the 6.6530 by $120,000 divided by 1000, to get a monthly payment of $798.36.

EXAMPLE 6:

Use the amortization table to find the monthly mortgage payment for a $135,000 loan at 5.5% for 30 years.

SOLUTION: Using the table, we find the payment factor of 5.5% for 30 years to be 5.6779. Then, 5.6779 × $135,000/1000 gives us a monthly payment of $766.5165, which must be rounded to $766.52.

From a Different Point of View: Online Calculators

Unfortunately, amortization tables are often incomplete and even hard to locate. This leads us to what can easily be considered one of the most useful websites we will ever encounter: http://www.interest.com/calculators/. Since we are only going to scratch the surface of the possibilities for the **mortgage calculators** on this site, you are strongly encouraged to explore it on your own. In fact, it would be wise to open that page in its own window, and bookmark it (or add it to your favorites folder) for future reference. Do realize, since the values printed in the amortization table shown in this section are rounded to four decimal places, the online calculators will be a little more accurate. But that difference, if any, should not be more than a couple of cents.

EXAMPLE 7:

Use the Mortgage Calculator at interest.com (URL listed above) to find the monthly mortgage payment for a $135,000 loan at 5.5% for 30 years.

SOLUTION: Go to the calculator webpage and select the Mortgage Calculator. Type in the mortgage amount, term, and rate (ignore the other information boxes for now), and then scroll down and click the calculate button to find the monthly payment is $766.52. It's that simple!

Image 1.5.3

Once the monthly payment is calculated, the total cost of the home can easily be found. In the example above, the 30-year loan would involve 360 payments of $766.52, or a total cost of $275,947.20. That means the finance charge for this loan is over $140,000, which is more than the cost of the house! This is typical, and, unfortunately, just a part of the home-buying process.

EXAMPLE 8:

Mason wishes to borrow $180,000, and he qualifies for a rate of 5.00%. Find the monthly payment for this loan if the term is 30 years. By how much will the payment go up if he reduces the loan to 20 years?

SOLUTION: For 5%, the payment factor on the amortization table for 30 years is 5.3682, which makes the monthly payment $966.28. For 20 years, the payment factor is 6.5996, which makes the monthly payment $1,187.93. So, for the shorter term, the monthly payment is $221.65 higher.

Additionally, for the 30-year loan, the total amount to be paid for the home is 360 × 966.28 = $347,860.80. Similarly, for the 20-year loan, the total amount to be paid is $285,103.20, which is a savings of $62,757.60.

The Entire Monthly Housing Payment

The monthly payment involved with a loan will constitute the majority of the cost of home ownership, but there are other costs that must be considered, as well. Probably the most important of all the topics in this section is the calculation of the *entire* monthly payment for a home buyer.

The complete monthly payment includes the **mortgage loan payment**, **real estate taxes**, and **homeowner's insurance**. Additionally, if the outstanding principal is more than 80% of the value of the home, **private mortgage insurance** (PMI) may also be required. However, since it is not required of every homeowner, to simplify our calculations a little bit, we will not deal with PMI.

EXAMPLE 9:

Find the entire monthly housing payment for the following.

Loan Amount: $105,000
Interest Rate: 8%
Term: 30 years
Assessed Value of the House: $120,000
Real Estate Taxes: 2.5% of assessed value (annually)
Homeowners Insurance: $480 per year

Image 1.5.4

Solution: Using an online calculator or the amortization table from earlier in this section, the monthly loan payment for principal and interest is found to be $770.45. Taxes will cost $(0.025) \times (\$120,000) = \$3,000$ per year, which adds $250 per month to the payment. Insurance, at $480 per year, will add $40 per month to the payment.

So, our total monthly payment will be $770.45 + $250 + $40 = $1,060.45.

EXAMPLE 10:

Find the total monthly payment for a $175,000 mortgage loan at 6.5% for 30 years. The assessed value of the home is $200,000. The annual taxes on the home are 1.5% of the assessed value, and the insurance on the home costs $600 per year.

Solution: Using the amortization table, the payment factor is 6.3207, which makes the mortgage payment $1,106.12 per month. The taxes are $3,000 per year, which adds $250 per month, and the monthly insurance payment is $50.

Thus, the total monthly payment is $1,406.12.

What Can You Afford?

The **Housing Recommendation #1** (the monthly housing expenses should not exceed 30% of the monthly gross income) presented earlier can be applied to buying a home, as well as renting. For buyers, the total monthly housing expenses should include the loan payment, taxes and insurance, as well as any homeowner's association dues and private mortgage insurance.

When you wish to purchase a home, the first question you should ask yourself is "How much of a mortgage loan can I afford?" As a rule of thumb, the amount of the mortgage loan should not exceed three times the borrower's annual gross income. Remember, this is just a recommendation on the amount of a loan and not the actual cost of the home. If you wish to purchase a home that is more expensive than this recommendation, you should save up enough money for a down payment that would cover the difference.

Image 1.5.5

Housing Recommendation #2:

The amount of a mortgage loan should not exceed three times a family's annual gross income.

Housing Recommendation #1 deals with *monthly* housing expenses and is based on a family's *monthly* gross income.

Housing Recommendation #2 deals with the amount of a loan and is based on a family's *annual* gross income.

Taking these recommendations into account, a family with an annual gross income of $45,000 should not take out a home loan of more than $135,000, and the monthly housing expenses—which include the loan payment, property taxes, and insurance—should not exceed ($45,000) × (1/12) × (0.3) = $1125.

EXAMPLE 11:

John Dough has a gross monthly income of $5,125. According to the Housing Recommendations, how much can he devote to monthly housing expenses?

SOLUTION: (0.3) × ($5,125) = $1,537.50.

EXAMPLE 12:

Joey has a gross monthly income of $4,500. According to the Housing Recommendations, how much of a home loan can he afford?

SOLUTION: Remember, the amount of the home loan is based on the annual income. Since the monthly income is $4500, the annual income is 12($4500) = $54,000. That means the loan amount should be no more than 3($54,000) = $162,000.

EXAMPLE 13:

The Wilsons have a combined annual gross household income of $128,000, and they wish to purchase a house priced at $430,000. According to the Housing Recommendations, how much of a down payment will they need?

Solution: The maximum mortgage loan amount they can afford a loan is three times their household income, which is 3($128,000) = $384,000. Thus, to afford a $430,000 home, they would need a down payment of $46,000.

SECTION 1.5 EXERCISES

Unless specifically directed to do otherwise, always round answers involving money to the nearest cent (hundredth).

1. Tina leases a new car by paying $2500 up front and $159 a month over three years. Assuming there are no other charges, what will be the total cost of the lease?

2. Maria leases a new car by paying $3000 up front and $189 a month over three years. Assuming there are no other charges, what will be the total cost of the lease?

3. Jose leases a new pickup by paying $3500 up front and $289 a month over three years. The lease also stipulates he will be charged $0.15 per mile for every mile over 36,000. If he puts 41,006 miles on the truck, what will be the total cost of the lease?

4. Scotty leases a new pickup by paying $4500 up front and $383 a month over three years. The lease also stipulates he will be charged $0.10 per mile for every mile over 36,000. If he puts 38,401 miles on the truck, what will be the total cost of the lease?

5. Lori wants to buy a new car for a down payment of $3000 and monthly payments of $435 for five years. What will be the total cost of the car?

6. Tasha wants to buy a new car for a down payment of $6000 and 48 monthly payments of $522. What will be the total cost of the car?

7. Pat wants to buy a new car for a down payment of $2000 and 48 monthly payments of $729. After 4 years, he will own the car and, based on projections, he will be able to sell it for $18,000. If he follows this plan, what will be the total net cost for the car?

8. Amber is going to purchase a new SUV. Of the following three options, which one will be the least expensive?

    a. $2000 Down Payment and $944/month for 36 Months

    b. $4000 Down Payment and $640/month for 48 Months

    c. $6000 Down Payment and $522/month for 60 Months

9. A property owner is asking for a $1200 security deposit and $1100/month rent. If half of the security deposit is forfeited, what will be the total cost for a two-year lease?

10. Adam paid a $950 security deposit and $1300/month rent for three years. $300 of the security deposit was forfeited, so what was the total cost for the lease?

11. Use the amortization table earlier in this section to find the monthly mortgage payment for loans with the following conditions.

    a. $150,000 for 20 years at 5.25%

    b. $172,000 for 30 years at 7.00%

    c. $210,000 for 30 years at 5.75%

    d. $275,000 for 15 years at 5.50%

12. Use an online mortgage calculator to find the monthly mortgage payment for loans with the following conditions.

    a. $150,000 for 20 years at 5.25%

    b. $172,000 for 30 years at 7.00%

    c. $210,000 for 30 years at 5.75%

    d. $275,000 for 15 years at 5.50%

13. Dave wishes to borrow $210,000, and he qualifies for a rate of 7.25%. Find the monthly payment for this loan if the term is 30 years. By how much will the payment change if he reduces the loan to 20 years?

14. Trevor wishes to borrow $280,000, and he qualifies for a rate of 5.50%. Find the monthly payment for this loan if the term is 30 years. By how much will the payment change if he reduces the loan to 15 years?

15. Laura wishes to borrow $175,000, and she qualifies for a rate of 6.25%. Find the monthly payment for this loan if the term is 20 years. By how much will the payment change if she takes out the loan to 30 years?

16. Find the entire monthly payment for a $275,000 mortgage loan at 5.5% for 30 years. The assessed value of the home is $300,000. The annual taxes on the home are 1.2% of the assessed value, and the insurance on the home costs $750 per year.

17. Find the entire monthly payment for a $205,000 mortgage loan at 5.25% for 20 years. The assessed value of the home is $240,000. The annual taxes on the home are 1.25% of the assessed value, and the insurance on the home costs $450 per year.

18. Find the entire monthly payment for a $185,000 mortgage loan at 4.5% for 30 years. The assessed value of the home is $200,000. The annual taxes on the home are 0.9% of the assessed value, and the insurance on the home costs $375 per year.

19. According to the Housing Recommendations, if a family has a gross annual income of $63,000, what is the maximum amount of their monthly income that could be devoted to housing expenses?

20. According to the Housing Recommendations, if a family has a gross annual income of $174,000, what is the maximum amount of their monthly income that could be devoted to housing expenses?

21. According to the Housing Recommendations, if a family has a gross annual income of $48,000, what is the maximum amount of their monthly income that could be devoted to housing expenses?

22. According to the Housing Recommendations, if a family has a gross annual income of $33,000, what is the maximum amount of their monthly income that could be devoted to housing expenses?

23. According to the Housing Recommendations, if a family has an annual income of $62,000, what is the maximum mortgage amount the family could afford?

24. According to the Housing Recommendations, if a family has a gross annual income of $122,000, what is the maximum mortgage amount the family could afford?

25. According to the Housing Recommendations, if a family has a gross annual income of $312,000, what is the maximum mortgage amount the family could afford?

26. The Littlepage family has a combined annual gross household income of $120,000, and they wish to purchase a house priced at $400,000. According to the Housing Recommendations, how much of a down payment will they need?

27. The Browns have a combined annual gross household income of $78,000, and they wish to purchase a house priced at $260,000. According to the Housing Recommendations, how much of a down payment will they need?

ANSWERS TO SECTION 1.5 EXERCISES

NOTE: If no method is specified, you are free to compute mortgage payments using a calculator or amortization tables. Depending on your choice of method, your answers may be off by a cent or two from the answers provided below. If, however, your answers are off by a greater amount, you may have made a calculation mistake or inappropriately rounded at an intermediate step.

1. $8224

2. $9804

3. $14,154.90

4. $18,528.10

5. $29,100

6. $31,056

7. $18,992

8. Option (b) is the least expensive.

9. $27,000

10. $47,450

11. **a.** $1010.76   **b.** $1144.32   **c.** $1225.50   **d.** $2246.97

12. **a.** $1010.77   **b.** $1144.32   **c.** $1225.50   **d.** $2246.98

13. The payment will go up $227.22.

14. The payment will go up $698.02 (using a calculator) or $698.01 (using the tables).

15. The payment will go down $201.61 (using a calculator) or $201.62 (using the tables).

16. $1923.92

17. $1668.88 (using a calculator) or $1668.87 (using the tables)

18. $1,118.62 (using a calculator) or $1,118.63 (using the tables)

19. $1575

20. $4350

21. $1200

22. $825

23. $186,000

24. $366,000

25. $936,000

26. $40,000

27. $26,000

CHAPTER 1 CREDITLINES

IMG 1.0.1: Copyright © 2012 Depositphotos/natis76.

IMG 1.1.1: Copyright © 2010 Depositphotos/Timmary.

IMG 1.1.2: Copyright © 2014 Depositphotos/asafeliason.

IMG 1.1.3: "Benjamin Franklin," http://commons.wikimedia.org/wiki/File:Benjamin_Franklin.PNG. Copyright in the Public Domain.

IMG 1.1.4: "Charles Ponzi," http://commons.wikimedia.org/wiki/File:Charles_Ponzi.jpg. Copyright in the Public Domain.

IMG 1.2.1: Copyright © 2013 Depositphotos/Elnur_.

IMG 1.2.2: Copyright © 2014 Depositphotos/zhaubasar.

IMG 1.2.3: "Capitol Building Full View," http://commons.wikimedia.org/wiki/File:Capitol_Building_Full_View.jpg. Copyright in the Public Domain.

IMG 1.2.4: "Froot-Loops-Cereal-Bowl," http://commons.wikimedia.org/wiki/File:Froot-Loops-Cereal-Bowl.jpg. Copyright in the Public Domain.

IMG 1.2.5: Copyright © 2012 Depositphotos/vnstudio.

IMG 1.2.6: Copyright © 2012 Depositphotos/vasabii777.

IMG 1.3.1: Copyright © 2012 Depositphotos/Gelpi.

SETS AND VENN DIAGRAMS

People love to group things together. We put all our socks in a drawer, our books on a shelf, and our keys on a keychain. Any collection of distinct objects is called a set, and believe it or not, sets are one of the most fundamental concepts in mathematics.

Set theory, including the study of Venn diagrams, was developed around the end of the nineteenth century. Basic set theory concepts are often taught to children, while more advanced concepts are usually part of a college education. Despite the simplicity of merely placing objects together, college-level set theory can be quite rigorous.

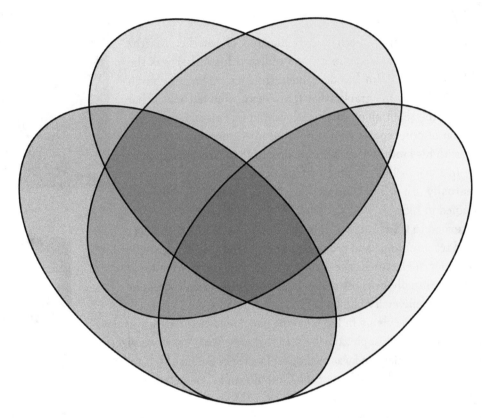

Image 2.0.1: Four-Set Venn Diagram

2.1 On the Shoulders of Giants: Biographies and Historical References

For Sets and Venn Diagrams ...

Much of what we study in relation to sets and Venn diagrams can be traced back to two individuals who provided many of their contributions around the end of the nineteenth century. Although there is no evidence suggesting the Englishman John Venn and the Russian-born Georg Cantor worked in collaboration, they were likely aware of each other's work and probably shared correspondences with other mathematicians from the same era.

The presentation of undeniable facts forms the basic foundation of set theory. That foundation was shaken in 1901 when a British mathematician and philosopher, Bertrand Russell, pointed out a paradox in that logistical reasoning.

The organizational structure of set theory used today allows some sets to have degrees of membership. For example, we could consider the set of all hot beverages. At first glance, we would think "hot" to be pretty clear, but at what *specific* temperature would you consider a cup of coffee to be hot?

John Venn

John Venn (1834–1923) was born in Hull, England. His mother, Martha Sykes, died when he was just three years old, and his father was the Reverend Henry Venn. John was descended from a long line of church evangelicals, including his grandfather John Venn, who led a sect that campaigned for the abolition of slavery, advocated for prison reform and the prevention of cruel sports, and supported missionary work abroad. He studied with his brother, Henry, in London in 1846, and moved on to Cambridge in 1853. In 1857, he obtained his degree in mathematics and would eventually follow his family vocation and become an Anglican priest, ordained in 1859.

Image 2.1.1: John Venn

Venn returned to Cambridge in 1862, as a lecturer in moral science, studying and teaching logic and probability theory, and beginning around 1869, giving intercollegiate lectures. These duties led to him developing the diagram which would eventually bear his name. A stained-glass window in one of the dining halls at the university, shown here, commemorates Venn's work.

He resigned from the clergy in 1883, having concluded that Anglicanism was incompatible with his philosophical beliefs. In that same year, Venn was elected a Fellow of the Royal Society and was awarded a Doctor of Science by Cambridge.

In 1903 he was elected President of the Gonville and Caius College at Cambridge, a post he held until his death, on April 4, 1923. In commemoration of the 180th anniversary of Venn's birth, on August 4, 2014, Google replaced its normal logo on global search pages with an interactive and animated "Google Doodle" that incorporated the use of a Venn diagram.

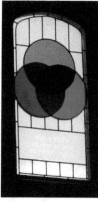

Image 2.1.2

Georg Cantor

Georg Ferdinand Ludwig Philipp Cantor (1845–1918) was born in the western merchant colony of Saint Petersburg, Russia, and was brought up in that city until he was eleven. Georg, the oldest of six children, was regarded as an outstanding violinist. Seeking winters milder than those of Saint Petersburg, his family moved to Germany in 1856. With exceptional skills in mathematics, Cantor entered the University of Zürich in 1862, and later studied at the University of Berlin, as well as the University of Göttingen. At the University of Berlin in 1867, Cantor completed his dissertation on the theory of numbers.

Image 2.1.3: Georg Cantor

Cantor's work between 1874 and 1884 is the origin of set theory. Prior to this work, the concept of a set was a rather elementary one. Before Cantor, there were only finite sets, which are relatively easy to understand. Everything else was "the infinite" and was considered a topic for philosophical, rather than mathematical, discussion. By proving that there are infinitely many possible sizes for infinite sets, Cantor established that set theory was not trivial and needed to be studied further. The basic concepts of set theory brought to the forefront by Cantor are now used throughout mathematics.

Cantor defined infinite and well-ordered sets and proved that the real numbers are "more numerous" than the natural numbers. As much of his work centered on the concept of infinity, many of his theories were originally regarded as so counter-intuitive—even shocking—that they encountered resistance from mathematical contemporaries such as Leopold Kronecker and Henri Poincaré. In a time when many Christians believed everything was tied to divinity, Kronecker's objections to Cantor's work on set theory were so vehement he was even quoted as having said, "God made the integers, all else is the work of man."

The objections to Cantor's work were occasionally fierce: Poincaré referred to his ideas as a "grave disease" infecting the discipline of mathematics, and Kronecker's public opposition and personal attacks included describing Cantor as a "scientific charlatan," a "renegade" and a "corrupter of youth" for teaching his ideas to a younger generation of mathematicians. Cantor's recurring bouts of depression from 1884 to the end of his life have been blamed on the hostile attitude of many of his contemporaries. In the 1880s heavy criticism of his work took a toll on Cantor's self-confidence, leading him to shift his research away from mathematics and toward philosophy. He also began an intense study of Elizabethan literature, thinking there might be evidence that Francis Bacon wrote the plays attributed to William Shakespeare.

Cantor retired in 1913, living in poverty and suffering from malnourishment during World War I. The public celebration of his 70th birthday was canceled because of the war, and he died on January 6, 1918, in the sanatorium where he had spent the final year of his life.

Bertrand Russell

Bertrand Russell (1872–1970), a British mathematician and philosopher, was born in Trellech, a small village in South East Wales. He was educated at Cambridge, where he was also a lecturer and fellow until 1916, when he was stripped of his position due to his outspoken opposition to World War I. In fact, his protestations were so severe, he spent six months in Brixton Prison.

Although Russell stated that mathematics was a subject he could love, but would not love him in return, he was presented with the Sylvester and deMorgan medals of the Royal Society in 1934, and in 1940, he received the Order of Merit. In addition to teaching at Cambridge, he spent time as a professor at Harvard, at the University of Chicago, and at the University of California at Berkeley before being imprisoned again in 1962, for leading movements in the opposition of nuclear weapons.

Russell's philosophical positions were critical of many societal institutions, stressing the importance of the individual. After his first marriage to Alys Pearsall Smith, who insisted on a Quaker ceremony, he said, "Don't imagine that I really seriously mind a

Image 2.1.4: Bertrand Russell

religious ceremony ... any ceremony is disgusting." Strangely enough, while on a bike ride in 1902, Russell came to the sudden realization that he no longer loved his wife. He would eventually be married four times, the last of which took place when he was 80 years of age.

Described as "a defender of humanity and the freedom of thought," Russell was friends with a wide range of people, including **Albert Einstein**, **Peter Sellers**, and **Winston Churchill**, and even received the Nobel Prize for Literature in 1950. Russell opposed communism, describing Karl Marx as "muddle-headed," and stating that "his thinking was almost entirely inspired by hatred." After meeting Lenin in 1920, he described the Soviet state as "an asylum of homicidal lunatics where the wardens are the worst."

The primary object of Russell's work was to show that mathematics was built on an unshakeable foundation of logic. It was in the field of set theory where this endeavor became jeopardized, as he became troubled by the existence of what would become known as **Russell's Paradox**, which, in generalized terms, states, "A barber is the one who shaves all those, and only those, who do not shave themselves. Does the barber shave himself?" No matter the answer, we have a contradiction. The barber cannot shave himself, because he only shaves those who do not shave themselves. But if he does not shave himself, he would be in the set of people that must be shaved by the barber. Contradiction. Given his passion for the study of logic, this paradox led Russell to say, "I felt about the contradiction much as an earnest Catholic must feel about wicked Popes."

Russell lived a very event-filled life and delayed writing his autobiography because, as he quipped, "I have a hesitation in starting too soon for fear of something important having not yet happened. Suppose I should end my days as President of Mexico; the biography would seem incomplete if I did not mention this fact."

Fuzzy Sets

Fuzzy sets are sets whose elements have degrees of membership. In contrast with well-defined sets in classical set theory, where an element either belongs to a set or it does not, fuzzy set theory allows gradual assessment of membership for the elements in a set. For example, the temperatures classified as "cold," "warm," or "hot" may change depending upon the situation being considered. Similarly, classifications of "young" or "old" could vary by one's chosen pro-

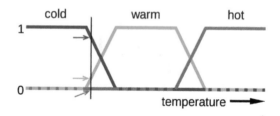

Figure 2.1.1 Fuzzy Logic with Temperature

fession. A 35-year-old doctor would probably be considered young, but a 35-year-old professional athlete would most likely be categorized as old. Membership in a fuzzy set is described using a membership function value, which ranges from 0 (completely false) to 1 (completely true). The closer to 1 a value is for an element, the higher the grade of membership in that set.

Fuzzy sets can be used in a variety of areas, but just for fun, let's look at an example of a fuzzy set that describes the actual fuzziness of different dog breeds. Ranging from 0 to 1 in terms of how fuzzy they are, a smooth-haired dachshund would not be very fuzzy and could be given a value of 0.1. A border terrier, in the middle of the fuzziness scale, could be assigned a 0.4, and then an Afghan, a very fuzzy breed, could be assigned a value of 0.9. This process of assigning a value to describe the degree of membership an element has in a set is commonly used for decision-making processes and is known as **defuzzification**.

Image 2.1.5a: Afghan

Image 2.1.5b: Border Terrier

Fuzzy set theory is used when information can be incomplete or imprecise, such as in the field of bioinformatics, a discipline that develops software tools for understanding biological data. Additionally, the concepts of fuzzy logic are applied to several areas of mathematics including fuzzy geometry, fuzzy graphs, and fuzzy subalgebra.

Many people remember that former president **George W. Bush** used the term "fuzzy math" in the months preceding the 2000 presidential election. It is probably unlikely that he was referring to this branch of mathematics.

References

Dauben, J. *Georg Cantor: His Mathematics and Philosophy of the Infinite*. Cambridge, MA: Harvard University Press. 1979.

Dubois, D. and H. Prade. *Fuzzy Sets and Systems*. Cambridge, MA: Academic Press, 1988.

Encyclopedia Britannica Online, s.v. "John Venn." Last modified January 17, 2017. https://www.britannica.com/biography/John-Venn.

Eves, H. *An Introduction to the History of Mathematics*. Philadelphia, PA: Saunders College Publishing, 1990.

Dunham, W. *The Mathematical Universe*. New York, NY. John Wiley & Sons, Inc.

"Russell, Bertrand Arthur William, Earl." In *The Lincoln Library of Essential Information*, vol. 2, 1966. Buffalo, NY: The Frontier Press Company, 1944.

World Book Encyclopedia, 1978 ed., s.v. "Russell, Bertrand Arthur William."

World Book Encyclopedia, 1978 ed., s.v. "Set Theory."

Zadeh, L. A. "Fuzzy Sets." *Information and Control* 8, no. 3 (1965): 338–353.

2.2 On Your Mark, Get Set, Go!: Basic Set Concepts and Notations

Forms of Sets

In order to better organize data, we often put them into sets. Simply stated, a **set** is a collection of distinct objects. Sets can be indicated several different ways, and three of the most common ways are using **roster form**, **set-builder notation**, or **verbal** (or written) **description**.

TABLE 2.2.1

Notation	Example
Roster Form	{2, 3, 5, 7, 11, 13, 17, 19}
Set Builder Notation	{x | x is a prime number less than 20}*
Verbal Description	The set of all prime numbers less than twenty.

*NOTE: In set-builder notation, the symbol | is called a pipe and means "such that."

One method to indicate a set is not necessarily better than another; they're just different.

If it is not possible (or practical) to list all of a set's elements using roster notation, an **ellipsis** (" ... ") can be used. But, before an ellipsis can be used, enough elements must be listed in order to establish a pattern. For example: {2, ... , 19} could mean all the prime numbers less than 20 or, possibly, all of the whole numbers from 2 to 19. When in doubt, it is usually best to describe larger sets with set-builder notation or a verbal description.

When writing a set in roster form, we need to be sure to separate each element with a comma. Also, be sure to use *braces* and not parentheses! For example, to indicate a set consisting of the lowercase letters a, b, and c in roster form, we must type the set as **{a, b, c}**. {a b c} and (a, b, c) are both incorrect because {a b c} lacks commas, and (a, b, c) uses parentheses.

> When writing ANY set in roster form or set-builder notation, we must be sure to encase the elements within a pair of braces, { }. The use of any other grouping symbols (parentheses or brackets) is incorrect.

When is a Letter Not a Letter?

In math, the symbols we use are just that—symbols. And, to make life easier, we frequently utilize the characters at our fingertips, which, more often than not, are the letters appearing on a computer keyboard. Keep in mind, however, they are just symbols. That means, since "A" and "a" are different characters, they are also different symbols. Even though they are both versions of the same letter, when we use them as symbols, they are as different as "A" and "B."

Think of the characters Δ and δ. Would you call them the same? Δ is the capital Greek letter delta, and δ is how we write the lowercase delta. In math, we would not necessarily think of them as Greek letters; we use them as symbols. The letters in the English alphabet need to be treated the same way. It is, however, worth noting that it is customary to use lowercase English letters as the symbols for elements and capital English letters as symbols for sets. We will see more of this in the next section.

Considering we are working with symbols and not letters, "A" is not an element in the set {a, b, c}, but "a" *is* an element of the set {a, b, c}. Using the symbols for "not an element" and "element," we have: A ∉ {a, b, c} and a ∈ {a, b, c}.

Another subtle but important characteristic of a set involves the word "distinct." To be precise, when using the roster form to write a set, we should not duplicate the elements in the list. For example, {a, b, b, c} is a list of objects, but we should not call it a set, because the b is listed twice. The order of the elements does not matter, but they should not be duplicated. Since we are doing a relatively short exploration into the topic of Set Theory, we will abuse this rule from time to time and refer to lists like {a, b, b, c} as sets to illustrate. Please afford us this luxury.

Infinite and Finite Sets

An **infinite set** has an unlimited number of elements. For example, the set of whole numbers, {0, 1, 2, 3, … } is an infinite set. If we know the number of elements in the set, or we know there is an end to the number of elements, we have a **finite set**. For example, the set {a, b, c} is a finite set that contains three elements.

EXAMPLE 1:

Are the following sets infinite or finite?

   a. The set of capital letters in the English alphabet

   b. The set of whole numbers

   c. All the gold bars in Fort Knox

Image 2.2.1

SOLUTIONS:

   a. Finite. There are 26 of them.

   b. Infinite. If you think you have the last one, just add 1 to it.

   c. Finite. We may not know how much is there, but there is a specific amount.

Well-Defined Sets

If there is no ambiguity or subjectivity as to whether an element belongs to a set, the set can be called **well-defined**. For example, the set of integers is well-defined, since it is clear whether a number is in that set, or not. Inversely, the set of good teachers at a school is not well-defined, because it is not clear whether a given teacher is to be considered "good" or not. In other words, if the contents of a set are subjective, it cannot be well-defined.

EXAMPLE 2:

Determine whether the following sets are well-defined.

   a. The set of capital letters in the English alphabet.

   b. The set of keys on John's keychain.

   c. The 10 best Disney characters of all time.

SOLUTIONS:

   a. Since we know the exact letters in the alphabet, the set is well-defined.

   b. Although we may not know what keys are on the keychain, a given key is clearly on his chain, or it is not. Also, no matter who makes the determination, the results are exactly the same every time. Thus, the set is well-defined.

   c. Since two different people will make two different lists, the set is not well-defined. Yes, we know there are 10 characters in the list, but we do not know which 10 characters are there.

Notations and Symbols

TABLE 2.2.2

SYMBOL	MEANING	EXAMPLE
~	Equivalent	$\{a, b, c\} \sim \{\#, \$, \%\}$ The sets have same number of elements.
=	Equal	$\{a, b, c\} = \{c, b, a\}$ The sets contain the exact same elements.
$\in$	Element Of	$a \in \{a, b, c\}$
$\notin$	Not an Element Of	$D \notin \{a, b, c\}$
$\varnothing$ or $\{\}$	The Empty Set	The set of all U.S. states sharing a land border with Hawaii is the empty set.

The Empty Set

Take a closer look at the symbols used for the empty set. In particular, look at the $\varnothing$. That symbol is *not* the number zero. Although many people like to distinguish between the letter O and the number 0 by placing a diagonal slash through the number 0, the $\varnothing$ symbol means something entirely different. Remember, the empty set has no elements in it. $\{0\}$ is the set containing the number 0, and $\{\}$ (or $\varnothing$) is the empty set. Additionally, $\{\varnothing\}$ is the set containing the $\varnothing$ symbol and, thus, is *not* empty.

Think of it this way: There is a big difference between having a checking account with no money in it and not having a checking account at all. For the former, you can walk into your bank, ask for your account balance, and be told, "Your balance is $0." If, however, you do not have an account (or you go into the wrong bank), the teller cannot quote you a balance for an account that does not exist.

If you are in the habit of putting slashes through your zeros, make an effort to limit your slash to the inside of the 0, itself. Then, for the empty set, extend your slash through the symbol on both the top and bottom. That is, 0, with the / completely contained within the symbol, is an alternative form for the number zero. While ∅, with the / extending through the symbol, is a way to indicate the empty set.

To help with the concept, throughout the remainder of this text, we will use the symbols for the empty set—both { } and ∅—interchangeably, but we will never put a / through any of our zeros.

EXAMPLE 3:

Each of the following statements is false. Without negating the symbol, rewrite the statement, so it is true. By the way, there are several ways to "fix" each statement.

    a. $7 \in \{2, 4, 6, 8, 10\}$

    b. $\{1, 2, 3, 4, 5, 6\} = \{q, w, e, r, t, y\}$

    c. $\{d, f, g\} \sim \{hat, coat, gloves, scarf\}$

    d. $\{a, b, c\} = (c, a, b)$

POSSIBLE CORRECTIONS

    a. Change the 7 into one of the elements in the set or put 7 into the set.

    b. Change the = to ~.

    c. Add an element to the set on the left or remove one from the set on the right.

    d. Change the parentheses to braces. Without braces, the list on the right is not even a set.

SECTION 2.2 EXERCISES

For Exercises #1 through #4, rewrite the statement using set notation.

1. 5 is not an element of the empty set.

2. t is an element of set B.

3. $13 < x < 19$

4. $x = 31$

For Exercises #5 through #9, list the elements in roster form.

5. The two-digit numbers on a standard analog clock.

6. The months of the year that do not have 31 days.

7. The set of all the states that touch the Pacific Ocean.

8. The set of all the oceans that border Nebraska.

9. {x | x is an odd whole number less than 10}

For Exercises #10 through #20, identify the statements as true or false.

10. Two sets that are equal must also be equivalent.

11. Zero is an element of the empty set.

12. The set of good students in our class is a well-defined set.

13. {0} is an empty set

14. {s, p, a, m} = {m, a, p, s}

15. {q, u, i, c, k} is a finite set.

16. Every well-defined set must also be finite.

17. The set of purple jellybeans is well-defined.

18. The set of purple jellybeans is infinite.

19. If two sets are equivalent, then they must be equal.

20. The set of ugly dachshunds is well-defined.

For #21 through #29, each of the statements is false. Provide at least two possible corrections. In each correction, change only one thing in the statement.

21. $14 \in \{2, 4, 6, 8, 10, 12\}$

22. {Fred, Barney, Betty, Wilma} ~ {Dino, Pebbles, Bam Bam}

23. $A \in \{a, b, c, d, f\}$

24. hat $\in$ {shirt, pants, shoes, coat, socks}

25. $\{1, 3, 4\} = \{a, c, e\}$

26. The set of people over 6 feet tall is an infinite set.

27. $a \notin \{a, e, i, o, u\}$

28. $\{1, 2, 3, 4, 5, 6, 7, ...\}$ is not well-defined.

29. $\{h, i\} = \{hi\}$

30. What is the empty set?

ANSWERS TO SECTION 2.2 EXERCISES

1. $5 \notin \{\}$ or $5 \notin \varnothing$

2. $t \in B$

3. $\{x \mid 13 < x \leq 19\}$

4. $\{31\}$

5. $\{10, 11, 12\}$

6. $\{February, April, June, September, November\}$

7. $\{Alaska, Washington, Oregon, California, Hawaii\}$

8. $\{\}$

9. $\{1, 3, 5, 7, 9\}$

10. True

11. False

12. False

13. False

14. True

15. True

16. False

17. True

18. False

19. False

20. False

For Exercises #21 through #29, answers may vary.

21. $14 \notin \{2, 4, 6, 8, 10, 12\}$, or
     $12 \in \{2, 4, 6, 8, 10, 12\}$

22. {Fred, Barney, Betty} ~ {Dino, Pebbles, Bam Bam}, or
     {Fred, Barney, Betty, Wilma} ~ {Dino, Pebbles, Bam Bam, Stan}

23. $A \notin \{a, b, c, d, f\}$, or $a \in \{a, b, c, d, f\}$

24. hat $\notin$ {shirt, pants, shoes, coat, socks}, or
     hat $\in$ {shirt, pants, shoes, coat, socks, hat}

25. $\{1, 3, 4\}$ ~ $\{a, c, e\}$, or
     $\{1, 3, 4\} \neq \{a, c, e\}$

26. The set of people over six feet tall is not an infinite set. Or the set of people over six feet tall is a finite set.

27. $a \in \{a, e, i, o, u\}$, or
     $y \notin \{a, e, i, o, u\}$

28. $\{1, 2, 3, 4, 5, 6, 7, ...\}$ is well-defined., or
     $\{1, 2, 3, 4, 5, 6, 7, ...\}$ is infinite.

29. $\{h, i\} = \{h, i\}$, or $\{h, i\} \neq \{hi\}$

30. A set that contains no elements.

2.3 How Many Are There?: Subsets and Cardinality

Subsets

When all of the elements of one set are found in a second set, the first set is called a **subset** of the second set. A formal definition is: If every element in set B is also an element in set A, then B is a subset of A.

EXAMPLE 1:

Given set A = {a, b, c, d, e}, B = {a, e}, and C = {c, d, f }, are sets B and C subsets of A?

SOLUTIONS: Since all of the elements in B are also in set A, set B is a subset of A.

Set C is not a subset of A, because the letter "f" is not a member of set A.

Every set has a certain number of subsets, and sometimes, it is useful to find all of them. We can determine the number of subsets using a systematic listing process.

EXAMPLE 2:

Let's say we would like to order a pizza from Phony Pizza, and the only toppings they offer are pepperoni, mushrooms, and anchovies. Taking into consideration that cheese has to be on every pizza Phony Pizza makes, how many different pizzas can we order?

Image 2.3.1

SOLUTION: Here is a set that contains all of the possible toppings: {p, m, a}. What we have been asked to do here is to find all of the subsets of that set.

The one-topping pizzas we could order are: {p}, {m}, and {a}
The two-topping pizzas we could order are: {p, m}, {p, a}, and {m, a}
We could also order a pizza with all the toppings: {p, m, a}

So far, we have found seven different pizzas we could order, but there is one more that we don't want to forget. We could order a pizza with no toppings—a plain cheese pizza. Since this pizza would contain none of the toppings, we would include this pizza in our list as the **empty set** and use either { } or ∅ to represent it. Sometimes it is difficult to accept the empty set as a subset. In terms of pizza, however, it is easy to see we can order a pizza with no toppings.

Thus, in total, there are eight different pizzas that we could order, which means the set {p, m, a} has a total of eight subsets.

Remember, there are no elements in the empty set. Thus, in the terms of our pizza toppings, there does not exist a topping in { } that is not in the set {p, m, a}. In other words, in order to *not* be a subset, there would have to be a topping listed in { } that you could not find in {p, m, a}. Given that there are no toppings in { }, there is nothing to compare with {p, m, a}. Since the empty set qualifies as a subset, this leads us to following important fact.

> By definition, the empty set is a subset of every set.

Additionally, the entire set also is a subset of itself. That is, {p, m, a} is, indeed, a subset of {p, m, a}.

Let's look at some other examples of subsets that don't involve pizza.

TABLE 2.3.1

A Given Set	{a}	{a, b}	{a, b, c}
Subsets of the set containing zero elements	{}	{}	{}
Subsets of the set with one element	{a}	{a}, {b}	{a}, {b}, {c}
Subsets of the set with two elements		{a, b}	{a, b}, {a, c}, {b, c}
Subsets of the set with three elements			{a, b, c}
Total number of subsets for the given set	2	4	8

If we continue to look at and count the number of subsets for a given set, we would notice an important fact. The total number of subsets of a given set—remember to include the empty set and the whole set, itself—is 2^n, where n is the number of elements in the given set.

In table 2.3.1, the set {a, b, c} has three elements. Thus, there are $2^3 = 8$ subsets for that set.

Intersection

Formally, the **intersection** of set A and set B, denoted $A \cap B$, is the set that consists of all the elements in *both* sets. That is, in order for an element to be in the intersection of set A and set B, that element must be in set A *and* in set B. Simply put, just like the intersection of two roads is where the roads cross, the intersection of two sets is the set of elements they have in common, which is essentially where the two sets overlap.

The Word "Or"

When we go to a restaurant and are presented with the choice of "soup or salad," this generally means we get to choose one item or the other, but not both. Here, the restaurant is using **exclusive "or,"** meaning the option of choosing both things has been excluded.

It is certainly possible, however, to use the word "or" in such a way that does not eliminate the possibility of having both. Let's say a friend asks you if you want to have "ketchup or mustard" on your hot dog. In this case, you could have ketchup only, mustard only, or you could have both. Here, your friend is using **inclusive "or,"** meaning the option of having both things is a possibility. Unless stated otherwise, when working with basic set theory, always use inclusive "or."

Union

The **union** of set A and set B, denoted $A \cup B$, is the set that consists of all the elements in at *least one* of the two sets. That is, if an element is in set A or in set B, then it is in the union of the two sets. Remember, we are using inclusive "or," so this means the set $A \cup B$ contains all of the elements that are in set A, joined with all the elements of set B, and it does include the elements that are common to both sets—but we don't list them twice.

Universal Set

Often a **universal set** is given to provide a point of reference for all of the possible elements under consideration. In other words, when forming a set, we cannot include any element that is not in the universal set. The universal set will be denoted with a capital letter U. Be careful not to confuse this with the symbol for union, ∪.

Complement

If set A is contained in the universal set, U, the **complement** of set A, denoted A', is the set consisting of all the elements in U that are not in A. The complement of a set can be indicated in a number of different ways, including the apostrophe (as above), a super-scripted c, or an overscore. Symbolically, these notations look like A', A^c, and $\bar{A}$. We will stick with the apostrophe notation, because, quite frankly, the other two are hard to type.

Notations

TABLE 2.3.2

Symbol	Meaning	Example
⊂	Subset of	{a, b} ⊂ {a, b, c, d}
∪	Union	A ∪ B consists of all the elements in ***at least one*** of the two sets.
∩	Intersection	A ∩ B consists of all the elements in ***both*** of the sets.
'	Complement	A' consists of all the elements in the given universal set that are ***not*** in set A.

EXAMPLE 3:

Given the Universal set U = {1, 2, 3, 4, 5}, and subsets A = {1, 4, 5} and B = {2, 4}, find the intersection of sets A and B, and union of sets A and B. Also, find the complement of A, and the complement of B.

Solutions: A ∩ B = {4} and A ∪ B = {1, 2, 4, 5}

A' = {2, 3} and B' = {1, 3, 5}

Proper Subsets

The subset symbol, ⊂, is actually used to indicate **proper subsets**, which are subsets that are not equal to the entire parent set. The word "proper" can be a bit misleading. We are not calling them right or wrong. Instead, we just mean a proper subset is smaller than the whole set. Remember our pizza example? {p, m, a} was the pizza that had all of the toppings Phony Pizza offered. It is certainly acceptable to order a pizza with everything. Just like the symbol ≤ means "less than *or* equal to," putting an underscore beneath the proper subset symbol, ⊆, gives us the "equal to" option.

By the way, the use of the word "proper" in this context is not unique to just sets. We have seen it before. When we studied fractions, we learned a proper fraction is a fraction with an absolute value between 0 and 1. In other words, a proper fraction has a numerator that is less than the denominator. The use of the term "proper" does not refer to the validity of fraction; it merely indicates the value of the fraction is less than a whole unit.

That said, to be technical, $\{a, b, c\} \subset \{a, b, c\}$ is incorrect, because we do not have the "equal to" option on the symbol. In order to indicate that the entire parent set is a subset, we would have to write $\{a, b, c\} \subseteq \{a, b, c\}$. Conversely, if we use the ⊆ symbol to indicate a proper subset, we are fine. That is, there is nothing wrong with $\{a, b\} \subseteq \{a, b, c\}$. Remember, ⊆ means the first set is either a proper subset OR equal to the set on the right of the symbol.

EXAMPLE 4:

Each of the following statements is false. Without negating the symbol, rewrite the statement so that it is true. Please note, there are several ways to "fix" each statement.

a. $\{a, b\} \subset \{a, c, e, f\}$

b. $\{\#, \$, \%, \&\} \cup \{\$, \#\} = \{\$, \#\}$

c. $\{\#, \$, \%, \&\} \cap \{\$, \%\} = \{\$\}$

d. $U = \{1, 2, 3, 4, 5\}$ and $A = \{2, 3, 4\}$, so $A' = \{1, 4\}$

POSSIBLE CORRECTIONS (YOUR ANSWERS MAY VARY)

a. Change the b to one of the elements in the set on the right (other than a), or put the b in the set on the right.

b. Change the union to an intersection, or put the % and & in the set on the right.

c. Put the % in the set on the right.

d. In A', change the 4 to 5.

Remember the order of operations for arithmetic? Specifically, we need to recall how parentheses are handled. In the expression $22 - 14 + 5$, we simplify it going from left to right to get 13. If, however, we have $22 - (14 + 5)$, we need to perform the operation within the parentheses first. $22 - (14 + 5) = 3$, not 13.

Unions, intersections, and complements can be thought of as the arithmetic operations for sets. Thus, if we introduce parentheses, we will need to begin any simplification by performing the operation(s) within the parentheses.

EXAMPLE 5:

Given the Universal set U = {2, 3, 4, 5, 6, 7, 8}, and subsets A = {5, 7, 8} and B = {2, 4, 5, 6, 7}, find:

a. $A \cup B$

b. $A \cap B$

c. A'

d. B'

e. $(A \cup B)'$

f. $(A \cap B)'$

g. $A' \cup B'$

h. $A' \cap B'$

SOLUTIONS:

a. {2, 4, 5, 6, 7, 8}

b. {5, 7}

c. {2, 3, 4, 6}

d. {3, 8}

e. {3}

f. {2, 3, 4, 6, 8}

g. {2, 3, 4, 6, 8}

h. {3}

Cardinality

The term **cardinality** refers to the number of elements in a set. The notation used to denote the cardinality of set A is **n(A)** and is read as "the number of elements in set A." Cardinality can also be considered with intersection and union of sets, for example n(A $\cup$ B), which would be "the number of elements in the union of sets A and B."

For a finite set, cardinality of the set should be determined and given as a single number. For example, if set A is the set consisting of all capital letters in the English alphabet, state n(A) = 26.

EXAMPLE 6:

For A = {a, b, c, d, e, f, g, h, i, j}, B = {a, b, c, d, e, f}, C = {a, e, i}, D = {b, c, d}, find:

a. n(A)

b. n(A $\cup$ B)

c. n(A $\cap$ B)

d. n(B $\cap$ C)

e. n(C $\cap$ D)

Image 2.3.2

SOLUTIONS:

a. 10

b. 10

c. 6

d. 2

e. 0

SECTION 2.3 EXERCISES

For Exercises #1 through #6, identify the statements as true or false:

1. $\{a, f\} \subset \{a, b, c, d, e, f, g, h\}$

2. $\{1, 4, 7\} \not\subset \{1, 2, 3, 4, 5, 6, 7, 8, 9\}$

3. $\varnothing \subset \{\text{red, white, blue}\}$

4. $4 \subset \{3, 4, 5, 6\}$

5. $\{\text{hawk, eagle, falcon, seagull}\} \subseteq \{\text{hawk, eagle, falcon, seagull}\}$

6. $(a, b, c) = \{c, a, b\}$

For Exercises #7 through #9, list all the possible subsets of the given sets:

7. $\{j, r\}$

8. $\{\text{Moe, Larry, Curly}\}$

9. $\{m, a, t, h\}$

10. A set contains 5 elements. How many subsets does this set have?

11. Explain, in your own words, why the empty set is a subset of every set.

For Exercises #12 through #14, given the groups of elements, name an appropriate universal set to which the elements could belong.

12. Apple, Dell, Gateway, Hewlett Packard

13. apple, banana, kiwi, orange, strawberry

14. basset hound, beagle, dachshund, poodle, St. Bernard

For Exercises #15 through #18, use the universal set, $U = \{1, 2, 3, 4, 5, 6, 7, 8, 9\}$

15. Find $\{1, 3, 5\}'$

16. Find $\{2, 4, 6, 8\}'$

17. Find $\{1, 2, 3, 4, 5\}'$

18. Find $\{1, 2, 3, 4, 5, 6, 7, 8, 9\}'$

19.   What does the notation, n(A) indicate?

For Exercises #20 through #22, the Universal set is U = {a, b, c, d, e, f, g}, with subsets A = {a, b, e, f}, B = {b, d, e, f, g}, and c = {b, d, e}.

20.   Find n(A)

21.   Find n(B')

22.   Find n(C)

For Exercises #23–34, the Universal set is U = {0, 1, 2, 3, 4, 5, 6, 7, 8}, with subsets A = {0, 3, 4, 5}, B = {0, 2, 6}, and c = {1, 3, 5, 7, 8}.

23.   Find A ∩ B

24.   Find A ∪ C

25.   Find B ∩ C

26.   Find B ∪ C

27.   Find A' ∪ B

28.   Find B ∪ C'

29.   Find A' ∩ C'

30.   Find (A ∩ B) ∪ C

31.   Find (B ∪ C)' ∩ A

32.   Find C ∩ (A' ∪ B)

33.   Find n(A ∪ B')

34.   Find n(B' ∩ C)

35.   Do we use inclusive "or" or exclusive "or" in this textbook?

36.   How do we find the intersection of two sets?

37.   How do we find the union of two sets?

ANSWERS TO SECTION 2.3 EXERCISES

1. True

2. False

3. True

4. False—without the braces, "4" is not a set, so it cannot be a subset. {4} is a subset of {3, 4, 5, 6}.

5. True

6. False—(a, b, c) is not a set

7. ∅, {j}, {r}, {j, r}

8. ∅, {Moe}, {Larry}, {Curly}, {Moe, Larry}, {Moe, Curly}, {Larry, Curly}, {Moe, Larry, Curly}

9. ∅, {m}, {a}, {t}, {h}, {m, a}, {m, t}, {m, h}, {a, t}, {a, h}, {t, h}, {m, a, t}, {m, a, h}, {m, t, h}, {a, t, h}, {m, a, t, h}

10. 32

11. answers may vary

12. computers

13. kinds of fruit

14. dog breeds

15. {2, 4, 6, 7, 8, 9}

16. {1, 3, 5, 7, 9}

17. {6, 7, 8, 9}

18. ∅ or { }

19. This notation indicates the cardinality of set A, which is the number of elements in that set.

20. 4

21. 2

22. 3

23. $\{0\}$

24. $\{0, 1, 3, 4, 5, 7, 8\}$

25. $\varnothing$ or $\{\ \}$

26. $\{0, 1, 2, 3, 5, 6, 7, 8\}$

27. $\{0, 1, 2, 6, 7, 8\}$

28. $\{0, 2, 4, 6\}$

29. $\{2, 6\}$

30. $\{0, 1, 3, 5, 7, 8\}$

31. $\{4\}$

32. $\{1, 7, 8\}$

33. 7

34. 5

35. As we are studying the basics of set theory, we use "inclusive or."

36. We find the elements that are in both sets.

37. We join the two sets together by finding all the elements that are in at least one of the sets.

2.4 Mickey Mouse Problems: Constructing Venn Diagrams

Venn Diagram Regions

Venn diagrams are representations of sets that use pictures. We will work with Venn diagrams involving two sets and three sets.

In order to ease our discussion of Venn diagrams, we can identify each distinct region within a Venn diagram with a label, as shown in figures 2.4.1 and 2.4.2. Our labels are actually the Roman numerals for the numbers one through four in the two-set diagram, and the numbers one through eight in the three-set diagram.

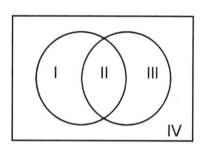

Figure 2.4.1 Two-Set Venn Diagram Regions

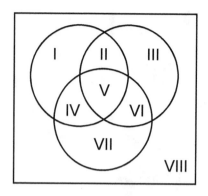

Figure 2.4.2 Three-Set Venn Diagram Regions

From a Different Point of View

In addition to identifying the region of a Venn diagram by a Roman numeral, we can also describe its shape. For example, in the two-set Venn diagram shown in figure 2.4.1, Regions I and III can be referred to as **crescents** (as in a crescent moon), while Region II in the middle of the diagram can be called a **football**. Figure 2.4.3 shows the crescent within Circle A, and figure 2.4.4 highlights the football-shaped region in the diagram.

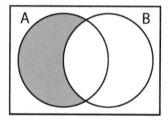

Figure 2.4.3 Crescent

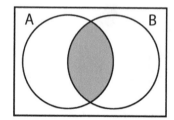

Figure 2.4.4 Football

In the three-set Venn diagram shown in figure 2.4.2, the crescent shape in the A circle would be Regions I and IV put together. If, however, we wanted to refer to the singular regions, we can use the term **double crescent** in reference to Region I, as well as Region III, and Region VII. Similarly, we can use the term **arrowhead** in reference to Region II, Region IV, and Region VI, while **center triangle** can be used to describe Region V in the middle of the diagram. Figures 2.4.5, 2.4.6, and 2.4.7 show examples of these descriptive shapes.

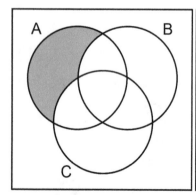

Figure 2.4.5 Double Crescent

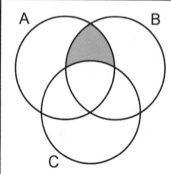

Figure 2.4.6 Arrowhead

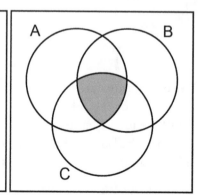

Figure 2.4.7 Center Triangle

The concepts of **intersection**, **union**, and **complement** (as well as the corresponding notation) are also used in the construction of Venn diagrams, as we can shade parts of a diagram to represent a certain set. Furthermore, any time parentheses are involved in a notation statement, that piece of the corresponding Venn diagram is shaded first.

The rest of this section contains several examples, but the concepts of this section will be learned primarily through practice.

Constructing Two-Set Venn Diagrams

To represent the set A in a two-circle Venn diagram, simply shade the circle corresponding to set A and ignore the rest of the figure, as shown in figure 2.4.8.

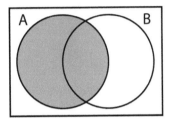

Figure 2.4.8   Set A

Likewise, the same idea would be used to indicate set B, as well as various intersections and unions with given sets.

EXAMPLE 1:

Create a Venn diagram for the set A ∩ B.

SOLUTION: While some may be able to visualize the set A ∩ B in the diagram right away, let's look at a step-by-step approach. That process looks a little bit like making a cartoon strip.

To represent the set A ∩ B in a two-set Venn diagram, realize we are looking for the intersection of sets A and B. Consider two separate Venn diagrams—one indicating set A in light red color and the other representing set B in light blue.

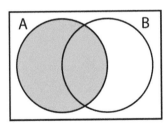

Figure 2.4.9a

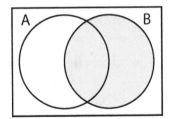

Figure 2.4.9b

When creating a diagram of the intersection of the sets shown in figures 2.4.9a and 2.4.9b, the result will be where the two sets overlap. We intentionally chose the light red and light blue colors to see the overlap turn purple, as in figure 2.4.9c. Since we may not have multiple colors available when working on these problems, an alternative approach is to use vertical and horizontal lines for the different sets. Here, we could fill the set A circle with vertical lines and set B circle with horizontal lines to make the overlapping region appear as cross-hatched, as in figure 2.4.9d.

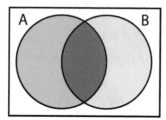

Figure 2.4.9c

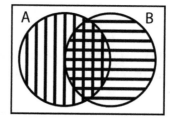

Figure 2.4.9d

Either way, since we are trying to get to only the INTERSECTION of these two sets, we finish our diagram by darkly shading the overlap of the two sets and erasing (if you used pencil!) the parts of sets A and B that are not in the overlap. If we can't erase the unwanted parts, we would simple redraw the diagram, as needed. This is shown in figure 2.4.9e.

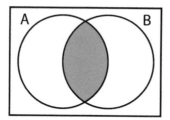

Figure 2.4.9e   Set A ∩ B

EXAMPLE 2:

Create a Venn diagram for the set A' ∪ B.

SOLUTION: Again, some may be able to visualize the set A' ∪ B and draw the diagram right away. This approach is fine if it works for you, but for others a step-by-step approach may be helpful.

Begin by drawing the diagrams for set A' and set B, as shown in figures 2.4.10a and 2.4.10b, respectively.

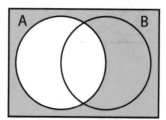

Figure 2.4.10a

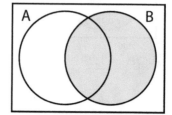

Figure 2.4.10b

Like in the previous example, when we merge figures 2.4.10a and 2.4.10b, the overlapping region turns purple as shown in figure 2.4.10c.

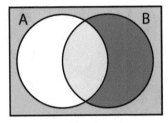

Figure 2.4.10c

Since we are trying to shade the UNION of sets A' and B, we finish our diagram by joining all the colored regions together. That is, we darkly shade everything we shaded in the previous image. This is shown in figure 2.4.10d.

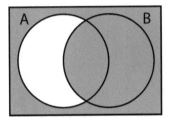

Figure 2.4.10d   Set A' ∪ B

Review: Order of Operations

When considering the Venn diagram representation for the union and/or intersection of more than two sets, just like with the order of operations for arithmetic, we need to work from left to right. And, once again, like the arithmetic order of operations, the only time we make an exception to the left-to-right process is when parentheses are used to group a specific operation.

Just like the arithmetic expressions "$10 - 2 + 5$" and "$10 - (2 + 5)$," simplify to two different values, the sets "A ∩ B ∪ C" and "A ∩ (B ∪ C)" will yield two different Venn diagrams.

Constructing Three-Set Venn Diagrams

Just like we saw with two-set Venn diagrams, to represent the set A in a three-circle Venn diagram, we simply shade the circle corresponding to set A and ignore the rest of the figure, as shown in figure 2.4.11. Likewise, the same idea would be used to indicate set B or set C. (By the way, can you see why some people refer to these as Mickey Mouse problems?)

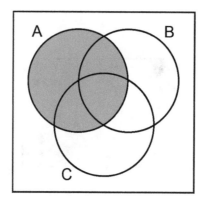

Figure 2.4.11   Set A

The creation of more involved three-set Venn diagrams is very similar to the process we followed for two-set Venn diagrams. They just take a little more time.

EXAMPLE 3:

Create a three-set Venn diagram for the set $A \cap B \cup C$.

SOLUTION: Again, some of us may be able to visualize all or part of this diagram right away. If that is true, great. If not, fall back on a step-by-step approach.

We start by shading the set A in light red, as shown in figure 2.4.12a. Next, shade set B in light blue, as shown in figure 2.4.12b. Like before, the purple, football-shaped region represents where the shadings overlap.

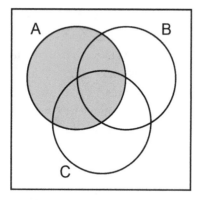

Figure 2.4.12a

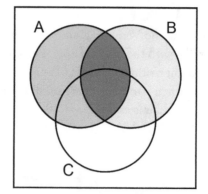

Figure 2.4.12b

We're not done yet; we've only completed the first half. At this point we use that overlap and have shaded the set A ∩ B, as shown in figure 2.4.12c. Next, we have to show the *union* of that football-shaped region with set C. So, we let the previously determined region be shaded in light red, and then add to it by shading set C in light blue, as shown in figure 2.4.12d.

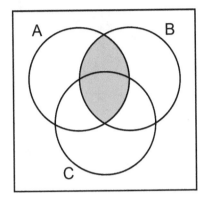

Figure 2.4.12c   Figure 2.4.12d

Finally, since we are trying to shade the *union* in this last step, we finish our diagram by joining the sets together. That is, we simply shade everything that was shaded in the previous image. The final image looks like figure 2.4.12e.

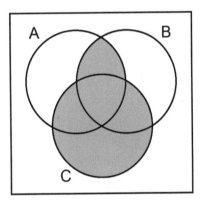

Figure 2.4.12e Set A ∩ B ∪ C

EXAMPLE 4:

Create a three-circle Venn diagram for the set A ∩ (B ∪ C).

SOLUTION: This time, because of the parentheses, we have to consider (B ∪ C) first. Thus, start by shading set B in light red, as shown in figure 2.4.13a. Next, we shade set C in light blue, as shown in figure 2.4.13b. Once again, the purple region represents where the shadings overlap.

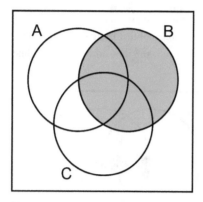

Figure 2.4.13a

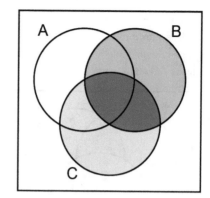

Figure 2.4.13b

Next, we need to find the *intersection* of B ∪ C and set A. So, we take the light red shading of B ∪ C, as shown in figure 2.4.13c, and then shade set A in light blue, as shown in figure 2.4.13d.

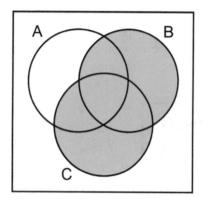

Figure 2.4.13c

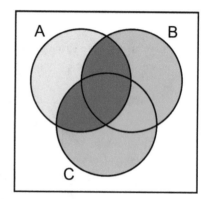

Figure 2.4.13d

Finally, since we are trying to shade the *intersection*, in this last step, we finish our diagram by shading only the overlap from the previous image. The Venn diagram should look like figure 2.4.13e.

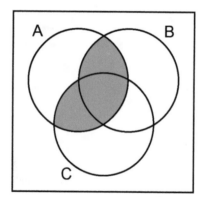

Figure 2.4.13e Set A ∩ (B ∪ C)

EXAMPLE 5:

Create a three-set Venn diagram for the set B′ ∩ (A ∪ C).

SOLUTION: Because of the parentheses, we must consider A ∪ C first. So, start by shading set A, as shown in figure 2.4.14a. Next, we shade set C, as shown in figure 2.4.14b.

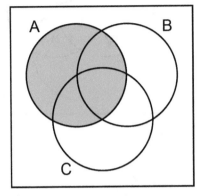

Figure 2.4.14a

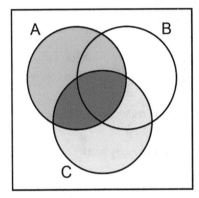

Figure 2.4.14b

Since we want A ∪ C, we join the sets together, as shown in figure 2.4.14c. Next, we shade the set B′, as shown in figure 2.4.14d.

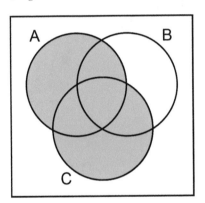

Figure 2.4.14c

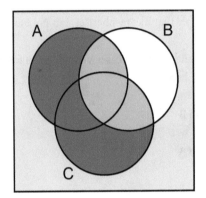

Figure 2.4.14d

Finally, since we are trying to shade the *intersection* in this last step, we finish our diagram by shading only the overlap from the previous image. The final image looks like figure 2.4.14e.

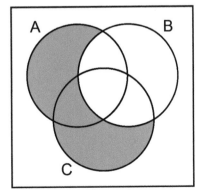

Figure 2.4.14e   Set B′ ∩ (A ∪ C)

SECTION 2.4 EXERCISES

1. Given that

   P = {people who like strawberries}
   Q = {people who like blueberries}
   R = {people who like raspberries}

   Use the three-set Venn diagram shown to determine the region(s) corresponding to the following.

   a. Identify the region you belong in.

   b. People that like raspberries and blueberries.

   c. People that like raspberries and blueberries, but not strawberries.

   d. People that like raspberries.

   e. People that like raspberries, but not blueberries.

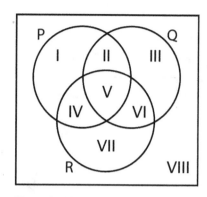

Figure 2.4.15

Image 2.4.1

2. Create and shade a two-set Venn diagram for each of the following.

   a. $A \cap B$

   b. $A \cup B$

   c. $A' \cap B$

   d. $A \cup B'$

3. Create and shade a three-set Venn diagram for each of the following.

   a. $A \cap C$

   b. $B \cup C$

   c. $B' \cap C$

   d. $A \cup B'$

   e. $A \cup (B \cap C)$

   f. $B \cap (A \cup C)$

g. $(A \cup B) \cap C'$

h. $B \cup (A' \cap C)$

4. Use set notation to describe the Venn diagrams shown below.

a.

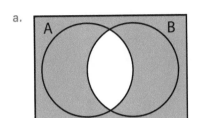

Figure 2.4.16a

b.

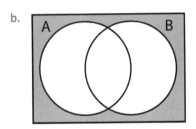

Figure 2.4.16b

c.

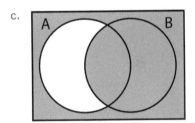

Figure 2.4.16c

d.

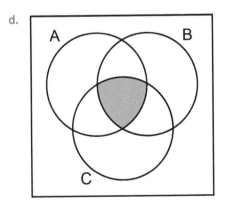

Figure 2.4.16d

e.

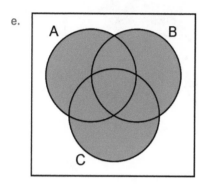

Figure 2.4.16e

f.

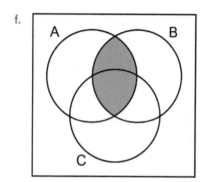

Figure 2.4.16f

g.

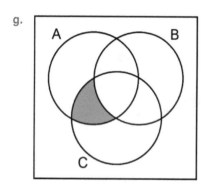

Figure 2.4.16g

h.

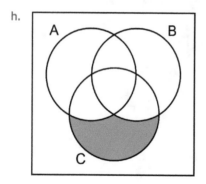

Figure 2.4.16h

5.   When drawing Venn diagrams, why do we use circles and not rectangles?

ANSWERS TO SECTION 2.4 EXERCISES

1. a. Answers will vary depending upon your personal preferences.

   b. Regions V and VI

   c. Region VI

   d. Regions IV, V, VI, and VII

   e. Regions IV and VII

2. a.
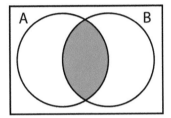
   Figure 2.4.17a

   b.
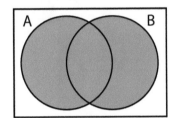
   Figure 2.4.17b

   c.
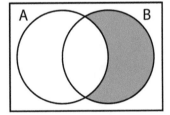
   Figure 2.4.17c

   d.
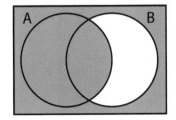
   Figure 2.4.17d

3. a.

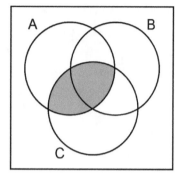

Figure 2.4.18a

b.

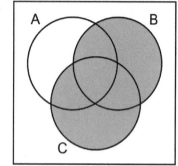

Figure 2.4.18b

c.

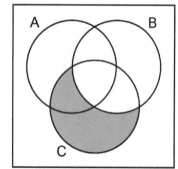

Figure 2.4.18c

d.

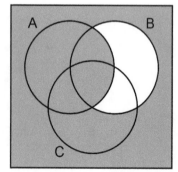

Figure 2.4.18d

e.

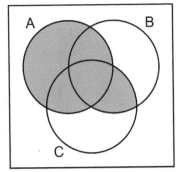

Figure 2.4.18e

f.

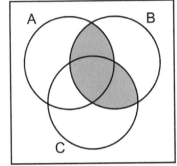

Figure 2.4.18f

g.

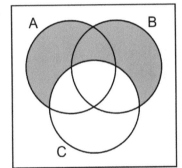

Figure 2.4.18g

h.

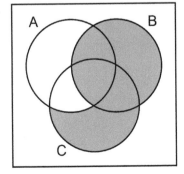

Figure 2.4.18h

4. a. $(A \cap B)'$ or $A' \cup B'$

    e. $(A \cup B)'$ or $A' \cap B'$

    f. $A' \cup B$

    g. $A \cap B \cap C$

    h. $A \cup B \cup C$

    i. $A \cap B$

    j. $A \cap C \cap B'$

    k. $(A \cup B)' \cap C$

5. It is easier to identify and describe the different regions with circles. Try drawing a three-set diagram with rectangles, and you'll find it may quickly turn into a situation where it is difficult to tell where one rectangle ends and a different one begins.

2.5 Putting Mickey to Work: Applications of Venn Diagrams

Applications of Two-Set Venn Diagrams

In addition to just being fun, we can also use **Venn diagrams** to solve problems. When doing so, the key is to work from the "inside out," meaning we start by putting information in the regions of the diagram that represent the intersections of sets.

Pay attention to the fundamental difference between the last section and the upcoming material. The previous material was limited to identifying the various regions in a Venn diagram. Now, we will be counting the *number* of items in those regions.

EXAMPLE 1:

In a group of 100 customers at Big Red's Pizza Emporium, 80 of them ordered mushrooms on their pizza, and 72 of them ordered pepperoni. 60 customers ordered both mushrooms and pepperoni on their pizza.

Image 2.5.1

a. How many customers ordered mushrooms but no pepperoni?

b. How many customers ordered pepperoni but no mushrooms?

c. How many customers ordered neither of these two toppings?

Solutions: Create a Venn diagram with two sets: mushrooms and pepperoni. To do this, first draw and label two intersecting circles inside a rectangle. Then, identify the number of items in each region, working from the inside out.

The innermost region is the football-shaped section corresponding to the intersection of the two sets. Since 60 customers ordered *both* mushrooms *and* pepperoni on their pizza, we begin by putting 60 in that center region.

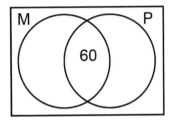

Figure 2.5.1a

Next, we know we need to have a total of 80 customers inside the "M" circle. We already have 60 of them in there, so we have to put 20 more of them into the circle for set M, making sure they are also NOT in the circle for set P.

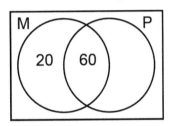

Figure 2.5.1b

Similarly, we know we need a total of 72 customers inside the "P" circle. We already have 60 of them in there, so we need to put 12 more into the circle for set P, making sure they are *not* in the circle for set M.

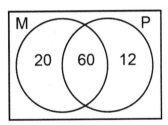

Figure 2.5.1c

Finally, there are supposed to be 100 people represented in our diagram. Up to this point we have accounted for $20 + 60 + 12 = 92$, so the remaining 8 customers must go into the region outside both of the circles, but still inside our rectangle.

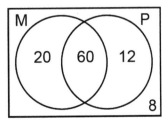

Figure 2.5.1d

Now, we can answer the questions.

a. 20 ordered mushrooms but not pepperoni.

b. 12 ordered pepperoni but not mushrooms.

c. 8 ordered neither of these two toppings.

EXAMPLE 2:

At Dan's Automotive Shop, 50 cars were inspected. 23 of the cars needed new brakes, 34 needed new exhaust systems, and 6 needed neither repair.

a. How many cars needed both repairs?

b. How many cars needed new brakes, but not a new exhaust system?

SOLUTIONS: Create a Venn diagram with two sets. To do this, first draw two intersecting circles inside a rectangle. Label the circles with a B for brakes and an E for exhaust.

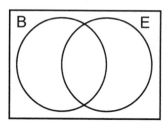

Figure 2.5.2a

Now, work from the inside out. That is, begin by determining the number of cars in the intersection of the two sets. Since 6 out of the 50 cars needed no repairs, that leaves 44 cars that did need repairs. 23 needed brakes, and 34 needed exhaust systems. That makes 57 cars (23 + 34) that got worked on, which is too many; we know only 44 cars needed repairs. This means 57 − 44 = 13 cars got counted twice, which means that 13 cars get placed into the overlapping part of the Venn diagram (the intersection). These 13 cars needed both brakes AND exhaust systems.

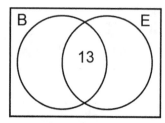

Figure 2.5.2b

Next, look at the circle that corresponds to brakes. There should be 23 cars inside that circle. 13 are already accounted for, so the remaining 10 must be added into the brakes circle, but are outside of the exhaust circle. Likewise, 34 vehicles must appear in the exhaust circle, so 21 more must be placed inside that circle, but not in the brakes circle.

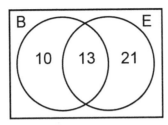

Figure 2.5.2c

Finally, 6 cars need to be indicated outside the circles but inside the rectangle.

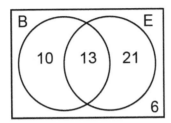

Figure 2.5.2d

By looking at the completed Venn diagram, answer the original questions.

   a. 13 cars needed both repairs.

   b. 10 cars needed brakes, but not an exhaust system.

EXAMPLE 3:

A survey was conducted in which 200 people were asked whether they preferred ketchup or mustard on a hot dog. Eighty-eight people said they like ketchup, 124 said they like mustard, and 16 liked neither of those condiments. How many of these people like both ketchup and mustard on their hot dogs?

Image 2.5.2

SOLUTION: We start by drawing a two-circle Venn diagram. One circle will tabulate the respondents who like ketchup and the other will be for those who like mustard.

   Usually, we begin by determining the number that would go into the intersection of the two sets. But, in this problem, that is the information we are being asked to find. We can, however, put the 16 people who like neither condiment into the region outside of the two circles.

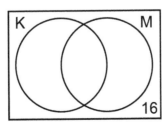

Figure 2.5.3a

This leaves 184 people who still need to be placed into our diagram. We were told that 88 people like ketchup and 124 like mustard, so it seems reasonable to put those numbers inside the appropriate circles. This might appear to be fine at first glance, but if we do this, we will see we have a total of 88 + 124 + 16 = 228 people represented in the diagram. But since only 200 people were surveyed, this cannot be correct.

Since our diagram is supposed to contain only 200 people (remember, only 200 people were surveyed), we can surmise that 28 people have been counted twice. Those 28 people are the ones who like both ketchup and mustard. They were counted once with the crowd who like ketchup and again with the mustard fans.

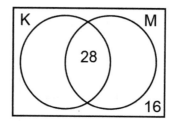

Figure 2.5.3b

The completed Venn diagram would show the 28 who like both ketchup and mustard in the intersection. Then, to get a total of 88 in the ketchup circle, we need to put 60 people in the part of the ketchup circle that does not intersect with the mustard circle. Likewise, 96 people are needed to be included in the portion of the mustard circle that does not intersect with the ketchup circle.

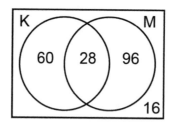

Figure 2.5.3c

We can verify that the numbers are correct by making sure the diagram meets the conditions given in the problem. There are 60 + 28 = 88 people in the ketchup circle, 28 + 96 = 124 in the mustard circle, and a total of 60 + 28 + 96 + 16 = 200 people in the entire diagram.

Applications of Three-Set Venn Diagrams

Applications with three-circle Venn diagrams are a bit longer and, consequently, a bit more involved. However, the strategy remains the same—we must work from the inside out.

EXAMPLE 4:

A survey asked 85 students about the subjects they liked to study. 35 students liked math, 37 liked history, and 26 liked physics. 20 liked math and history, 14 liked math and physics, and 3 liked history and physics. 2 students liked all three subjects.

a. How many of these students like math or physics?

b. How many of these students didn't like any of the three subjects?

c. How many of these students liked math and history but not physics?

SOLUTIONS: Create a Venn diagram with three sets, and label the circle M for math, H for history, and P for physics. Then, be sure to work from the inside out. Start by placing the two students that like all three subjects into the center, which is the part of the diagram that represents the intersection of all three sets.

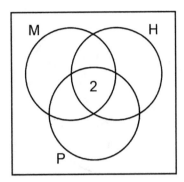

Figure 2.5.4a

We know 20 students like math and history, so the intersection of those two sets must contain 20 students. We already have 2 of them in that intersection, so we put the remaining 18 in the intersection of the M and H circles, but not in the portion that also intersects the P circle. Using similar reasoning, we put 12 students and 1 student into the regions shown on the diagram.

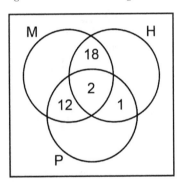

Figure 2.5.4b

Next, we know we need to have a total of 35 students inside the M circle. We already have 32 in there, so we put 3 students into Region I—the part of the M circle that does not intersect with any other region. Similarly, we put 16 students into the remaining section of the H circle and 11 students into the remaining section of the P circle.

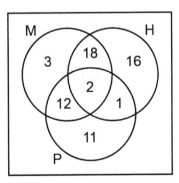

Figure 2.5.4c

Finally, there are supposed to be 85 students included in our diagram. Up to this point, we have included 63 of them, so the remaining 22 students must go into the portion of the diagram that is outside all of the circles, but still inside the rectangle.

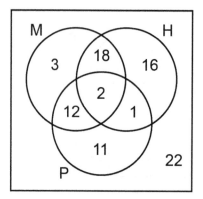

Figure 2.5.4d

Now, we can answer the original questions:

a. 47 of the students liked math or physics.

b. 22 of the students didn't like any of these subjects.

c. 18 of the students liked math and history but not physics.

EXAMPLE 5:

Schmancie's Restaurant keeps track of all of the orders made by their customers. One evening, they found that 64 customers ordered an appetizer, 110 ordered a main dish, and 76 ordered dessert. 48 customers ordered an appetizer and a main dish, 25 ordered an appetizer and a dessert, and 64 ordered a main dish and a dessert. 21 customers ordered all three, and every customer ordered something.

Image 2.5.3

a. How many customers ordered only a main dish?

b. How many customers ordered a main dish or a dessert?

c. How many customers ordered an appetizer and a main dish but not a dessert?

SOLUTIONS: Create a Venn diagram with three sets, and label the circles A for appetizer, M for main dish, and D for dessert.

Working from the inside out, start by placing the 21 customers who ordered all three types of menu items into the triangular region corresponding to the intersection of all three sets.

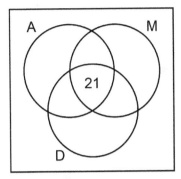

Figure 2.5.5a

We are told that 48 customers ordered an appetizer and a main dish, so the football-shaped intersection of those two sets must contain 48 people. We already have 21 people in half of that region, so we put the remaining 27 people into the other half of that region. In other words, there were 27 customers who ordered an appetizer and a main dish but not a dessert. Using similar reasoning, we will put 4 people into Region IV (the part of the diagram corresponding to customers who ordered appetizers and desserts but not main dishes) and 43 people into Region VI (the part corresponding to the customers who ordered main dishes and desserts but not appetizers).

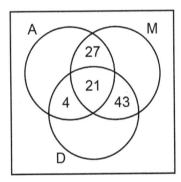

Figure 2.5.5b

Next, we know we need a total of 64 customers inside the appetizer circle. We already have 52 in there, so we put 12 people into Region I. Similarly, we put 19 people into Region III and 8 people into Region VII. Since we know that every customer ordered something from one of these three categories, zero people will be in Region VIII.

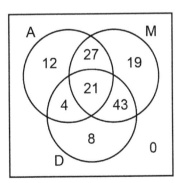

Figure 2.5.5c

Now that our diagram is complete, we can answer the original questions:

a. 19 customers ordered only a main dish

b. 122 customers ordered a main dish or a dessert

c. 27 customers ordered an appetizer and a main dish but not a dessert

SECTION 2.5 EXERCISES

1. The enrollment of 80 students at a college was examined. It was determined 39 students were taking a math class, 44 of them were taking an English class, and 18 of them were taking a math and an English class.

   a. How many students are not taking an English class?

   b. How many students are not taking a math class?

   c. How many students are taking neither of these types of classes?

   d. How many students are taking a math class or an English class?

2. A survey of 145 people was conducted, and the following data were gathered: 94 people use the Internet to find out about the news, 85 people use television to find out about news, and 62 people use the Internet and television to find out about news.

   a. How many of the people use only television to find out about news?

   b. How many of the people do not use the Internet to find out about news?

   c. How many of the people do not use television to find out about news?

   d. How many of the people use the Internet or television to find out about news?

3. A survey was conducted using 88 people. Of these people, 63 liked drinking coffee, 27 liked drinking tea, and 11 did not like either of these beverages. How many of the people surveyed liked both of these beverages?

4. 135 people were asked whether they like to watch basketball or hockey games. Of those, 91 said they like to watch basketball, 83 said they like to watch hockey, and 3 said they don't watch either game. How many of these people like to watch both games?

5. 120 people participated in a survey about their finances, and the following data were collected: 83 people have a checking account, 51 people have a savings account, and 26 have stocks. Forty people have a checking and a savings account, 11 have a checking account and stocks, and 7 have a savings account and stocks. Three people have all three types of accounts.

    a. How many people have only a savings account?

    b. How many people surveyed have none of the three types of accounts?

    c. How many people have a checking account and stocks, but do not have a savings account?

    d. How many people have only one of the three types of accounts?

6. A survey of 105 sports fans was conducted to determine which websites they read. Fifty-two read *CBS Sports*, 43 read *ESPN*, and 38 read *Fox Sports*. Eighteen read *CBS Sports* and *ESPN*, 11 *CBS Sports* and *Fox Sports*, and 8 read *ESPN* and *Fox Sports*. Six people read all three websites.

    a. How many of these sports fans read only *Fox Sports*?

    b. How many of these sports fans did not read any of these websites?

    c. How many of these sports fans read *CBS Sports* or *Fox Sports*?

    d. How many of these sports fans read *ESPN* and *Fox Sports* but not *CBS Sports*?

7. A survey of 160 people at a casino was conducted to determine the casino games that they typically play, and the following data were collected: Ninety-three played blackjack, 77 played roulette, and 39 played craps. Fifty-one played blackjack and roulette, 22 played blackjack and craps, and 11 played roulette and craps. Nine people played all three games.

    a. How many of these people played only craps?

    b. How many of these people did not play craps?

    c. How many of these people played at least one of the three games?

    d. How many of these people played blackjack or roulette?

8. The students in Mr. Jones' 5th grade class who owned pets filled out a survey. The Venn diagram below shows the number of students who belong to each region, with set D representing students who own dogs, set C representing students who own cats, and set F representing students who own fish.

    a. How many students own dogs?

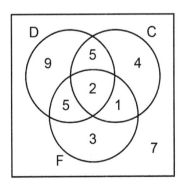

Figure 2.5.6

    b. How many students own cats or fish?

    c. How many students own cats and fish?

    d. How many students do not own dogs, cats, or fish?

9. The provided Venn diagram represents the cardinality of the specific disjoint regions. Use that information to find the following cardinalities:

    a. $n(A)$

    b. $n(C)$

    c. $n(A')$

    d. $n(B \cap C)$

    e. $n(A \cup B')$

    f. $n((A \cup C)')$

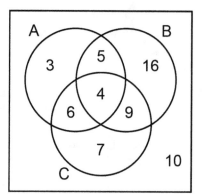

Figure 2.5.7

ANSWERS TO SECTION 2.5 EXERCISES

1. a. 36	b. 41	c. 15	d. 65		
2. a. 23	b. 51	c. 60	d. 117		
3. 13					
4. 42					
5. a. 7	b. 15	c. 8	d. 53		
6. a. 25	b. 3	c. 79	d. 2		
7. a. 15	b. 121	c. 134	d. 119		
8. a. 21	b. 20	c. 3	d. 7		
9. a. 18	b. 26	c. 42	d. 13	e. 35	f. 26

CHAPTER 2 CREDITLINES

STATISTICS

3

In statistics, we study **random systems**. We take samples, organize data, and draw conclusions. If, however, the systems we studied were not random, they would be completely predictable, and there would be no need for statistics at all.

More and more businesses and other entities are employing statisticians. Through random, unbiased sampling, a statistician can save a company millions of dollars and better prepare them for upcoming events. Professional sports teams analyze players' performances in different situations, so the teams can increase their chances of winning. And, if one team is doing it, the others had better follow suit or risk falling behind.

Insurance companies employ actuaries to analyze data and help determine how much policyholders will pay for insurance policies. A wealth of information is used to determine the likelihood a non-smoking, single mother of three has of getting a speeding ticket, having an accident, or even passing away. Based on that data, the insurance company sets its rates.

According to its website, http://www.nielsen.com/us/en.html, **The Nielsen Company** provides timely data on media and consumer trends, including TV ratings, smartphone trends, and video game purchase intent. That data provides other companies with a better understanding of consumers, but it also paints a rich portrait of the American audience.

Statistics are all around us. If we have a better understanding of how the data are obtained and who interprets the results, we can get a better idea of what to believe and, unfortunately, what not to believe.

Do be cautious, though. An old adage states, "90% of all statistics can be made to say anything ... 50% of the time."

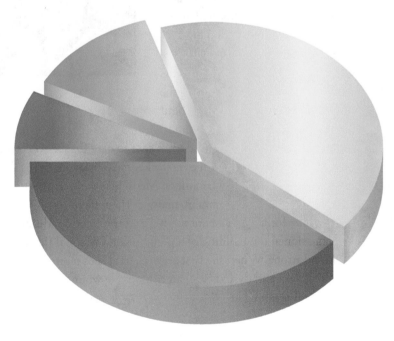

Image 3.0.1

3.1 On the Shoulders of Giants: Biographies and Historical References

For Statistics ...

Quick! Think of a famous nurse. Many people respond to this prompt by naming Florence Nightingale. What you may not have realized is she became that famous nurse through the effective use of statistics.

On the other side of the statistics spectrum is an infamous picture. In 1948, **Harry Truman** defeated **Thomas Dewey** for the Presidency of the US. In a well-published photograph, the day after the election, the president-elect laughingly waved a *Chicago Tribune* with the headline that mistakenly read "DEWEY DEFEATS TRUMAN." George Gallup was the one ultimately responsible for that headline.

Florence Nightingale

Florence Nightingale (1820–1910) was a celebrated English social reformer and statistician, and the founder of modern nursing. She was born on May 12, 1820, into a rich, upper class, well-connected British family in Florence, Italy, and was named after the city of her birth. In her youth, she was respectful of her family's opposition to her working as a nurse, only announcing her decision to enter the field in 1844. Despite the intense anger and distress of her mother and sister, she eventually rebelled against the expected role for a woman of her status, which was to become a wife and mother. Despite opposition from her family, and the restrictive social code for affluent young English women, Nightingale worked diligently to educate herself in the art and science of nursing.

Image 3.1.1: Florence Nightingale

Florence Nightingale's most famous contributions came during the Crimean War, which became her central focus when reports about the horrific conditions for the wounded were sent back to Britain. She and the staff of 38 women volunteer nurses that she trained were sent to care for the soldiers that were fighting in the Ottoman Empire. Her team found that an overworked medical staff, in the face of official indifference, was delivering poor care for wounded soldiers. Medicines were in short supply, hygiene was being neglected, and mass infections were common, many of them fatal.

After Nightingale sent a plea to *The Times* for a government solution to the poor condition of the facilities, the British Government commissioned the building of a prefabricated hospital that could be built in England and shipped to Southern Europe. When she first arrived, ten times more soldiers died from illnesses such as typhus, typhoid, cholera and dysentery than from battle wounds. Nightingale's directives in the war hospital, such as hand washing and other hygiene practices, helped reduce the death rate from 42% to 2%.

Nightingale became a pioneer in the visual presentation of information and statistical graphics. She is credited with developing a form of the pie chart, now known as the polar area diagram, to illustrate seasonal sources of patient mortality in the military field hospital she managed. She called a compilation of such diagrams a **coxcomb**, and frequently used them to present reports on the nature and magnitude of the conditions of medical care. These visual representations of the data helped the members of Parliament and civil servants to read and understand traditional statistical reports. In 1859, Nightingale was elected the first female member of the **Royal Statistical Society**. She later became an honorary member of the **American Statistical Association**.

Sir Ronald Fisher

Image 3.1.2: Sir Ronald Fisher

Sir Ronald Fisher (1890–1962) was a British statistician and geneticist. Poor eyesight prevented him from joining the British Army but led him to an ability to mentally visualize problems and formulate solutions. While a teenager, he won the Neeld Medal in mathematics, and secured a scholarship to study mathematics at Cambridge. Soon thereafter, he worked as a statistician and a teacher in a few different English villages and cities, including London.

As a researcher and an analyst, Fisher studied crop data at the Rothamsted Experimental Station, and later became a well-known biostatistician while working at University College London and the University of Cambridge. He published several papers that encouraged proper statistical design techniques and applications and went on to develop many prominent theories about evolution and population genetics. Among those theories was the **Sexy Son Hypothesis**, which states a female will choose an attractive mate with the belief that the two will produce an attractive male offspring, thereby increasing the likelihood of passing along her own genes to future generations.

In the 1950s researchers for the *British Medical Journal* began publishing data that suggested smoking tobacco caused lung cancer. Fisher, who was an avid pipe smoker, argued lung cancer was likely genetic and, even though there may a correlation between the two, it was not the same as causation. Fisher even suggested that certain people were genetically predisposed to crave cigarettes, but lost credibility when it was pointed out some of his research was funded by tobacco manufacturers.

A true genius, Fisher was elected to the **Royal Society** in 1929, and was knighted by **Queen Elizabeth II** in 1952. According to his biographers, Fisher was noted for being fiercely loyal to his supporters, but equally hostile to his critics. Even though modern beliefs run contrary to some of the viewpoints he championed in the early-to-mid 1900s, many of the statistical tools and techniques he developed are still prominent in today's research and experimental designs.

George Gallup

Image 3.1.3: George Gallup

George Horace Gallup Jr. (1901–1984) was born in Jefferson, Iowa. As a teen, George would deliver milk, and he used his salary to start a newspaper at the local high school. Later he attended the University of Iowa, where he became the editor of *The Daily Iowan*, an independent newspaper that covered the university campus. He earned his BA in 1923, his MA in 1925 and his PhD in 1928. After earning his doctorate, he moved to Des Moines, Iowa, where he served as head of the Department of Journalism at Drake University until 1931. Later that year, he moved to Evanston, Illinois, as a professor of journalism and advertising at Northwestern University. A year later, he moved to New York City to join the advertising agency of Young and Rubicam as director of research. He was also a professor of journalism at Columbia University, but he had to give up this position shortly after he formed his own polling company, the American Institute of Public Opinion (Gallup Poll), in 1935.

Gallup is often credited as the developer of public polling, as he wished to objectively determine the opinions that were held by the people. To ensure his independence and objectivity, Gallup resolved to undertake no polling that was paid for or sponsored, in any way, by special interest groups such as the Republican and Democratic parties.

In 1936, his new organization achieved national recognition by correctly predicting, from the replies of only 50,000 respondents, that **Franklin Roosevelt** would defeat **Alf Landon** in the US presidential election. This was in direct contradiction to a poll in the widely respected *Literary Digest* magazine. Twelve years later, his organization had its moment of greatest ignominy, when it predicted that Thomas Dewey would defeat Harry S. Truman in the 1948 presidential election, by five to fifteen percentage points. Gallup believed the error was mostly due to ending his polling three weeks before Election Day.

Today, the Gallup Organization conducts 1,000 interviews per day, 350 days out of the year, using both landline and cell phones across the US for its surveys. Their tracking methodology relies on live interviewers, dual-frame random-digit-dial sampling, and uses a multi-call design to reach respondents not contacted on the initial attempt. The data are weighted daily by the number of adults in the household and the respondents' reliance on cell phones, to adjust for any disproportion in selection probabilities. The data are then further weighted to compensate for nonrandom nonresponse, using targets from the US Census Bureau for age, region, gender, education, Hispanic ethnicity, and race. The resulting sample represents the opinions of an estimated 95% of all US households.

Lies, Damned Lies, and Statistics

American author **Mark Twain** wrote in his autobiography, "Figures often beguile me, particularly when I have the arranging of them myself." Following along with this theme, Twain popularized a saying that he attributed to former British Prime Minister **Benjamin Disraeli**, who said, "There are three kinds of lies: lies, damned lies, and statistics."

Actually, that line has been credited to Disraeli, **William Shakespeare**, **Woody Allen**, and several others. It is a way to describe the persuasive power of numbers, especially when statistics are used to support weak arguments or to mislead the public. Generally speaking, people are not experts in understanding statistical data, and for that reason, they can often misinterpret information. Compounding the impact of these types of "lies," people tend to believe specific data when someone who is considered to be an expert presents it.

Many variations of Disraeli's statement can be found, and one particularly notable version is from the British newspaper *National Observer*, published on June 8, 1891. Commenting on statistics related to national pensions, the published statement was, "It has been wittily remarked that there are three kinds of falsehood: the first is a 'fib,' the second is an outright lie, and the third and most aggravated is statistics."

The practice of misleading the public through the use of statistics is so well known that journalist Darrell Huff, in 1954, published the book, ***How to Lie with Statistics***. The book is brief and entertaining, and it outlines common errors involved when statistics are interpreted and how these errors can create incorrect conclusions. Additionally, the book describes the way graphs can be used to distort reality and mislead the reader. Throughout the 1960s and 1970s, this book was used as a standard textbook for the introduction of statistics to college students. It has been widely translated and is one of the best-selling books in history.

References

Cohen, B. "Florence Nightingale." *Scientific American*, March 1984. https://www.scientificamerican.com/article/florence-nightingale/.

Encyclopedia.com: Fisher, Ronald https://www.encyclopedia.com/people/history/historians-miscellaneous-biographies/ronald-aylmer-fisher

Encyclopedia of World Biography, s.v. "George Gallup Biography." http://www.notablebiographies.com/Fi-Gi/Gallup-George.html.

Small, H. *Florence Nightingale: Avenging Angel*. London: Palgrave Macmillan, 1999.

Steele, J. M. "Darrell Huff and Fifty Years of How to Lie with Statistics." *Statistical Science* 20, no. 3 (2005): 205–209.

Velleman, P. F. "Truth, Damn Truth and Statistics." *Journal of Statistics Education* 16, no. 2 (2008).

World Book Encyclopedia, 1978 ed., s.v. "Gallup, George."

World Book Encyclopedia, 1978 ed., s.v. "Nightingale, Florence."

World Book Encyclopedia, 1978 ed., s.v. "Public Opinion Poll."

Yates, F., and Mather, K. (1963). "Ronald Aylmer Fisher 1890–1962". *Biographical Memoirs of Fellows of the Royal Society*.

3.2 Right Down the Middle: Measures of Central Tendency

Mean, Median, and Mode

The thing commonly referred to as the "average" is actually the mean of a set of data. *Average* is a general term that actually applies to one of several different measures of central tendency. A couple of these measures are the mean and the median.

The **mean** is commonly known as the "average," and this is what we get when we "add them all up and divide by how many there are." You are probably very familiar with the mean.

The **median** is the middle number in the data set. Be careful; the data values must be arranged in order before we can determine the median. This order can be from lowest to highest, or from highest to lowest, but either way, the median is the value in the middle. For example, if our data set is {3, 3, 8, 7, 5}, we might be confused into thinking that the median is 8, because it appears in the middle. But remember, the numbers must be ordered first. So, since our ordered data set is actually {3, 3, 5, 7, 8} when arranged from lowest to highest, we can easily see the median of this data set is 5.

So, how do we find the median if there is an even number of data values? The median is then found by finding the mean of the two numbers in the middle of the data set. For example, if the data set is {2, 3, 5, 7, 8, 9}, there is not a single middle number. Since the 5 and 7 are the two numbers in the middle, the median would be the mean of those two numbers: $5 + 7 = 12$, and $12/2 = 6$. Thus, the median for that set would be 6.

Another descriptive measure of a data set is the mode. The **mode** is the single data value that occurs most often within the data set. If there are two data values that occur more often than the others, then we refer to the set as **bimodal**. For example, the set of data {2, 3, 4, 5, 7, 2, 7, 8, 2, 7, 7, 2} is bimodal, as the 2 and the 7 each occur four times. If there is not a single value (or a pair of values) that occurs most often, we say there is **no mode**. It is very common to see the mode grouped with the mean and median when discussing measures of central tendency, but since modal values don't have to appear around the middle of a data set, it is a misnomer to say they are describing the central tendencies of a set. That said, the mode is still useful in describing the overall appearance of the set.

EXAMPLE 1:

Find the mean, median, and mode of the exam scores listed below. Round your answers to the nearest tenth, as necessary.

93, 97, 59, 71, 57, 84, 89, 79, 79, 88, 68, 91, 76, 87, 94, 73, 58, 85, 82, 38

SOLUTIONS: Mean: The sum of the numbers is 1,548, and 1,548/20 = 77.4

Median: First order the numbers from lowest to highest. Since there is an even number of values, we must find the mean of the two values in the middle. (79 + 82)/2 = 80.5.

Mode: The mode is 79, as it is the most common value.

Frequency Tables

A **frequency table** is a way to arrange all of the data values from a given situation into chart form, which can be extremely useful for large data sets. The "frequency" column indicates the number of times a given data value occurs in the set. Occasionally, to reinforce the cardinality of the data set, we will also see a "total" row added to the bottom of the table

EXAMPLE 2:

The table below shows the size of the litter for 23 different cats. Find the mean, median and mode for the litter sizes.

TABLE 3.2.1

NUMBER OF KITTENS IN LITTER	FREQUENCY
1	2
2	5
3	6
4	7
5	3

Image 3.2.1

SOLUTIONS: The chart above represents the following data set: {1, 1, 2, 2, 2, 2, 2, 3, 3, 3, 3, 3, 3, 4, 4, 4, 4, 4, 4, 4, 5, 5, 5}, but using the chart allows us to avoid writing it out. We could certainly list out all 23 data values to find the mean, median, and mode, but let's take a different and more efficient approach.

Mean: To find the mean, we need to add the data values together and then divide by the total number of data values. Instead of adding together 23 individual numbers, we can make use of multiplication for groups of the same number. That is, the sum is: $(1 \times 2) + (2 \times 5) + (3 \times 6) + (4 \times 7) + (5 \times 3) = 73$. Since there are 23 total data values, the mean (rounded to the nearest tenth) will be $73/23 = 3.2$.

Median: Since we have 23 data values, an odd number, there will be a single middle number. There will be eleven data values greater than the median and eleven data values less than the median. Using the chart to our advantage, we can just count up from the bottom and find the location of the 12th data value. Counting the three 5s and the seven 4s gets us to the 10th data value. Since there are six 3s, we can see that the 12th data value would be a 3, and thus, 3 is the median. If we preferred, we could have counted down from the top to find the 12th data value. Counting the two 1s and the five 2s gets us to the 7th data value. Since there are six 3s, the 12th data value will be in that group, and the median will (again) be 3.

Mode: The mode is the value that occurs most often and is easily found by looking at the table. There are seven 4s, which is the most common of the data values. So, the mode is 4.

EXAMPLE 3:

Create a frequency table for the data set {2, 3, 4, 5, 7, 2, 7, 8, 2, 7, 7, 2, 8, 5, 5, 5, 5}, and then find the mean, median and mode, rounding to the nearest tenth, as necessary.

SOLUTIONS: First, create the frequency table. Be sure to order the data.

TABLE 3.2.2

DATA VALUE	FREQUENCY
2	4
3	1
4	1
5	5
7	4
8	2
Total:	17

Mean: Multiply each data value by its frequency. Add up those products and divide by the total number of data values. $(2 \times 4 + 3 \times 1 + 4 \times 1 + 5 \times 5 + 7 \times 4 + 8 \times 2)/17 = 84/17 \approx 4.9412$. Thus, to the nearest tenth, the mean is 4.9

Median: Since there are an odd number of data values, the median will be the single value in the middle of the ordered data set. With 17 data values, there will be eight values greater than the median and eight values less than the median, meaning the median is the value in the ninth position. There are four 2s, one 3, and one 4. That makes six values less than 5, so the ninth data value will be the third 5. Thus, the median is 5.

Mode: The value of 5 occurs most often, so the mode is 5.

How to Lie with Averages

Sometimes misinterpretations of statistics are the direct result of the use of the word "average." As we have seen, there are several different ways to compute averages. The two most common ones are the mean and median, but those two values can be enough to create a "lie." A company with several low paid employees and a couple highly paid executives may have a median salary of $35,000 (remember, half the employees earn more and half earn less than the median) and a mean salary of $120,000. Both numbers, however, can be called the "average" salary for the company.

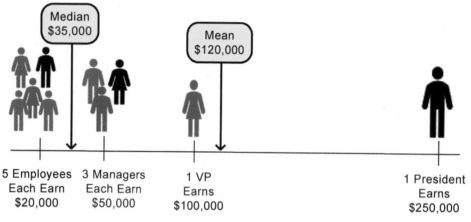

Figure 3.2.1   Mean vs. Median Salaries

EXAMPLE 4:

John has two job offers and his decision on which one to take rests solely on the salary. Company A states its average employee salary is $40,000, and Company B claims its average employee salary is $45,000. So, does this mean Company B is the better choice? Not necessarily. Examine the figures in the following table. Find the mean and median salary for each company.

TABLE 3.2.3

Company A Salaries	Company B Salaries
$30,000	$30,000
$35,000	$30,000
$40,000	$30,000
$45,000	$30,000
$50,000	$105,000

Solution:

Company A: mean = $40,000, median = $40,000
Company B: mean = $45,000, median = $30,000
Company B intentionally used the mean, instead of the median, when reporting its "average" salary. This isn't lying, but it is misleading to a potential employee. In this case, Company A is probably the better choice for John.

As we can see, often, the easiest way to lie with an average is to just use the word "average" and let the reader misinterpret the actual meaning of the statement. Here are a couple of "average" statements that are commonly misinterpreted. What should the proper interpretation of each be?

1. On average, most auto accidents occur on Saturday night. This means that people do not drive carefully on Saturday night.

   Proper Interpretations: This "average" is a mode. More people are on the road Saturday nights. Also, it is very likely that more people drink and drive on Saturday nights than other nights of the week.

2. At East High School, half of the students score below average in mathematics. Therefore, the school should receive more federal aid to raise standards.

   Proper Interpretation: If the reported "average" is the median, half the students will *always* be below average.

Review: Order of Operations

If several people are asked to simplify the same multi-step arithmetic **expression**, a standard set of rules must be established for the order in which the operations are performed. Otherwise, different people may get different answers. For example, let's say Bill and Ted are asked to simplify the expression $3 + 4 \times 5$. Bill adds the $3 + 4$, and then multiplies that result by 5 to get a total of 35. Ted performs the multiplication first, and then adds 3 to get a total of 23. Who is right? In case you aren't sure yet ... it is Ted.

Arithmetic started with addition (and subtraction). Repeated addition led to multiplication (and division), and repeated multiplication led to the use of exponents. In addition to those procedures, parentheses or other grouping symbols can also be used in an expression. Let's consolidate all of these processes into a single list, known as the "order of operations."

Arithmetic **Order of Operations:**

1. All operations contained within parentheses ( ) or other grouping symbols, such as brackets [ ], or braces { }, should be done first.

2. Secondly, simplify all expressions containing exponents.

3. Multiplication and division are done next, as we come to them going from left to right.

4. Addition and subtraction are done last, again, as we come to them going from left to right.

To help remember this order, many students like to memorize the acronym **PEMDAS** (Parentheses, Exponents, Multiplication, Division, Addition, Subtraction). This can be really helpful, but be careful! If you do not realize multiplication and division are done as we come to them going from the left to the right, you may fall into the trap of thinking multiplication always precedes division—it does not. The same holds true for addition and subtraction.

EXAMPLE 5:

Simplify: $5 + 6 \times 3$

SOLUTION: Since multiplication is performed before addition, start by multiplying 6×3. Then, add 5 to that result.

$5 + 6 \times 3$
$= 5 + 18$
$= 23$

EXAMPLE 6:

Simplify: $13 - 5 + 6$

SOLUTION: Remember, perform addition and subtraction as we come to them going from left to right. Here, that means the subtraction must be done first.

$13 - 5 + 6$
$= 8 + 6$
$= 14$

EXAMPLE 7:

Simplify: $13 - (5 + 6)$

SOLUTION: Since $(5 + 6)$ is inside parentheses, that operation is performed first.

$13 - (5 + 6)$
$= 13 - 11$
$= 2$

EXAMPLE 8:

Simplify: $3 \times (5) + 2 \times (4) + 4 \times (3)$

SOLUTION: There are parentheses in this expression but take note that there is no operation to perform inside these parentheses. We have multiplication and addition to perform here, so we will perform the multiplications first, and the additions afterward.

$3 \times (5) + 2 \times (4) + 4 \times (3)$
$= 15 + 8 + 12$
$= 35$

EXAMPLE 9:

Simplify: $5 \times (2 + 3)^2 - (6 - 4) + 1$

SOLUTION: Here, we start with the operations that are inside the parentheses. Then, perform the operation using the exponent. After that, the multiplication is done. Finally, we have addition and subtraction, which are performed as we come to them going from left to right.

$$5 \times (2 + 3)^2 - (6 - 4) + 1$$
$$= 5 \times (5)^2 - 2 + 1$$
$$= 5 \times 25 - 2 + 1$$
$$= 125 - 2 + 1$$
$$= 123 + 1$$
$$= 124$$

Grade Point Averages

Students should to be able to compute their own **Grade Point Average**, also known as the **GPA**. The GPA is a weighted average. That is, each grade has a weight associated with it. This weight is typically the number of credits of the course for which the grade was earned. Thus, an A in a 4-credit class carries more weight than an A in a 3-credit class.

First, we need to know the values of specific grades. The following table is taken from the College of Southern Nevada (CSN) Catalog.

TABLE 3.2.4 GRADE VALUES AT CSN

GRADE	VALUE	GRADE	VALUE
A	4.0	C	2.0
A-	3.7	C-	1.7
B+	3.3	D+	1.3
B	3.0	D	1.0
B-	2.7	D-	0.7
C+	2.3	F	0.0

Courses with grades of I (Incomplete), P (Pass), S (Satisfactory), U (Unsatisfactory), W (Withdrawal), NR (Not Reported), or AU (Audit) are not included in the GPA calculation.

To compute a GPA, we first multiply the value of the grade by the corresponding weight, which is the number of credits for the course. That product gives us the number of grade points earned for the course. Then, we add together the grade points for all the courses and divide by the total number of credits taken. Even though the individual grade values are listed to the tenth of a point, published GPAs are usually rounded to the nearest hundredth or thousandth.

common mistake:

When computing GPAs, a common mistake is to divide by the number of classes.

Remember, we should divide the sum of the grade points by the total number of credits.

EXAMPLE 10:

The table below represents a student's grades for a given semester at CSN. Find the student's GPA for that semester. Make sure to note that this student took a total of 12 credits. Round your answer to the nearest thousandth.

TABLE 3.2.5

COURSE	CREDITS	GRADE
ENG 103	3	A-
HIST 107	4	B
MATH 120	3	C+
IS 241	2	A

SOLUTION: For ENG 103: $3 \times 3.7 = 11.1$
For HIST 107: $4 \times 3.0 = 12.0$
For MATH 120: $3 \times 2.3 = 6.9$
For IS 241: $2 \times 4.0 = 8.0$
Semester GPA: $(11.1 + 12.0 + 6.9 + 8.0)/12 = 38.0/12 = 3.16666 ...$, which is then rounded to 3.167.

SECTION 3.2 EXERCISES

For Exercises #1 through #4, find the mean, median, and mode of each data set. Round any decimal answers to the nearest tenth.

1. {1, 3, 5, 5, 7, 8, 9, 11}

2. {5, 13, 8, 4, 7, 2, 11, 15, 3}

3. {37, 52, 84, 99, 73, 17}

4. {4, 16, 9, 4, 2, 4, 1}

5. During the month of November 2008, the Oakland Raiders played five football games. In those games, the team scored the following number of points: 0, 6, 15, 31, and 13. Find the mean, median, and mode for this data set. Round any decimal answers to the nearest tenth. Did the Raiders win all five games?

6. The mean score on a set of 15 exams is 74. What is the sum of the 15 exam scores?

7. A class of 12 students has taken an exam, and the mean of their scores is 71. One student takes the exam late and scores 92. After including

Image 3.2.2

the new score, what is the mean score for all 13 exams? If you get a decimal answer, you should round to the nearest hundredth.

8. The 20 students in Mr. Edmondson's class earned a mean score of 76 on an exam. Taking the same exam, the 10 students in Mrs. Wilkinson's class earned a mean score of 86. What is the mean when these teachers combine the scores of their students? If you get a decimal answer, you should round to the nearest hundredth.

9. After six exams, Carl has a mean score of 78.5. With only one exam remaining in the class, what is the minimum score Carl will need on that exam to have an overall mean of 80?

10. Create a set of seven data values in which the mean is higher than the median.

11. Can the mean be a negative number? Explain your answer and give an example.

12. Table 3.2.6 gives the ages of cars (in years) in a supermarket parking lot. Using the information given in the table, find the mean, median, and mode of the data. Round any decimal answers to the nearest tenth.

TABLE 3.2.6

Age of the Car in Years	Number of Cars
1	5
2	9
3	13
4	14
5	6
6	2

13. Table 3.2.7 gives the distance (in miles) students in a class travel to get to campus. Using the information given in the table, find the mean, median, and mode of the data. Round any decimal answers to the nearest tenth of a mile.

TABLE 3.2.7

Miles Traveled	Number of Students
2	4
5	8
8	5
12	6
15	3
20	2
30	1

14. The number of years of experience of the kindergarten teachers at a school are as follows:

    Mr. Amazing: 2   Mrs. Super: 1
    Ms. Terrific: 10   Mrs. Dynamite: 2
    Mr. Great: 12   Ms. Fantastic: 3

    a. Find the mean, median, and mode for the number of years of experience for these teachers.

    b. If you were a parent, and you wanted to emphasize the fact that the teachers did not have very much experience, would you use the mean, median, or mode to support your argument?

    c. If you were the principal, and you were pointing out that your kindergarten teachers did have sufficient experience, would you use the mean, median, or mode to support your argument?

15. The following statement is misleading. Provide a proper interpretation.
    The average depth of the pond is 3 feet, so it is safe to go wading.

16. A student earned an A in her 5-credit CHEM class, a C in her 1-credit ART class, and a B in her 3-credit Spanish class. What is her GPA for the term? For grade values, use the CSN values listed earlier in this section. Round your answer to the nearest hundredth.

17. A student earned a C+ in his 3-credit MATH class, a B in his 3-credit English class, a C in his 4-credit HIST class, and an A in his 1-credit PE class. What is his GPA for the term? For grade values, use the CSN values listed earlier in this section. Round your answer to the nearest thousandth.

18. Would it make sense to have a frequency table for a set of data without repeated values? Why or why not?

ANSWERS TO SECTION 3.2 EXERCISES

1. mean = 6.1, median = 6, mode = 5

2. mean = 7.6, median = 7, mode = none

3. mean = 60.3, median = 62.5, mode = none

4. mean = 5.7, median = 4, mode = 4

5. mean = 13, median = 13, mode = none
   Since they could not win a game in which they scored zero points, they did not win all five games.

6. 1,110

7. 72.62

8. 79.33

9. 89

10. Answers may vary. Find the mean and median to check and see if your data set meets the conditions of the problem.

11. Yes. An example would be the mean low temperature in Anchorage, Alaska, during the month of January.

12. mean = 3.3, median = 3, mode = 4

13. mean = 9.5, median = 8, mode = 5

14. a. mean = 5, median = 2.5, mode = 2

    b. The mode, by saying something like: "The most common number of years of experience is 2."

    c. The mean, by saying something like: "The average number of years of experience is 5."

15. Proper Interpretation: The pond could be very shallow in some spots, but very deep in others.

16. 3.44

17. 2.536

18. No. Without repeated values, you would end up listing all the data values. In that case, just leave them in a set, rather than building a table to indicate there is only one of each value.

3.3 Mine Is Better Than Yours: Percentiles and Quartiles

Percentiles

When data sets are relatively small, one of the best ways to spot clusters of values, as well as the relationships between the individual values, is to simply list and inspect them. However, when data sets get large, say over 100 values, listing the values out becomes impractical. As an alternative, **percentiles** are used to describe the relative position of certain data values when compared to the entire data set. Simply put, a data value at the 70th percentile is above 70% of the data values in the set. We often hear the term **percentile rank** when discussing test results. If a student scored at the 82nd percentile, then that student scored above 82% of the people who took the test.

Read that last sentence again. If a student scored at the 82nd percentile, then that student scored *above* 82% of the people that took the test. The biggest mistake when dealing with percentiles is computing them as straightforward percents. They are actually a little bit different. If we have a set of 10 ranked values, 70% of them would be 7 out of the 10. However, the value at the 70th percentile is the first value greater than 70% of the values in the set. So, if the data consists of the set {1, 2, 3, 4, 5, 6, 7, 8, 9, 10}, the score at the 70th percentile is the 8, as it is the first value in the set *greater than* 70% of the values in the set. Once again, in most cases, if a mistake is made in working with percentiles, it is finding the value *at* the stated percent, rather than finding the first value *above* the stated percent.

Additionally, we need to make sure to know whether we are looking for an overall rank or a percentile rank. Overall rank is based on the total number of data values, and the highest value is ranked first. Percentile ranks are indicated with whole numbers ranging from 0 to 99. There is no 100th percentile, as a value at the 100th percentile would be above 100% of the values in the set. This wouldn't make sense, as it would mean the value was higher than itself.

EXAMPLE 1:

In a class of 375 students, Sarah has a rank of 15th. What is her percentile rank?

SOLUTION: We first find the number of students below her: $375 - 15 = 360$. We then divide that number by the total number of students in the class: $360/375 = 0.96$. So, Sarah is ranked above 96% of the students in her class, which means she is ranked at the 96th percentile.

EXAMPLE 2:

415 people ran a marathon, and Shane finished at the 27th percentile. In what place did Shane finish?

SOLUTION: We use the knowledge that he finished ahead of 27% of the runners to determine that he finished ahead of $0.27 \times 415 = 112.05 \rightarrow 112$ runners. Since 415 runners were in the race, we can subtract the 112 that finished behind him: $415 - 112 = 303$, to find out that he finished in 303rd place.

How to Lie with Comparisons

Caveat Emptor. Let the Buyer Beware. Warning ... When comparing things, a frequent practice in advertising is to compare items but leave out key data, thereby allowing the target audience to assume conditions that are preferable to themselves.

For example, the Miracle Juicer Company can claim their electric juicer "extracts 40% more juice," implying it is superior to other juicers on the market. By neglecting to point out their juicer was tested against an old-fashioned manual juice extractor, they have lied by omission. Sadly, even though it is intentionally deceptive, it is not illegal.

Image 3.3.1

We've all heard the claim (or something similar), "Four out of 5 dentists recommend sugar-free gum for their patients who chew gum." Can you see some problems with that claim?

- Were only 5 dentists surveyed?

- How many times did they have to do this survey to get these results?

- Is it possible that only 1 out of 100 dentists even recommend chewing gum at all?

Below are a few fictional advertisements, all of which are true in some way, but all also "lie" by leaving out some relevant information. Can you spot the omissions?

1. 8 News Now: The Valley's top rated 4 PM newscast.

    Omission: What Channel 8 conveniently omitted was they were the only station with a 4 PM newscast.

2. Coke beats Pepsi! In a recent taste test, an amazing 60 percent said Coke tasted as good as or better than Pepsi.

    Omission: In reality, 36% of the people surveyed liked Coke better, but 40% liked Pepsi better. When 24% said the two were equal in taste, the claim made becomes true. That's why the ad used the words "as good as or better."

3. Hospitals recommend acetaminophen, the aspirin-free pain reliever in Ache-Free, more than any other pain reliever!

    Omission: Pay attention; the recommendation is for acetaminophen, not the product that contains it. They casually neglected other national brands that also contain acetaminophen, and hospitals recommended some of those other brands more than Ache-Free.

4. In a fall fashion survey of college students, 90% say Votam Jeans are "in" on campus.

    Omission: What was not mentioned was that Votam Jeans were the only jeans listed in the survey. Other entries included T-shirts, 1960s-style clothing, overalls, and neon-colored clothing. So, anyone who wanted to choose any type of jeans had no choice but to pick Votam Jeans.

As we can see, advertisers—and, sadly, political candidates—love to let the general public fill in the blanks. This is usually done in a positive fashion, as we all would like the presented information to be skewed in our favor. Essentially, if you find yourself making an assumption that agrees with a presented statistical analysis, there's a chance some facts surrounding that assumption were intentionally omitted.

Quartiles

Instead of discussing the position of a data value in relation to all the values in the set, alternative descriptive measures used in large data sets are known as quartiles. **Quartiles** cut the data into four equal parts. As we saw in the previous section, the middle of the ranked data set is called the **median**. The median cuts the data set in half, but it does not have to be one of the data values in the set. In fact, if there is an even number of data values, the median is the mean of the two values in the middle. Thus, the median can be thought of as a boundary between the lower half and the upper half of the data set.

Counting from the bottom up, the **first quartile** (also called the **lower quartile**) is the median of the lower half of the data set. Similarly, the **third quartile** (also called the **upper quartile**) is the median of the upper half of the data set. Like the median (which is sometimes called the **second** or **middle quartile**), the first and third quartiles do not have to be specific values in the data set. The first quartile, median, and third quartile are boundaries that divide the data set into four equal parts. Remember, percentiles describe the location of a specific data values, and quartiles cut the entire set into four equally sized parts.

Once again, although it is possible to have data values fall at the quartile boundaries, it is not necessary for the quartiles to be numbers in the data set. It is also important to note, when considering an odd number of data points, the median is *not* in either the upper or lower half; it is the boundary between the two. For example, in the set {1, 2, 3, 4, 5, 6, 7}, the lower half of data points is {1, 2, 3}, not {1, 2, 3, 4}.

The Five-Number Summary

When working with quartiles, it is also useful to identify the lowest and highest values in the data set. All together, that group of five quantities—the lowest value (L), the first quartile (Q_1), the median (M), the third quartile (Q_3), and the highest value (H)—is called the **five-number summary**.

EXAMPLE 3:

Find the 5-number summary for the data set {1, 2, 2, 4, 6, 9, 13, 14, 17, 19, 20}.

SOLUTION: The easiest ones to find are the lowest and highest values: L = 1 and H = 20.

To find the first and third quartiles, we first have to find the median. This data set consists of eleven data points (an odd number), so there will be a data point right in the middle. This number will be the median, so M = 9.

Note: When we have an odd number of data points, as we do in this example, the data point that is the median is not in the lower half, and it is not in the upper half of the data set. It is the border between the upper and lower halves.

To find the first quartile, we need to find the median of the lower half of the data set. Here, the lower half of the data set is made up of the data points 1, 2, 2, 4, 6, so $Q_1 = 2$.

To find the third quartile, we need to find the median of the upper half of the data set. Here, the upper half of the data set is made up of the data points 13, 14, 17, 19, 20, so $Q_3 = 17$.

Putting it all together: L = 1, $Q_1 = 2$, M = 9, $Q_3 = 17$, and H = 20.

EXAMPLE 4:

Find the five-number summary for the data set {35, 50, 51, 55, 56, 58, 62, 62, 66, 72, 74, 74, 74, 77, 81, 87, 90, 95, 95, 99}.

SOLUTION: The easiest ones to find are the lowest and highest values: L = 35 and H = 99.

To find the first and third quartiles, we have to find the median first. Of the 20 values in the data set, the 72 and the first 74 are in the middle. Thus, M = (72 + 74)/2 = 73.

For the first quartile, Q_1, consider only the lower half of the data set, which is {35, 50, 51, 55, 56, 58, 62, 62, 66, 72}. Of those 10 values, the 56 and 58 are in the middle. Thus, $Q_1 = (56 + 58)/2 = 57$.

Similarly, for the third quartile, Q_3, we consider only the upper half of the data set, which is {74, 74, 74, 77, 81, 87, 90, 95, 95, 99}. Of those 10 values, the 81 and 87 are in the middle. So, $Q_3 = (81 + 87)/2 = 84$.

Putting it all together: L = 35, $Q_1 = 57$, M = 73, $Q_3 = 84$, and H = 99.

Box-and-Whisker Plots

A primary reason for finding the five-number summary is to create a visual representation of the data set. This visual representation is known as a **box-and-whisker plot** (or a **boxplot**). The five-number summary indicates the boundaries that cut the data set into four equal parts, each of which contains approximately 25% of the data points. For example, the number of data values between the lowest value (L) and the first quartile (Q1) is the same as the number of data values between the median (M) and the third quartile (Q_3).

Be careful with this. The length of the intervals on the number line are often quite different from quartile to quartile. But remember, the quartiles cut the data set into four equal parts, so each interval contains approximately 25% of the values that are in the entire data set. Also, keep in mind that we are usually dealing with large sets of data.

On a boxplot, the values appear in order from least to greatest with a "box" drawn in the center, using the first and third quartile values as the left and right sides of the box. The median will be located somewhere inside the box, and the highest and lowest values are used to draw the "whiskers" on the box.

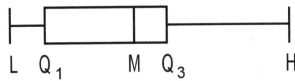

Figure 3.3.1 Boxplot

The values of the five-number summary should appear immediately above or below the boxplot. Alternatively, for indexing purposes, we may also see a number line drawn underneath the entire boxplot. Without the values of the five-number summary or a number line index, the boxplot is just a strange-looking figure.

EXAMPLE 5:

Figure 3.3.2 is the boxplot that represents the amount of snowfall, in inches, recorded at 240 weather stations around a large city in a given week last December.

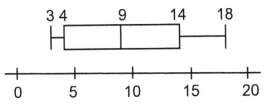

Figure 3.3.2 Inches of Snowfall

a. What was the median snowfall level?

b. Approximately how many weather stations recorded between 9 and 14 inches of snow?

c. Approximately how many weather stations recorded between 3 and 14 inches of snow?

d. What was the largest snowfall reading?

e. Did more weather stations record 3 to 4 inches or 4 to 9 inches of snow?

Solutions:

a. The median is the value indicated inside the "box" part of the diagram. Thus, the median snowfall was 9 inches.

b. Since each vertical mark on the diagram is a quartile label, approximately 25% of the values fell within each interval. There are 240 weather stations, and 25% of them were in that interval. So, (0.25)(240) = 60 stations recorded 9 to 14 inches of snow.

c. The span from 3 to 14 inches covers three intervals, which is 75% of the data set. So, (0.75)(240) = 180 weather stations recorded 3 to 14 inches of snow.

d. The largest snowfall reading is at the end of the rightmost whisker, which is 18 inches.

e. Remember, each interval represents 25% of the data values. Thus, although these two intervals do not appear to be the same length on the number line, they contain the same number of data points. The smaller sections (like between 3 and 4) indicate there are several data points squeezed into a small space, and larger sections (like between 4 and 9) show places the data points are more spread out.

EXAMPLE 6:

Figure 3.3.3 is the boxplot that represents the test results for 560 students who took the CHEM 120 final exam at State University last fall.

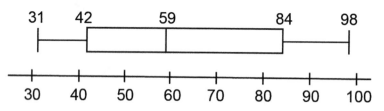

Figure 3.3.3 CHEM 120 Final Exam Scores

a. A student with a score of 84 did better than how many students?

b. What was the highest score?

c. Did more students score above 59 or below 59?

d. What percent of students scored lower than 42?

Solutions:

a. 84 is at the third quartile, which is the 75th percentile. Thus, a student with a score of 84 did better than 75% of the students, which is (0.75)(560) = 420 of them.

b. The highest score was 98.

c. 59 is the median. Half the students scored above 59, and half scored below it.

d. 42 is at the first quartile. So, 25% of the scores were below it.

Another practical use of boxplots is in the comparison of multiple sets. By stacking two or more boxplots onto the same graph, we can quickly compare the various aspects of the data at hand.

EXAMPLE 7:

Walmart, Amazon, and Target all sell a number of different blankets. The stack of boxplots in figure 3.3.4 represents the prices for the blankets at each of the stores.

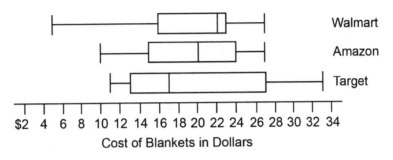

Cost of Blankets in Dollars

Figure 3.3.4 Blanket Prices

a. How much is the least expensive blanket at Amazon?

b. Which of the three stores sells the most expensive blanket? How much is that blanket?

c. Which store has the lowest-priced blanket? How much is that blanket?

d. Which store has the largest price range?

e. Which store has the highest median price?

f. For Target, are there more blankets priced above or below $17?

g. For Walmart, are there more blankets priced above or below $20?

SOLUTIONS:

a. $10

b. Target has the most expensive blanket, and it costs $31.

c. Walmart has the lowest priced blanket, and it costs $5.

d. Walmart's price range of $22 is the largest.

e. Walmart has the highest median price.

f. Neither. $17 is the median, so half the blankets are priced above $17, and half are priced below $17.

g. Be careful. Do not look at the length of the boxplot above and below $20. Remember, a longer region on the boxplot just means the values are more spread out. Then, realize the median is $22. That means half the blankets are priced above $22. Thus, *more than half* of the blankets must be priced above $20.

SECTION 3.3 EXERCISES

1. In a graduating class of 300 students, Erin has a rank of 18th. What is her percentile rank in the class?

2. In a 13-mile half-marathon, Todd finished in 33rd place. If there were 175 runners, what was Todd's percentile rank?

Image 3.3.2

3. In a class with 35 students, Gil scored at the 60th percentile on an exam. How many students scored lower than Gil?

4. Crystal has a percentile rank of 20 in her graduating class, which consists of 400 students. What is her rank in the class?

5. Amy and Joe are in the same senior class. Amy is ranked 40th out of the 280 seniors, and Joe has a percentile rank of 15. Of these two seniors, which one is ranked higher?

6. In a class of 30 students, Bruce is ranked 29th. What is his percentile rank? In that same class, Jennifer is ranked 3rd. What is her percentile rank?

7. Karen is ranked at the 75th percentile in her class of 440 students. What is her rank in the class?

8. The following statement is misleading. Provide a proper interpretation.
   Eighty percent of all car accidents occur within 10 miles of the driver's home. Therefore, it is safer to take long trips.

9. ABC Crackers claims, "Our crackers have 1/3 fewer calories." What is misleading about this claim?

10. What is misleading about the claim "Eating fish may help to reduce your cholesterol"?

11. What is improper about the survey question, "Are you going to vote for Candidate Jones, even though the latest survey shows he will lose the election?"

12. We can claim 71% of adults do not use sunscreen. Although 71% is a large percentage, explain what about that claim can be misleading.

13. For any data set, approximately what percent of the data points are above the median?

14. For any data set, approximately what percent of the data points are above the first quartile?

15. For any data set, approximately what percent of the data points are between the first and third quartiles?

16. For the boxplot in figure 3.3.5, find the five-number summary.

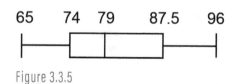

Figure 3.3.5

17. Use the following set of data to find the five-number summary.

12, 12, 13, 13, 13, 16, 16, 16, 16, 18, 18, 18, 21, 21, 21, 26, 26, 28, 31, 51, 51, 75

18. Use the following set of data to find the five-number summary.

65, 65, 67, 68, 74, 74, 75, 77, 77, 77, 79, 80, 83, 85, 85, 86, 89, 92, 93, 94, 96

For Exercises #19 through #22, use the boxplot in figure 3.3.6, which represents number of points scored by 160 different basketball players during a tournament.

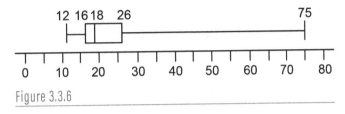

Figure 3.3.6

19. What was the highest number of points scored?

20. What was the median number of points scored?

21. Approximately how many players scored more than 26 points?

22. Were there more players who scored between 16 and 18 points or more who scored between 26 and 75 points?

For Exercises #23 through #25, use the pair of boxplots in figure 3.3.7, which indicate the cost per credit for community colleges in Indiana and Texas. Note, these numbers are for this exercise only, and may not be reflective of the actual costs.

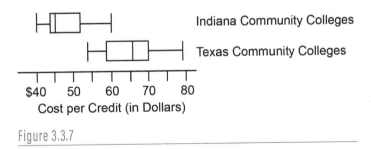

Figure 3.3.7

23. Estimate the values for the five-number summary for each state.

24. As a general statement, is it less expensive to attend a community college in Indiana or Texas?

25. Do the costs vary more in Indiana or Texas? How can you tell?

26. Create a data set in which the median, Q_1 and Q_3 are not numbers in the data set.

ANSWERS TO SECTION 3.3 EXERCISES

1. 94

2. 81

3. 21

4. 320th

5. Amy is ranked higher. Amy's percentile rank is 86. Joe's rank in the class is 238th.

6. Bruce's percentile rank is 3. Jennifer's percentile rank is 90.

7. 110th

8. Proper Interpretation: Most accidents occur close to home because when people drive, most trips are within 10 miles.

9. What are the crackers being compared to? If they had 1/3 fewer calories than a large piece of chocolate cake, that's not very good.

10. Notice the use of the word "may." We could just as easily claim, "Eating fish may not help to reduce your cholesterol."

11. Most people do not like to vote or will not admit voting for the losing candidate. This may lead people to say "No," thereby injecting bias into the results.

12. Not everyone spends a significant amount of time in the sun. Also, where was the survey conducted? If it was done in Seattle, the percent would be high. However, if it was done in Southern California, the results may indicate the majority of people do use sunscreen.

13. 50%

14. 75%

15. 50%

16. $L = 65, Q_1 = 74, M = 79, Q_3 = 87.5, H = 96$

17. $L = 12, Q_1 = 16, M = 18, Q_3 = 26, H = 75$

18. $L = 65, Q_1 = 74, M = 79, Q_3 = 87.5, H = 96$

19. 75

20. 18

21. 40

22. There were 40 players in both those intervals.

23. IN: L = \$40, Q_1 = \$44, M = \$45, Q_3 = \$52, H = \$60;
    TX: L = \$54, Q_1 = \$57, M = \$66, Q_3 = \$70, H = \$79

24. Although it is possible to find some community colleges in Texas that are less expensive than some community colleges in Indiana, in general, the cost is less expensive in Indiana.

25. Costs vary more in Texas. We know this because the width of the box-and-whisker plot is larger for Texas.

26. Answers will vary, but the entire data set, the upper half and the lower half will all contain an even number of data points.

3.4 Pretty Pictures: Graphs of Data

Stem-and-Leaf Plots

The following are the scores on an exam.

93, 97, 59, 71, 57, 84, 89, 79, 79, 88, 68, 91, 76, 87, 94, 73, 57, 85, 82, 38

A **stem-and-leaf plot** is a method of organizing data that helps us put the numbers in order, from lowest to highest. This type of chart uses the leading digit of the score as the "stem" and the trailing digit of each score as the "leaf." To organize the exam scores listed above into a stem-and-leaf plot, we first create the necessary "stems." Since our data set ranges from the 30s to the 90s, we need to establish the stems from 3 to 9.

TABLE 3.4.1

STEM	LEAVES
9	
8	
7	
6	
5	
4	
3	

Next, we put each of the data points by using the ones digits as the "leaves." The first number listed in our data set is 93. To place this value on our plot, we start by identifying the proper "stem." This data value has a 9 in the tens place, so the stem will be 9. The value 93 has a 3 in the ones place, so we write a 3 in the Leaves column to the right of the "9" Stem. Thus, the 3 in the top row of the Leaves column represents the number 93, because it uses the 9 in the Stem column as the tens digit. In similar fashion, the 8 in the bottom row of the Leaves column represents the number 38. Then we fill in the remaining leaves, as in table 3.4.2.

TABLE 3.4.2

STEM	LEAVES
9	3, 7, 1, 4
8	4, 9, 8, 7, 5, 2
7	1, 9, 9, 6, 3
6	8
5	9, 7, 7
4	
3	8

We finish our stem-and-leaf plot by rearranging the leaves for each stem from lowest to highest. After doing so, we have a very nice chart that lists all of the data points in increasing order for each stem, as shown in table 3.4.3.

TABLE 3.4.3

STEM	LEAVES
9	1, 3, 4, 7
8	2, 4, 5, 7, 8, 9
7	1, 3, 6, 9, 9
6	8
5	7, 7, 9
4	
3	8

Frequency Tables

As we previously discussed, a **frequency table** is a way to organize all of the data from a given situation into chart form. Using the exam scores from before, table 3.4.4 is an example of a frequency table, where the data has been grouped into categories that we have deemed to be important. Whereas a stem-and-leaf plot lists the actual values in the data set, a frequency table lists the *number* of data values included within each specific category.

TABLE 3.4.4

GRADE	FREQUENCY
A	4
B	6
C	5
D	1
F	4
Total:	20

Take a look at the last row in table 3.4.4. It represents the total number of data values. The total number of data values is important when we want to examine the percent of the data values within each category. Later in this section we will extend this to a **relative frequency table**. But for now, we will focus on the individual frequencies of the specific grades.

Bar Graphs

A **bar graph** (also called a **bar chart**) is a visual way to present categories of data. The specific categories (also called **bins**) are typically listed across a horizontal axis, and the number of items within each category (a.k.a., the frequency) is indicated by the height of the corresponding bar. In a bar graph, we also see spaces between the bars to indicate each category is separate and distinct. The bars on a bar graph can be horizontal, but we will stick with a vertical representation.

> To represent quantities of discrete data, use a bar graph.

EXAMPLE 1:

A bag contains four red jellybeans (R), six green jellybeans (G), two purple jellybeans (P), seven yellow jellybeans (Y), and four blue jellybeans (B). Create a bar graph that displays the data.

SOLUTION:

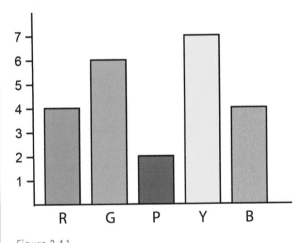

Figure 3.4.1

Histograms

A **histogram** is a specialized type of bar graph in which the categories displayed on the horizontal axis represent a *continuous* set of data. Being continuous (as in time), there should not be any gaps in the data and, subsequently, no spaces between the individual bars.

> To represent quantities of continuous data over designated intervals, use a histogram.

EXAMPLE 2:

Table 3.4.5 represents the annual number of babies born in a hospital's maternity ward. Create a histogram that represents the data.

TABLE 3.4.5

Year	Babies
2015	981
2016	1895
2017	2027
2018	651
2019	432

Solution:

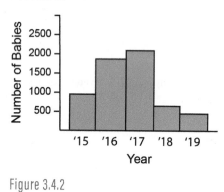

Figure 3.4.2

In appearance, histograms and bar charts look very similar. But remember, bar charts show data sets that are independent of each other and can make sense in any order. Histograms show ordered data and are designed to have no spaces between the bars to reflect their data of continuous measurement. For example, in the histogram for the babies shown in the previous example, it would not make sense to put the categories—which represent consecutive years—in a different order.

Line Graphs

Line graphs are another useful tool when working with data that is collected over time. The horizontal axis is used to create a timeline, while the data points that change over time are plotted along the vertical axis. You may already be quite familiar with these types of graphs. Remember, these are best used to represent *change over time*. We also see line graphs when examining supply and demand charts in business. In those cases, the continuous data is usually money.

To emphasize the changes in quantities of continuous data over designated intervals, use a line graph.

For our example displaying the number of babies over a 5-year period, the line graph for the data would look like figure 3.4.3.

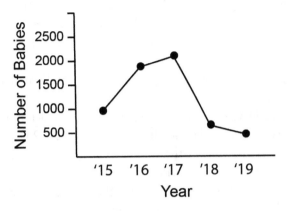

Figure 3.4.3   Line Graph

Relative Frequency Tables

The **relative frequency** is the percentage of the data values that belong to a certain category. A **relative frequency table** is an extension of the frequency table that shows the relative frequency (or percentage) of each category that is listed. The relative frequency is calculated by dividing the number of data values in a given category by the total number of data values. Relative frequencies can be displayed in their decimal form or listed as a percent by simply moving the decimal point two places to the right and adding the % sign. If we do that, however, we should list the percents in their own column. Keep in mind, unless we are specifically directed to do so, converting the decimal values to percents is not required. In their decimal forms, the sum of all the relative frequencies needs to be 1. In terms of percents, the sum of the percents needs to account for 100% of the data.

Recall the set of 20 exam scores from earlier in this section. Since there were 4 As, to find the relative frequency for an A grade, we divide the number of As by the total number of grades, which is 4/20 = 0.20. When columns for the relative frequencies for each letter grade and, if desired, the corresponding percents are added to the frequency table from table 3.4.4 (from earlier in the section), the revised version is as displayed in table 3.4.6. The information in this table shows us 20% of those who took the exam received As, 30% received Bs, etc. And, notice that the sum of the relative frequencies is equal to 1, while the sum of the percents is 100%.

TABLE 3.4.6

Grade	Frequency	Relative Frequency	Percent
A	4	0.20	20%
B	6	0.30	30%
C	5	0.25	25%
D	1	0.05	5%
F	4	0.20	20%
Total:	20	1	100%

Pie Charts

Pie charts (also called **circle graphs**) are used to show relative proportions, which are similar to relative frequencies. Again, you are probably very familiar with these types of graphs, but creating them may be new for you. With that in mind, we will use the same exam data from earlier in the section to create a pie chart.

An essential number to have when creating a pie chart is the total number of data values, which is the sum of the frequencies. In this case, we have 20 data values.

There are 360° in a circle, and when making a pie chart, we need to determine the number of degrees to be given to each category within the data set. In this case, we have 20 total data values sorted into the five letter grade categories. To determine the number of degrees to give to each portion of the circle graph (called a **sector**), we will set up a proportion for each one.

Let's start by finding the number of degrees to give to the A grades. In this data set, there are 4 As out of the 20 total grades. Our thought process in creating the proportion is, "The first ratio indicates there are 4 A grades out of 20 total grades, and this equals the second ratio, which is the number of degrees for the A sector out of a total of 360° for the whole circle."

Setting up a proportion gives us:
4/20 = A/360

Cross-multiplying and then dividing by 20 to get the A by itself, we have:
20A = 1,440
A = 72
Thus, the A grades will be given 72° in our pie chart.

Using the same process for the B grades, we have:
6/20 = B/360
20B = 2,160
B = 108
This means the B grade sector of the circle will take up 108°.

Following a similar procedure for the C, D, and F grades, we have A = 72°, B = 108°, C = 90°, D = 18°, and F = 72°. At this point, we should note that the sum of those five numbers is 72° + 108° + 90° + 18° + 72° = 360°, which accounts for the entire circle.

Now we can draw our pie chart. We start by drawing a circle, which can be a little daunting when doing so by hand. To help create a more professional looking circle, we can trace a circular object or use a compass. If we don't have a compass, we can use a piece of string or a paperclip by anchoring one side with a pencil and then using a second pencil to rotate the opposite end.

Once we have our circle, draw a vertical line from the center to the top of the circle. From the spot where the line touches the circle, we will move 72° clockwise around the circle and then draw another line from the center of the circle to that new spot. We have created the "slice" of the pie chart (again, sector) that represents the A grades. At this point, a question you may be asking is, "how big is 72°?"

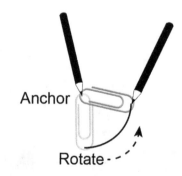

Figure 3.4.4 Making a Circle with a Paperclip

Picture an analog clock. Every hour on the clock constitutes 1/12 of a circle, which corresponds to $(1/12)(360°) = 30°$. So, if we open up a sector from 12 o'clock to 1 o'clock, it would be 30°. Likewise, a sector from 12 o'clock to 4 o'clock would be $(4/12)(360°) = 120°$.

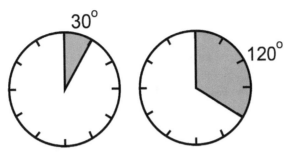

Figure 3.4.5 30° and 120° Sectors

What about 72°? Since the sector from 12 to 2 would be 60° and the sector from 12 to 3 would be 90° we can see that 72°, is equal to a sector from 12 o'clock to a little less than halfway between 2 and 3 o'clock.

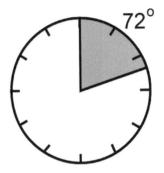

Figure 3.4.6 72° Sectors

The sector of the circle that will represent the B grades will contain 108°. One side of this sector will be the line that we have already drawn (at 72°). From that spot on the circle, we need to move 108° clockwise and then draw the line that completes the sector. Since $72° + 108° = 180°$, we can see the terminal side of this sector will be drawn at the 180° mark.

We continue moving clockwise around the circle as we draw in the remaining lines. The next line we draw will create the sector for the C grades, so we will need to move 90° from the last line. $180° + 90° = 270°$, so we draw in the line that completes the sector for C grades at 270°. From there, we move clockwise 18° and draw the line completing the sector for the D grades at $270° + 18° = 288°$. Being the last piece of the pie, the sector for the F grades is complete at this point, but we should take the time to count and make sure that it does, indeed, measure 72°.

Finally, we need to make sure to label each of the sectors in the pie chart.

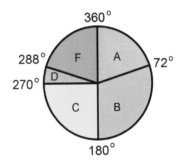

Figure 3.4.7 Grade Pie Chart

How to Lie with Graphs and Pictures

An old, well-known adage states, "A picture is worth a thousand words." And, since many people prefer looking at pictures over reading, using graphs and pictures to intentionally mislead an audience is common practice.

When the designer of a graph wants to make the difference between data bins look more significant, one way is to truncate the graph and show a zoomed-in view of the vertical axis. Manipulating graphs by deleting part of the vertical axis isn't really lying if the accompanying numbers are accurate, but it certainly can be a way of misleading the reader. This technique works with bar graphs, histograms and line graphs.

EXAMPLE 3:

Mr. Glick wanted to show that his students performed better on a standardized test than Ms. Jones's and Mr. Smith's students, and he produced the bar graph shown in figure 3.4.8. Although technically correct, what is misleading about his graph?

SOLUTION: At first glance, with the bar for Mr. Glick's students being dramatically taller that the bars for the other teachers, it appears the students in Mr. Glick's class performed significantly better than the students in the other two classes. If, however, we zoom out and show the entire scale for the vertical axis, we can see the performance of the students is nearly identical in each of the three classes.

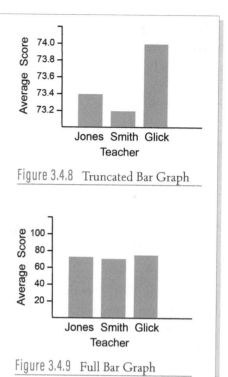

Figure 3.4.8   Truncated Bar Graph

Figure 3.4.9   Full Bar Graph

Another way to mislead an audience with a bar graph is to take advantage of displaying one-dimensional information with two- or three-dimensional images. In a bar graph, the information being conveyed is indicated by the height of the bars, while the width and depth (if 3D) of the bars do not carry any actual information. If the graph maker uses images instead of simple colored bars (called a **pictograph**) the width and depth of the images take on a subconscious role.

EXAMPLE 4:

The Twisted Graph Investment Firm wants you to invest in bitcoin and shows you figure 3.4.10 while stating the value has doubled in the last month. What is misleading about their graph?

SOLUTION: By doubling both the height *and* the width, the coin displayed for "This Month" is actually *four* times as big as the initial coin. A more realistic representation would be to just "double" the height by adding another coin, as in figure 3.4.11.

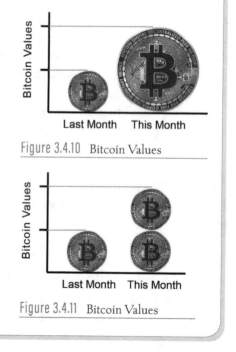

Figure 3.4.10   Bitcoin Values

Figure 3.4.11   Bitcoin Values

If three-dimensional images are used, the perceived change is even more dramatic. For example, if a student wants to create a simple bar graph showing how the cost of textbooks has doubled in the last decade, the graph can be made more appealing if the student uses a three-dimensional image of a stack of books for each bar, making the stack for the current year contain twice as many books as the bar representing the cost from ten years ago, as in figure 3.4.12.

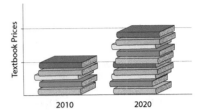

Figure 3.4.12 Book Prices Doubled

If, however, the student wants to give the impression that the increase is even larger, instead of having just a taller stack of books for the current year, he can also increase the size of the image corresponding to the 2020 cost, so that it is twice as tall as the initial image, as in figure 3.4.13.

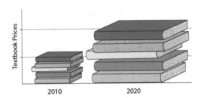

Figure 3.4.13 Book Prices Doubled?

The resulting image for 2020 has the stack being not only twice as tall as the stack for 2010, but since the whole image has been scaled up, the stack is also twice as wide and twice as deep. That makes the new book stack appear *eight* times larger.

SECTION 3.4 EXERCISES

1. Average class sizes at a college are given in table 3.4.7. Create a bar graph that represents this data.

TABLE 3.4.7

CLASS	SIZE
Math	34
English	27
History	22
Philosophy	17

2. The number of speeding tickets issued by the Mayberry police department during the months of May, June, and July of the years 2016, 2017, and 2018 are shown in figure 3.4.14.

   a. How many tickets were issued in June of 2016?

   b. For the months shown on the graph, during which year were the most tickets issued?

   c. Over the 3-year period, during which month were the most tickets issued?

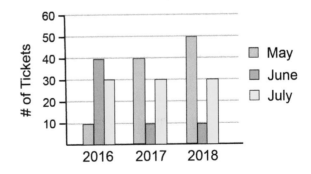

Figure 3.4.14 Speeding Tickets

3. A survey of college students that asked them about the mode of transportation that they used to travel to campus resulted in the following information: 120 students drove a car to school, 80 students rode a bike, 70 students took the bus, and 30 students walked to school. Find the number of degrees that should be given to each category, and create a pie chart that represents this data.

4. In a physics class, 4 students earned As, 9 earned Bs, 14 earned Cs, 7 earned Ds, and 6 students earned Fs. Find the number of degrees that should be given to each category, and create a pie chart that represents this data.

5. A teacher marked down the color of the shirt each child in her class was wearing. Five kids were wearing blue shirts, 12 had yellow shirts, 9 were wearing green, and the remaining 4 were wearing red. Use these data to create a relative frequency table and a bar chart. Round all decimals to the nearest hundredth.

6. The amount of time (in minutes) that it took a class of students to complete a short quiz was recorded in Table 3.4.8. Use the data to create a histogram.

TABLE 3.4.8

Minutes	# of Students
4	3
5	5
6	4
7	1
8	2
9	8
10	12

7. Use the following data to create a stem-and-leaf plot:

15, 23, 31, 17, 13, 20, 26, 23, 35, 11, 17

8. Use the following data to create a stem-and-leaf plot:

56, 84, 64, 91, 75, 59, 85, 58, 87, 66, 89, 73, 72, 66, 91, 81, 98, 63

9. Which type of graph would you use for the data in table 3.4.9? Justify your choice.

TABLE 3.4.9

Year	Population of Fictionland
1940	3,400
1960	3,900
1980	4,900
2000	6,300
2020	7,500

10. Which kind of graph is best for each of the following?

    a. Displaying change over time.

    b. Showing a comparison and including the raw data.

    c. Showing a comparison that displays the relative proportions.

11. On a line graph that shows the change over time that occurs in the data, what can be done to make the change appear more drastic?

12. On a line graph that shows the change over time that occurs in the data, what can be done to make the change appear less drastic?

13. Figures 3.4.15 and 3.4.16 show information regarding the price of widgets. Both graphs use the same data for their creation.

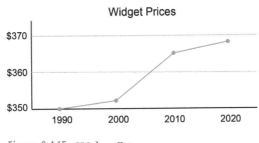

Figure 3.4.15 Widget Prices

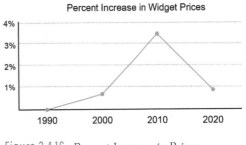

Figure 3.4.16 Percent Increase in Prices

    a. Describe ways in which each of these graphs could be used to mislead the reader.

    b. What could the manufacturer of widgets do with the graph that shows the price data, in order to improve public perception of the price increase over time?

14. Figure 3.4.17 represents how a student's Science College Readiness Test score (SCRT) was reported to his parents. What is misleading about the graph?

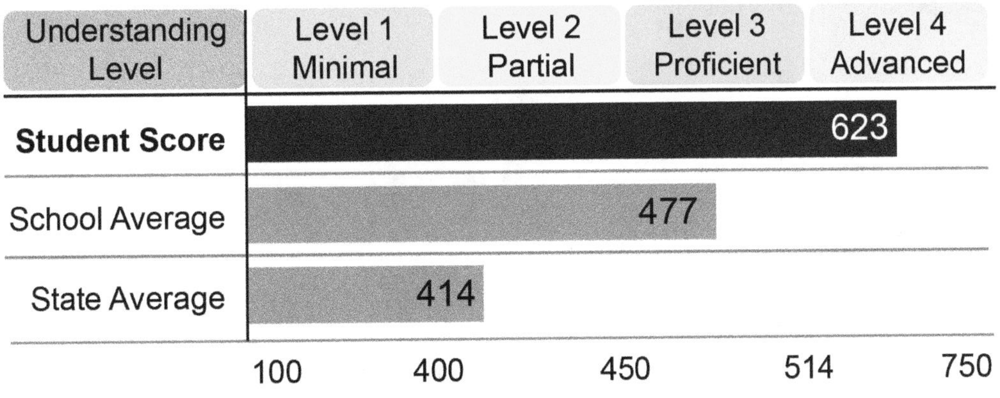

Understanding Level	Level 1 Minimal	Level 2 Partial	Level 3 Proficient	Level 4 Advanced
Student Score				623
School Average			477	
State Average	414			
	100	400	450	514	750

Figure 3.4.17 SCRT Scores

ANSWERS TO SECTION 3.4 EXERCISES

1. While we could arrange the classes in any order, one version looks like figure 3.4.18.

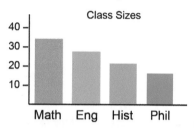

Figure 3.4.18   Class Sizes

2. **a.** 40   **b.** 2018   **c.** May

3. While we could arrange the sections in any order within the graph, the number of degrees for each section are: Car = 144°; Bike = 96°; Bus = 84°; Walk = 36°

One option for creating this graph and being correct is:

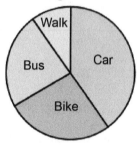

Figure 3.4.19   Getting to School

4. While we could arrange the sections in any order within the graph, the number of degrees for each section are: A = 36°; B = 81°; C = 126°; D = 63°; F = 54°

One option for creating this graph and being correct is:

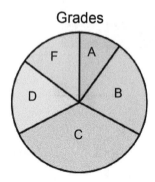

Figure 3.4.20   Grades

5. Frequency Table

TABLE 3.4.10

Color	# of Kids	Relative Frequency
Blue	5	0.17
Yellow	12	0.40
Green	9	0.30
Red	4	0.13

Bar Chart

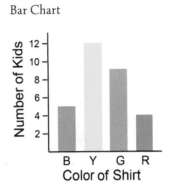

Figure 3.4.21 Shirt Color

6. Histogram

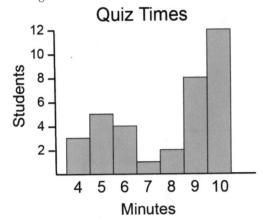

Figure 3.4.22 Quiz Times

7.

TABLE 3.4.11

Stem	Leaves
3	1, 5
2	0, 3, 3, 6
1	1, 3, 5, 7, 7

8.

TABLE 3.4.12

Stem	Leaves
9	1, 1, 8
8	1, 4, 5, 7, 9
7	2, 3, 5
6	3, 4, 6, 6
5	6, 8, 9

9. For these data, which shows change over time, the best choice would be to use a line graph or a histogram.

10. **a.** line graph,   **b.** bar graph,   **c.** pie chart

11. Zoom in on the data by truncating the vertical axis in the graph.

12. Zoom out by using the entire vertical axis in the graph.

13. **a.** The graph showing the price of widgets could be used by *consumers* to show how the price has gone up dramatically over the years. The graph showing the percent increase in price could be used by the *manufacturer* to show the tremendous drop in the amount of increase from 2010 to 2020.

    b. The manufacturer could zoom out and show the entire vertical axis, resulting in a graph that looks like figure 3.4.23.

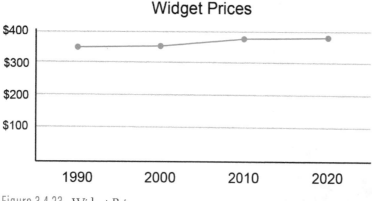

Figure 3.4.23 Widget Prices

14. The scale across the bottom is not uniform and starts at 100, instead of 0. This makes the bar for the student's score appear about 2.5 times longer than the bar for the state. Instead of being 250% greater, the student's score is only about 50% greater than the state average. Also, the bar for the school average is about halfway between the bars for the student and state, implying the school's average score is about halfway between those scores. Doing the calculation, halfway between the student and state scores is about 519. Thus, with an average of 477, the bar for the school should be shorter (assuming the scale across the bottom was corrected to be uniform).

3.5 Is Anything Normal?: Standard Deviation and the Normal Curve

Review: Order of Operations

If several people are asked to simplify the same multi-step arithmetic **expression**, a standard set of rules must be established for the order in which the operations are performed. Otherwise, different people may get different answers. For example, let's say Bill and Ted are asked to simplify the expression $3 + 4 \times 5$. Bill adds the $3 + 4$, and then multiplies that result by 5 to get a total of 35. Ted performs the multiplication first, and then adds 3 to get a total of 23. Who is right? In case you aren't sure yet ... it is Ted.

Arithmetic started with addition (and subtraction). Repeated addition led to multiplication (and division), and repeated multiplication led to the use of exponents. In addition to those procedures, parentheses or other grouping symbols can also be used in an expression. Let's consolidate all of these processes into a single list, known as the "order of operations."

Arithmetic **Order of Operations:**

1. All operations contained within parentheses ( ) or other grouping symbols, such as brackets [ ], or braces { }, should be done first.

2. Secondly, simplify all expressions containing exponents.

3. Multiplication and division are done next, as we come to them going from left to right.

4. Addition and subtraction are done last, again, as we come to them going from left to right.

To help remember this order, many students like to memorize the acronym **PEMDAS** (Parentheses, Exponents, Multiplication, Division, Addition, Subtraction). This can be really helpful, but be careful! If you do not realize multiplication and division are done as we come to them going from the left to the right, you may fall into the trap of thinking multiplication always precedes division—it does not. The same holds true for addition and subtraction.

EXAMPLE 1:

Simplify: $5 + 6 \times 3$

SOLUTION: Since multiplication is performed before addition, start by multiplying 6×3. Then, add 5 to that result.

$5 + 6 \times 3$
$= 5 + 18$
$= 23$

EXAMPLE 2:

Simplify: $13 - 5 + 6$

SOLUTION: Remember, perform addition and subtraction as we come to them going from left to right. Here, that means the subtraction must be done first.

$13 - 5 + 6$
$= 8 + 6$
$= 14$

EXAMPLE 3:

Simplify: $13 - (5 + 6)$

SOLUTION: Since $(5 + 6)$ is inside parentheses, that operation is performed first.

$$13 - (5 + 6)$$
$$= 13 - 11$$
$$= 2$$

EXAMPLE 4:

Simplify: $42 \div 3(2)$

SOLUTION: There are parentheses in this expression but take note that there is no operation to perform inside these parentheses. We have division and multiplication to perform here, and those are done going from left to right.

$$42 \div 3(2)$$
$$= 14(2)$$
$$= 28$$

EXAMPLE 5:

Simplify: $\dfrac{(5-3)^2 + (2-3)^2 + (2-3)^2}{3}$

SOLUTION: In this problem we have a long division bar separating the numerator from the denominator. In cases like this, we simplify everything in the numerator, simplify everything in the denominator, and then divide as the last step. Here, our denominator is already simplified but there is plenty to do in the numerator. The numerator contains operations inside parentheses, exponents, and addition, which will be done in that order.

$$\frac{(5-3)^2 + (2-3)^2 + (2-3)^2}{3}$$
$$= \frac{(2)^2 + (-1)^2 + (-1)^2}{3}$$
$$= \frac{4 + 1 + 1}{3}$$
$$= \frac{6}{3}$$

Standard Deviation

Standard Deviation is a way to describe the amount of spread that is inherent in a data set. The standard deviation measures spread by finding the average distance of each data point from the mean. The more spread out the data, the higher the standard deviation will be.

To calculate the standard deviation of a data set, we will use the formula shown below. While this formula may appear to be intimidating at first, once you understand what all of the symbols represent, it really isn't a hard formula to use. You just have to be careful to remember the order of operations and execute them properly.

The symbol σ, which is the lowercase Greek letter "sigma," represents the standard deviation. The symbol μ, which is the lowercase Greek letter "mu," (pronounced "m-you") represents the mean of the data set.

The letter "n" is the total number of data points that are included in the data set.

Finally, we have these guys: $x_1, x_2, x_3, \ldots x_n$

These are abbreviations for "x subscript 1," "x subscript 2," and so on, which are often pronounced using the shortened versions ... "x sub 1," "x sub 2," etc. These represent the individual data points, with x_1 being the first data point, x_2 being the second data point, and continuing until we get to x_n which is the last of the data points.

After all that buildup, here it is, the formula for calculating the standard deviation of a data set:

$$\sigma = \sqrt{\frac{\left(x_1 - \mu\right)^2 + \left(x_2 - \mu\right)^2 + \ldots + \left(x_n - \mu\right)^2}{n}}$$

To help take some of the mystery out of this formula, let's take a look at an example showing how it works. The key is to plug all of the proper numbers into the proper spots, and then, be careful as you simplify.

EXAMPLE 6:

Calculate the standard deviation of the following data set. Round your answer to the nearest hundredth.

45, 62, 73, 75, 90

Solution: First, we must find the mean of the data set.

$\mu = (45 + 62 + 73 + 75 + 90)/5 = 345/5 = 69$

Next, we will plug in the values of $x_1, x_2, x_3, x_4, x_5, \mu$, and n into the formula, and simplify:

$$\sigma = \sqrt{\frac{\left(45-69\right)^2 + \left(62-69\right)^2 + \left(73-69\right)^2 + \left(75-69\right)^2 + \left(90-69\right)^2}{5}}$$

$$\sigma = \sqrt{\frac{\left(-24\right)^2 + \left(-7\right)^2 + \left(4\right)^2 + \left(6\right)^2 + \left(21\right)^2}{5}}$$

$$\sigma = \sqrt{\frac{576 + 49 + 16 + 36 + 441}{5}}$$

$$\sigma = \sqrt{\frac{1118}{5}}$$

$$\sigma = \sqrt{223.6} = 14.95 \text{ (to the hundredth)}$$

So, the standard deviation for this data set is 14.95.

A data set with a smaller standard deviation would be less spread out than this one, and a data set with a higher standard deviation would be more spread out.

At this point, the concept of the standard deviation probably doesn't have a great deal of meaning for you, but as we move forward studying the normal curve, we will see that the standard deviation plays a critical role in some generalizations that can be made about certain types of data sets.

NOTE: We have used the Greek letters mu (μ) and sigma (σ) to represent the mean and standard deviation of a data set. These letters, and the formula given in this section, are used when the data represents an entire population. If, instead, you are working with a data set that is a *sample* of the population, the symbol $\bar{x}$ would be used to represent the mean, and s would be used to represent the standard deviation. Additionally, when working with a sample, the formula for standard deviation is slightly different. The standard deviation of a sample will not be covered in this text.

The Normal Curve

The general idea of a standard normal distribution is a symmetric distribution of the data points with the majority of them clustered around the mean. Also, there is a decreasing amount of data points as we get further and further from the middle. For example, if we made a histogram of the data set with only five bins, it would look similar to figure 3.5.1. (We have left slight gaps between the bars for emphasis.)

Figure 3.5.1 5-Bin Histogram

If, however, we dramatically increased the number of bins, we may see a histogram like figure 3.5.2.

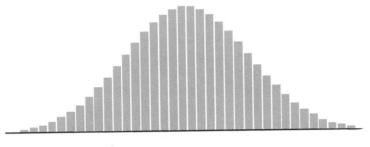

Figure 3.5.2 Multi-Bin Histogram

Notice how the increase in the number of bins makes the histogram appear more rounded at the top. If we drew a smooth curve that closely estimates the heights of the bars and removed the bars from the diagram, as shown in figure 3.5.3, what remains is a shape known as the **bell curve**, or a **normal curve**. Do you see why it is sometimes called a "bell" curve?

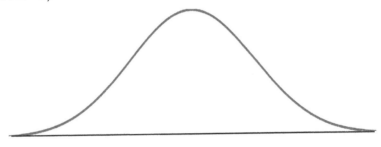

Figure 3.5.3 Bell Curve

Again, a data set like this one, in which the majority of the data points are close to the middle and the number of data points gradually tapers off in a symmetric fashion as we move further away from the middle—with a very small number of data points in the extremes—is known as "normally distributed." When graphed, this type of data set creates a normal curve.

Image 3.5.1

As it turns out, a great deal of real-world data actually fits into a shape like this. When graphed, normally distributed data form a symmetric, bell-shaped appearance. Also, the mean, median, and mode of a normally distributed data set will be right in the center of the curve.

Some examples of normally distributed data include:

- SAT/ACT scores. Most are close to the mean, and as you move further away from the mean, the number of scores tapers off. A small number of scores are very low, and a small number are very high.

- Birth weights of infants. Most are close to the mean, a small number of babies are extremely light, and a small number are extremely heavy.

- IQ scores. Most people are close to the mean, a small number of people have very low IQs, and a small number have very high IQs.

- Annual yields for a crop. Most years are close to the mean level of production, a small number of years will result in very low production, and a small number of years will result in very large production.

- Life spans of batteries. Most batteries will last an amount of time close to the mean, a small number will have very short life spans, and a small number will have very long life spans.

Applications of Standard Deviations

Here we reach the point at which the concept of standard deviation becomes extremely useful, as it is closely tied to our study of the normal curve. On the normal curve shown in figure 3.5.4, the dotted line in the middle represents the mean, μ, of a normally distributed data set, and the other dotted lines represent multiples of the standard deviation away from the mean.

That is, the "$\mu + 1\sigma$" visible under the curve indicates the location at which we are one standard deviation above the mean. The "$\mu - 2\sigma$" indicates two standards deviations below the mean, and so on. Keep in mind, the height of the curve corresponds to the number of data points at a specific frequency (remember how we started with a histogram?).

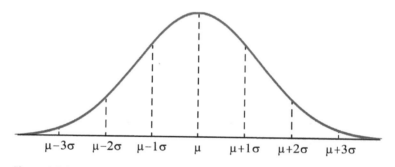

Figure 3.5.4   Normal Curve with Standard Deviations

The 68−95−99.7 Rule

A normally distributed data set is defined by its mean and standard deviation. Once we know that a data set is normally distributed, some very powerful observations can be made about the amount of data that is a given number of standard deviations from the mean. One of these observations is particularly useful, and it is known as the **68−95−99.7 Rule**. This can also be called the **Empirical Rule**, but it is far more useful to refer to it using the numbers, as they indicate the percent of data values within 1, 2, and 3 standard deviations from the mean.

For a normally distributed data set, the 68-95-99.7 Rule states:

- 68% of the data points lie within 1σ of the mean.

- 95% of the data points lie within 2σ of the mean.

- 99.7% of the data points lie within 3σ of the mean.

Remember, "within one standard deviation" means we can be one deviation above *or* one deviation below the mean.

As shown in figure 3.5.5, we can use the dashed lines that align with the standard deviation multiples to examine the percent of data that falls into the regions identified by the 68—95—99.7 Rule.

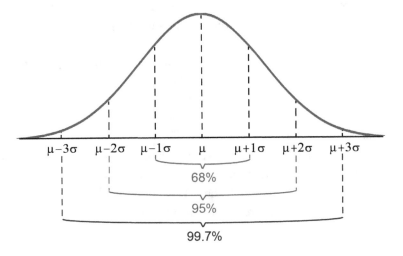

Figure 3.5.5   The 68-95-99.7 Rule

If we want to be more specific, we can narrow the percentages down to single regions. For example, as shown in figure 3.5.6, since we know that 68% of the data is within one standard deviation of the mean, the symmetric nature of the curve allows us to conclude 34% of the data is between the mean and 1σ *above* the mean, while 34% of the data is between the mean and 1σ *below* the mean.

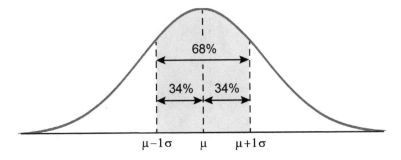

Figure 3.5.6   34% + 34% = 68% of the Data

Using that same logic, we can determine the amount of data that is within each specific region of the graph, as shown in figure 3.5.7.

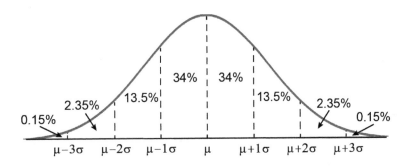

Figure 3.5.7   Percent of Data in Each Region

Even though each of the eight regions are discrete, we can use simple addition to find the percent of data in a desired combination of the various regions. For example, if we want to know the percent of data above two standard deviations from the mean, we simply add together the percentages found in the regions that are above $\mu + 2\sigma$, which are the two right-most regions in the graph. Thus, $2.35\% + 0.15\% = 2.5\%$ of the data are above two standard deviations from the mean. Using a similar process, we can determine that $13.5\% + 34\% = 47.5\%$ of the data lie between the mean and two standard deviations below the mean.

Disclaimer

Sometimes students fight the notion that we can be so sure about the location of all of these data points. Keep in mind, the 68–95–99.7 Rule, and other properties discussed in this section, only apply when we are *certain* the data is normally distributed. If the data is not normally distributed, then these rules do not apply. Remember, in this section, we will be working with data that do fit the normal curve. They are far more common than you might think.

EXAMPLE 7:

The weights, in pounds, of the children in a third-grade class were recorded, and the data was found to be normally distributed. The normal curve and the associated values for this data set are shown in figure 3.5.8.

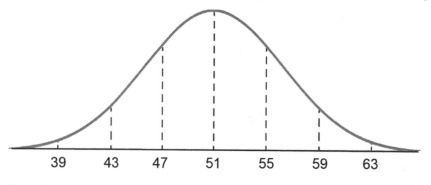

Figure 3.5.8 Student Weights

a. What is the mean weight of the children in this class?

b. What is the value of the standard deviation?

c. What percent of the weights are below 55 pounds?

d. What percent of the weights are above 43 pounds?

e. What percent of the weights are between 51 and 59 pounds?

SOLUTIONS:

a. The mean is in the middle of the curve: $\mu = 51$ pounds.

b. Since 55 represents one standard deviation above the mean, $\sigma = 4$.

c. Since the mean is exactly in the middle, 50% of the data is below the mean. Adding this to the 34% of the data that is between 51 and 55 pounds, a total of 84% of the weights are below 55 pounds.

d. Adding the percentages within the necessary regions, we see 13.5% + 34% + 50% = 97.5% of the children are heavier than 43 pounds.

e. Adding the percentages within the necessary regions, we see 34% + 13.5% = 47.5% of the weights are between 51 and 59 pounds.

EXAMPLE 8:

Given a set of normally distributed exam scores with a mean of 70 and a standard deviation of 8, find:

a. What percent of the scores were below 62?

b. What percent of the scores were above 70?

c. What percent of the scores were above 86?

d. What percent of the scores were between 54 and 78?

SOLUTIONS: Even though we could answer the questions without an examination of the normal curve, it is a bit easier to do so. When drawing the curve, be sure to include the specific numbers for the mean and standard deviation.

1σ above the mean is: $70 + 1(8) = 70 + 8 = 78$.
2σ above the mean is: $70 + 2(8) = 70 + 16 = 86$.
3σ above the mean is: $70 + 3(8) = 70 + 24 = 94$.
Likewise, 1, 2, and 3σ below the mean are 62, 54, and 46, respectively. If we drew the normal curve and labeled the deviations, it would look like figure 3.5.9.

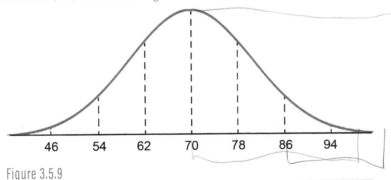

Figure 3.5.9

a. As we can see from the curve, 0.15% + 2.35% + 13.5% = 16% of the exam scores are below 62.

b. The mean score for this exam is 70. Since the data is normally distributed, 50% of the data is above this point.

c. 2.5% of the scores are above 86.

d. Adding the percentages within the necessary regions, 13.5% + 34% + 34% = 81.5% of the scores are between 54 and 78.

SECTION 3.5 EXERCISES

1. Find the standard deviation for the following data set. Round your answer to the nearest hundredth. {11, 16, 17, 20}

2. Find the standard deviation for the following data set. Round your answer to the nearest hundredth. {30, 30, 31, 35, 39}

3. Considering the data sets from Exercises #1 and #2, which of the sets is more spread out? Why?

4. IQ scores are normally distributed with a mean of 100 and a standard deviation of 15.

   a. What percent of IQ scores are between 85 and 115?

   b. What percent of IQ scores are between 70 and 130?

   c. What percent of IQ scores are between 55 and 145?

   d. If the MENSA organization requires an IQ score higher than 130 for membership, what percent of the population would qualify for membership in MENSA?

5. The heights (in inches) of the students at a large college were recorded, and the data was normally distributed. Use the normal curve in figure 3.5.10 to answer the following questions:

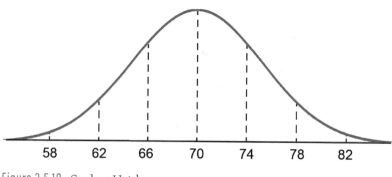

Figure 3.5.10   Student Heights

   a. What is the mean height for these students?

   b. What is the standard deviation?

   c. What percent of the students are taller than 62 inches?

   d. What percent of the students are shorter than 66 inches?

   e. What percent of the students are between 62 and 74 inches tall?

   f. What was the range (in inches) for the middle 68% of student heights?

6. The scores on a chemistry exam were normally distributed with a mean of 65 and a standard deviation of 9.

   a. What percent of the students scored above 65?

   b. What percent of the students scored above 56?

   c.   What percent of the students scored below 47?

   d.   What percent of the students scored between 65 and 74?

   e.   What percent of the students scored between 56 and 83?

   f.   If 1,000 students took the exam, and all students with grades between 74 and 83 earned a B, how many students earned a B?

   g.   How high must a student score in order to be in the top 2.5% of scores?

7.   The life span for a certain brand of tires is normally distributed, with a mean of 35,000 miles and a standard deviation of 6,000 miles.

   a.   What percent of these tires will last more than 29,000 miles?

   b.   What percent of these tires will last fewer than 47,000 miles?

   c.   What percent of these tires will last between 23,000 and 35,000 miles?

   d.   What is the range (in miles) for the middle 95% of the life spans of these tires?

8.   The length of human pregnancies from conception to birth is normally distributed with a mean of 266 days and a standard deviation of 16 days.

   a.   What percent of human pregnancies last fewer than 266 days?

   b.   What percent of human pregnancies last between 266 and 298 days?

   c.   What percent of human pregnancies last more than 282 days?

9.   A factory produces light bulbs that have a normally distributed life span, with a mean of 900 hours and a standard deviation of 150 hours. What is the percent chance that one of the light bulbs from this factory will last at least 750 hours?

10.   A standardized test has a mean of 400 and a standard deviation of 50. A total of 2,000 students took this test.

   a.   How many students scored over 500?

   b.   How many students scored at least 350?

11.   The term "grading on a curve" is often used. When teachers assign grades based on the notion that grades should be normally distributed, grades are assigned as follows:

   ▪   Grades within 1 standard deviation of the mean earn a C.

   ▪   Grades between 1 standard deviation above the mean and 2 standard deviations above the mean earn a B.

   ▪   Grades greater than 2 standard deviations above the mean earn an A.

   ▪   Grades between 1 standard deviation below the mean and 2 standard deviations below the mean earn a D.

   ▪   Grades greater than 2 standard deviations below the mean earn an F.

   If grading is done in this manner for a very large lecture class containing 400 students, how many of them would earn a C? How many would earn an A?

12. A student scored 73 on a standardized test that had a mean of 79 and a standard deviation of 3. Based on this score, what score would you expect for this student if he were to take another standardized test that has a mean of 95 and a standard deviation of 9?

13. Bonnie and Clyde attend different schools. Bonnie scored 84 on a math test that was normally distributed with a mean of 75 and a standard deviation of 9. Clyde scored 81 on a math test that was normally distributed with a mean of 70 and a standard deviation of 10. Which student did better on their exam?

ANSWERS TO SECTION 3.5 EXERCISES

1. 3.24

2. 3.52

3. Because it has a higher standard deviation, the data from Exercise #2 is more spread out.

4. **a.** 68%   **b.** 95%   **c.** 99.7%   **d.** 2.5%

5. **a.** 70 in   **b.** 4 in   **c.** 97.5%   **d.** 16%   **e.** 81.5%   **f.** 66−74 in

6. **a.** 50%   **b.** 84%   **c.** 2.5%   **d.** 34%   **e.** 81.5%   **f.** 135   **g.** 83

7. **a.** 84%   **b.** 97.5%   **c.** 47.5%   **d.** 23,000 miles to 47,000 miles

8. **a.** 50%   **b.** 47.5%   **c.** 16%

9. 84%

10. **a.** 50 students   **b.** 1,680 students

11. 272 students would be given a C, and 10 students would get an A.

12. 77, which is a score 2 standard deviations below the mean.

13. Clyde scored better. His score is more than 1 standard deviation above the mean.

CHAPTER 3 CREDITLINES

PROBABILITY

What's the difference between probability and statistics?

Simply put, to describe an entire set by looking at a few specific items randomly selected from the set, we use statistics. To attempt to predict the results of one particular event based on information that describes a set, we use probability.

Randomness is extremely important in the worlds of probability and statistics. If the systems under consideration were not random, they would be predictable. If they were predictable, then there would not be a need to study them like we do. Thus, to keep things worth studying, we will assume all events we discuss are random in nature and all outcomes are equally likely. Furthermore, in this book we will assume all dice and coins are fair and balanced, all decks of cards are well shuffled, and all balls in urns have been thoroughly mixed.

Image 4.0.1

4.1 On the Shoulders of Giants: Biographies and Historical References

For Probability ...

During the summer of 1654, in a series of five letters with each other, Frenchmen Pierre de Fermat and Blaise Pascal laid the foundation for the theory of probability. They considered the dice problem, which asks how many times pair of six-sided dice must be thrown before one expects a double six.

Even though Fermat and Pascal are credited with establishing the foundations of probability theory, a rather quirky Italian doctor and mathematician named Girolamo Cardano was an expert in the probabilities associated with games of chance nearly 100 years earlier.

Blaise Pascal

Blaise Pascal (1623–1662) was a French mathematician, physicist, inventor, writer and Christian philosopher. His mother passed away when he was just three years old and his father, Étienne, decided that he alone would educate his children. Each of them showed extraordinary intellectual ability, particularly his son Blaise, who showed an amazing aptitude for mathematics and science.

Image 4.1.1: Blaise Pascal

While not yet 19 years old, in an effort to ease his father's endless, exhausting calculations and recalculations of taxes owed and paid, Pascal constructed a mechanical calculator capable of addition and subtraction. This device, created in 1642, was called **Pascal's Calculator** or the **Pascaline**.

In 1654, Pascal corresponded with Pierre de Fermat on the subject of gambling problems, and from that collaboration was born the mathematical theory of probability. The specific problem considered was that of two players who want to finish a game early and, based on the chance each has of winning the game from that point, want to divide the stakes fairly. From this discussion, the notion of expected value was introduced. Pascal later used a probabilistic argument, which became known as **Pascal's Wager**, to justify belief in God and a virtuous life. It reads:

> If God does not exist, one will lose nothing by believing in him, while if he does exist, one will lose everything by not believing. Thus, we are compelled to gamble.

The work done by Fermat and Pascal in the study of probability laid important groundwork for the formulation of calculus. In addition to Pascal's Calculator, his inventions include the hydraulic press (using hydraulic pressure to multiply force) and the syringe. Additionally, in his search for a perpetual motion machine, Pascal introduced a primitive form of roulette and the roulette wheel.

After a religious experience in 1654, Pascal mostly gave up working with mathematics. His death came in 1662, just two months after his 39th birthday, with his last words being "May God never abandon me." An autopsy performed after his death revealed grave problems with his stomach and other organs of his abdomen, along with damage to his brain. Despite the autopsy, the cause of his poor health was never precisely determined, though speculation focuses on tuberculosis, stomach cancer, or a combination of the two.

Pierre de Fermat

Pierre de Fermat (1601–1665) was a French lawyer and mathematician who is given credit for early developments that led to the discovery of calculus. He made notable contributions in the fields of number theory, analytic geometry, probability, and optics. And, being fluent in French, Latin, Occitan, classical Greek, Italian, and Spanish, he was also regularly sought out regarding the translation of foreign texts.

Image 4.1.2: Pierre de Fermat

In 1623, he entered the University of Orléans and earned a bachelor's degree in civil law in 1626. Soon after, he began his first serious mathematical research, communicating most of his ideas in letters to friends. Although Fermat claimed to have proven all his theorems of arithmetic, few records of his proofs were actually included in these letters. This led many mathematicians to doubt several of his claims, especially given the difficulty of some of the problems and the limited mathematical methods available to Fermat at the time. His famous **Last Theorem** was first discovered by his son in the margin of one of his father's books and included the statement that "the margin was too small to include the proof."

Through their correspondence in 1654, Fermat and Blaise Pascal helped lay the fundamental groundwork for the study of probability, and from this brief but productive collaboration, they are now regarded as joint founders of probability theory. Together with René Descartes, Fermat was one of the two leading mathematicians of the first half of the seventeenth century. According to Peter L. Bernstein, in his book *Against the Gods*, Fermat "was a mathematician of rare power."

Girolamo Cardano

Girolamo (or **Gerolamo**) **Cardano** (1501–1576), also known as **Jerome Cardan**, is one of the most interesting people in the history of mathematics. He was a mathematician, physician, astrologer, philosopher and gambler. He wrote more than 200 works on medicine, mathematics, physics, philosophy, religion, and music, and his gambling led him to formulate elementary rules in probability, making him one of the founders of the field.

He was born the illegitimate child of Fazio Cardano, a mathematically gifted lawyer, who was a friend of Leonardo da Vinci. After he earned a degree in medicine, Cardano managed to develop a considerable reputation as a physician and his services were highly valued. He was the first to describe typhoid fever, and in 1553 he cured the Scottish Archbishop of St Andrews of a disease that had left him speechless and was thought incurable—for which he was paid 1,400 gold crowns.

Image 4.1.3: Girolamo Cardano

Today, he is best known for his achievements in algebra. Cardano was the first mathematician to make systematic use of numbers less than zero. He acknowledged the existence of what are now called **imaginary numbers** (although he did not understand their properties), and introduced binomial coefficients and the **binomial theorem**.

Cardano was notoriously short of money and kept himself solvent by being an accomplished gambler and chess player. His book about games of chance, **Liber de Ludo Aleae** ("Book on Games of Chance"), was written around 1564, but not published until 1663, nearly 90 years after his death. The book contains the first systematic treatment of probability, as well as a section on effective cheating methods. He used the game of throwing dice to understand the basic concepts of probability, and defined odds as the ratio of favorable to unfavorable outcomes.

Cardano invented several mechanical devices including the combination lock and universal joints, which allow for the transmission of rotary motion at various angles and are used in vehicles to this day. In a fit of rage, he cut off the ears of his youngest son, who had stolen money from him. Cardano himself was accused of heresy and had to spend several months in prison in 1570 because he had computed and published the horoscope of Jesus in 1554. Cardano's life came to a dramatic end. Years before, he had made an astrological prediction of the date of his own death. When the day arrived and he was still alive, he committed suicide so that his prediction would come true.

Dice and Playing Cards

Some of the most common tools used in the study of probability are dice and playing cards. It's easy to take these common items for granted, but, like many things, their origins and development are quite fascinating.

Keeping in mind that the development of probability did not come about until the sixteenth and seventeenth centuries, dice have ancient origins. They were originally used for **divination**, which is an organized, systematic attempt to determine the will of spiritual deities. This is similar to fortune-telling, but instead of general predictions about a person's life, divination is steeped in religious connotations.

Dice have been found in Middle Eastern archeological sites that date to 2800-2500 BC, which is well before the development of the scientific method and probability theory. Much like today's fantasy role-playing games, specific outcomes were assigned to the various results, thereby removing the potential personal biases of the people involved. This specific form of divination is referred to as **casting lots**, which involves using a tool to determine a random outcome, and in ancient times, results determined in this manner would then be assumed to represent the will of a chosen god. Of course, in semi-developed cultures that lacked milling and construction techniques, the perfectly shaped dice we know and love today were not the tools of choice. Instead, some of the most common objects used in divination were **knucklebones**, which were typically the ankle bones from sacrificial sheep or buffalo. It is from these earliest forms of dice that we get the phrase "**rolling the bones.**"

Even though divination practices eventually became viewed as superstitious and were outlawed in many cultures, casting lots using uniform tools continued to occur and develop. As interest in recreational games expanded and there became a need for more than six random outcomes, mathematics came to the rescue with the five **Platonic solids**. These three-dimensional objects, named for the Greek philosopher Plato, have sides that are equilateral triangles, squares, or regular pentagons. When used as dice, each of the identically shaped sides has an equal chance of displaying its result. A **hexahedron** is the traditionally accepted cubical die with six square faces. A 4-sided die, which is a **tetrahedron**, has four triangular faces. An 8-sided die, which is an **octahedron**, has eight triangular faces. A **dodecahedron**, which can be used as a 12-sided die, has faces that are all pentagons. And, an **icosahedron** has twenty triangular faces, and can be used as a 20-sided die. Then, with the faces labeled with either a unique number or patterns of round dots, called **pips**, each side corresponds to a specific, predetermined outcome.

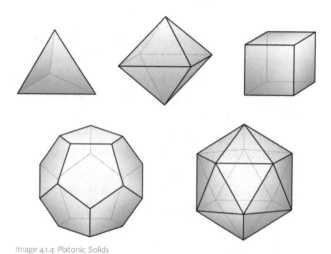

Image 4.1.4: Platonic Solids

If you have ever played with a **Magic 8-Ball**, you may have found there were twenty unique responses to a simple yes-no question. Ten of the responses were affirmative, five were negative, and five were non-committal (e.g., "REPLY HAZY, TRY AGAIN"). To make all of the twenty outcomes equally likely, the responses were each printed on one side of an icosahedron, which was suspended in a tube of dark blue liquid. The user asked a question and rotated the 8-Ball so that the polyhedron floated up to a window, displaying a single answer shown on one of its triangular sides. Of course, the displayed "answer" is more likely a result of physics and probability, rather than divination. ☺

Image 4.1.5: Magic 8-Ball

After the Chinese invented paper and the Germans developed techniques for printing, decks of **playing cards** started becoming popular for recreational activities. Different cultures, however, modified the appearance of the cards to make them more familiar to their own citizens. For example, the four suits in early European decks were the chalice, sword, money, and baton, while other countries used hearts, acorns, bells, and leaves. Eventually, the French and English adopted the suits of **spades** to represent royalty, **hearts** to represent the clergy, **diamonds** to represent the merchant class, and the lowest-ranked suit of **clubs** to represent the peasants.

Given the portable nature of a deck of cards, there are many coincidences that allow a traveler to treat it as a calendar and almanac.

- The four suits can be aligned with the four seasons of Spring, Summer, Autumn, and Winter.

- The two colors, red and black, can correspond to daytime and nighttime.

- There are 52 cards in a deck, and there are 52 weeks in a year.

- There are 13 ranks (Ace, 2, 3, 4, 5, 6, 7, 8, 9, 10, Jack, Queen, and King), which can correspond to the 13 lunar cycles (four-week periods) in a year.

- There are 12 face cards (the Jacks, Queens, and Kings), which align with the 12 months in a year.

- If we consider value of each rank and allow the Jack to be worth 11, the Queen worth 12, and the King to be worth 13 points, we can say the value of the entire deck is $4 \times (1 + 2 + 3 + 4 + 5 + 6 + 7 + 8 + 9 + 10 + 11 + 12 + 13) = 364$. If we include a Joker that is worth a single point, we arrive at 365, which is the number of days in a year. And, if we throw in a second Joker, we have 366, which is the number of days in a leap year!

It is also easy to correlate the varying cards, their appearances and deck structures to specific aspects of different religions, which often points to occult-like fortune telling using **tarot cards**. That, in turn, circles us back to a deck of cards as another form of casting lots. In fact, in some US States, like **Nevada**, a common practice for breaking a tie in an election is drawing cards. Using cards may not be specifically mandated—**Nevada Revised Statute 293.400.1 (c)** simply states some election ties will be decided "by lot"—but, if any state is going to settle a tie in an election by using playing cards, it should be Nevada!

References

Bernstein, P. L. *Against the Gods: The Remarkable Story of Risk.* Hoboken, NJ: John Wiley & Sons, 1966.

Bicycle Cards, https://bicyclecards.com/article/cards-and-the-calendar/

"Cardan, Jerome." In *The Lincoln Library of Essential Information*, vol. 2, 1754. Buffalo, NY: The Frontier Press Company, 1944.

Encyclopedia Britannica, Dice, https://www.britannica.com/topic/dice

Encyclopedia Britannica, Playing Cards https://www.britannica.com/topic/playing-card

Eves, H. *An Introduction to the History of Mathematics.* Philadelphia, PA: Saunders College Publishing, 1990.

Fletcher, P., H. Hoyle, and C. W. Patty. *Foundations of Discrete Mathematics.* Boston, MA: PWS Publishing Company, 1990.

International Playing Card Society, https://www.i-p-c-s.org/

Nevada Revised Statue 293.400, https://www.leg.state.nv.us/NRS/NRS-293.html#NRS293Sec400

"Pascal, Blaise." In *The Lincoln Library of Essential Information*, vol. 2, 1943. Buffalo, NY: The Frontier Press Company, 1944.

The Burnt City and the Evolution of the Concept of "Probability" In the Human Brain, *Iran J Public Health.* 2015 Sep; 44(9): 1306–130: https://www.ncbi.nlm.nih.gov/pmc/articles/PMC4645795/

World Book Encyclopedia, 1978 ed., s.v. "Fermat, Pierre de."

World Book Encyclopedia, 1978 ed., s.v. "Pascal, Blaise."

4.2 I'm Counting on You: Counting, Permutations, and Combinations

Review: Order of Operations

If several people are asked to simplify the same multi-step arithmetic **expression**, a standard set of rules must be established for the order in which the operations are performed. Otherwise, different people may get different answers. For example, let's say Bill and Ted are asked to simplify the expression $3 + 4 \times 5$. Bill adds the $3 + 4$, and then multiplies that result by 5 to get a total of 35. Ted performs the multiplication first, and then adds 3 to get a total of 23. Who is right? In case you aren't sure yet ... it is Ted.

Arithmetic started with addition (and subtraction). Repeated addition led to multiplication (and division), and repeated multiplication led to the use of exponents. In addition to those procedures, parentheses or other grouping symbols can also be used in an expression. Let's consolidate all of these processes into a single list, known as the "order of operations."

Arithmetic **Order of Operations:**

1. All operations contained within parentheses ( ) or other grouping symbols, such as brackets [ ], or braces { }, should be done first.

2. Secondly, simplify all expressions containing exponents.

3. Multiplication and division are done next, as we come to them going from left to right.

4. Addition and subtraction are done last, again, as we come to them going from left to right.

To help remember this order, many students like to memorize the acronym **PEMDAS** (Parentheses, Exponents, Multiplication, Division, Addition, Subtraction). This can be really helpful, but be careful! If you do not realize multiplication and division are done as we come to them going from the left to the right, you may fall into the trap of thinking multiplication always precedes division—it does not. The same holds true for addition and subtraction.

EXAMPLE 1:

Simplify: $5 + 6 \times 3$

Solution: Since multiplication is performed before addition, start by multiplying 6×3. Then, add 5 to that result.

$5 + 6 \times 3$
$= 5 + 18$
$= 23$

EXAMPLE 2:

Simplify: $13 - 5 + 6$

SOLUTION: Remember, perform addition and subtraction as we come to them going from left to right. Here, that means the subtraction must be done first.

$13 - 5 + 6$
$= 8 + 6$
$= 14$

EXAMPLE 3:

Simplify: $13 - (5 + 6)$

SOLUTION: Since $(5 + 6)$ is inside parentheses, that operation is performed first.

$13 - (5 + 6)$
$= 13 - 11$
$= 2$

EXAMPLE 4:

Simplify: $42 \div 3(2)$

SOLUTION: There are parentheses in this expression, but take note that there is no operation to perform inside these parentheses. We have division and multiplication to perform here, and those are done going from left to right.

$42 \div 3(2)$
$= 14(2)$
$= 28$

EXAMPLE 5:

Simplify: $5 \times (2 + 3)^2 - (6 - 4) + 1$

SOLUTION: Here, we start with the operations that are inside the parentheses. Then, perform the operation using the exponent. After that, the multiplication is done. Finally, we have addition and subtraction, which are performed as we come to them going from left to right.

$5 \times (2 + 3)^2 - (6 - 4) + 1$
$= 5 \times (5)^2 - 2 + 1$
$= 5 \times 25 - 2 + 1$
$= 125 - 2 + 1$
$= 123 + 1$
$= 124$

Counting

Counting. Seems simple, right? We all know how to count, or we wouldn't have made it into this math class. Well, yes and no. What we're going to examine are some different situations that require different types of counting.

Let's pretend we've gone into a restaurant, and the very basic menu looks like this:

- Appetizers: Breadsticks, Salad

- Main Dishes: Lasagna, Chicken, Meatloaf

- Desserts: Pie, Ice Cream

We are instructed by the server to choose exactly one item from each column to create a meal. How many different meals are possible?

One approach we can take in trying to answer this question is to make a list of all the possible meals. If we're going to do this, we should be as systematic as possible, so that we don't leave out any of the meals.

Image 4.2.1

Going across the top row, the first meal that we could make would be: Breadsticks-Lasagna-Pie (we will abbreviate this as B-L-P). We could also have Breadsticks-Lasagna-Ice Cream (B-L-I). This takes care of every possible meal that includes Breadsticks and Lasagna.

So far, we have:

B-L-P and B-L-I

Continuing, we will create every meal that has breadsticks as the appetizer:

B-C-P and B-M-P
B-C-I and B-M-I

That's it. That's every meal that has breadsticks as the appetizer. Now, we must consider the meals that have salad as the appetizer:

S-L-P, S-C-P, and S-M-P
S-L-I, S-C-I, and S-M-I

Whew. Well, there they are; all 12 possible meals. If you're thinking, "there *must* be a better way," you're right. It is known as the **Fundamental Counting Principle**. The heart of the matter is as follows:

Fundamental Counting Principle

To find the number of options for a multi-part event, find the number of options for each stage and multiply those numbers together.

When we look at our menu from above, we had **two** choices of appetizer, **three** choices of main dish, and **two** choices of dessert. Multiplying these together gives us $2 \times 3 \times 2 = 12$ possible meals. Yep, it really is that easy.

Do keep in mind, however, the Fundamental Counting Principal tells us the *number* of meals, but not the specific meals. As we progress with our discussion of probability, our primary concern will be the number of options, not the specific options.

EXAMPLE 6:

A four-character code is required for entering a high-security room. This code is entered on a keypad that consists of the numbers 1 through 9 and the letters A, B, and C. How many different four-character codes are possible?

SOLUTION: We have four spots to fill with possible outcomes and we are going to use the Counting Principle. So, we will find the number of possibilities for each spot, and then multiply those numbers together.

$$\underline{\quad} - \underline{\quad} - \underline{\quad} - \underline{\quad}$$

The first spot in the code could be any of the 12 possible characters, so there are 12 possibilities for that spot.

$$\underline{12} - \underline{\quad} - \underline{\quad} - \underline{\quad}$$

The second spot could also be any of the 12 possible characters, so there are 12 possibilities for that spot, as well.

$$\underline{12} - \underline{12} - \underline{\quad} - \underline{\quad}$$

Similarly, the third and fourth spots also have 12 possibilities. That gives us a total of $12 \times 12 \times 12 \times 12 = 20{,}736$ possible four-character codes.

EXAMPLE 7:

A four-character code is required for entering a high-security room. This code is entered on a keypad that consists of the numbers 1 through 9 and the letters A, B, and C. *If repetition is not allowed*, how many different four-character codes are possible?

SOLUTION: Here, since repetition is not allowed, once a character has been used it cannot be used again.

As in the previous example, we have four spots to fill with possible outcomes, and we are going to use the Counting Principle. So, we will find the number of possibilities for each spot, and then multiply those numbers together.

$$\underline{\quad} - \underline{\quad} - \underline{\quad} - \underline{\quad}$$

The first spot in the code could be any of the 12 possible characters, so there are 12 possibilities for that spot.

$$\underline{12} - \underline{\quad} - \underline{\quad} - \underline{\quad}$$

Since one of the characters has been used in the first spot, we are left with 11 possibilities for the second spot.

$$\underline{12} - \underline{11} - \underline{\quad} - \underline{\quad}$$

Similarly, the third spot will have 10 possible characters and the fourth spot will have 9 possible characters, giving us a total of $12 \times 11 \times 10 \times 9 = 11{,}880$ different four-character codes, when repetition is not allowed.

Factorials

I have a class with six students in it and their names are Red, Yellow, Green, Blue, Indigo, and Violet. We're going to line up all of the students in a single row for a class photograph. How many different photographs are possible? We will apply the Fundamental Counting Principle, putting a different student in each of the six spots.

$$\underline{\quad} - \underline{\quad} - \underline{\quad} - \underline{\quad} - \underline{\quad} - \underline{\quad}$$

How many options do we have for the first spot? Well, no students have been used yet, so we have all six to pick from. We have six options for the first spot.

$$\underline{6} - \underline{\quad} - \underline{\quad} - \underline{\quad} - \underline{\quad} - \underline{\quad}$$

Now that we have placed a student (any one of them, it really doesn't matter which one) in the first spot, how many are left to choose from for the next spot? There would be five left to pick from, so we have five options for the second space. (I'm hoping you see the Fundamental Counting Principle at work here.)

$$\underline{6} - \underline{5} - \underline{\quad} - \underline{\quad} - \underline{\quad} - \underline{\quad}$$

Continuing on with the same logic, until we have only one student left to fill the last spot, our options look like:

$$\underline{6} - \underline{5} - \underline{4} - \underline{3} - \underline{2} - \underline{1}$$

We multiply these all together and wind up with $6 \times 5 \times 4 \times 3 \times 2 \times 1 = 720$ different ways the kids can line up. If this number seems too large to be correct, start listing them out. Begin with RYGBIV, then RYGBVI, and so on. After you write down the first couple hundred arrangements, you may get tired and accept that 720 is correct. ☺

What if we were asked the same question about a deck of cards? How many different ways can you place all 52 cards from a standard deck in a straight line? Well, there are 52 cards, so that will be: $52 \times 51 \times 50 \times$ ... WAIT A MINUTE! You don't want to write that all the way down to 1 and doing all that multiplying on a calculator would be hard to do without making a mistake.

"There's got to be a better way to write this," you might say, and you would be correct. It makes use of something known as **factorials**.

The factorial symbol (commonly known as the exclamation point) gives us a shorthand way to write such problems down. For example, 4! (pronounced "four factorial") $= 4 \times 3 \times 2 \times 1 = 24$.

Factorials get really large really fast.

$1! = 1$

$2! = 2 \times 1 = 2$

$3! = 3 \times 2 \times 1 = 6$

$4! = 4 \times 3 \times 2 \times 1 = 24$

$5! = 5 \times 4 \times 3 \times 2 \times 1 = 120$

$6! = 6 \times 5 \times 4 \times 3 \times 2 \times 1 = 720$

$7! = 7 \times 6 \times 5 \times 4 \times 3 \times 2 \times 1 = 5040$

$8! = 8 \times 7 \times 6 \times 5 \times 4 \times 3 \times 2 \times 1 = 40,320$

$9! = 9 \times 8 \times 7 \times 6 \times 5 \times 4 \times 3 \times 2 \times 1 = 362,880$

$10! = 10 \times 9 \times 8 \times 7 \times 6 \times 5 \times 4 \times 3 \times 2 \times 1 = 3,628,800$

$11! = 11 \times 10 \times 9 \times 8 \times 7 \times 6 \times 5 \times 4 \times 3 \times 2 \times 1 = 39,916,800$

$25! = 15,511,210,043,330,985,984,000,000$

Remember the question about the different arrangements for a standard deck of cards? Well, 52! is greater than 8.0658×10^{67}. That's a 68-digit number. The number one hundred trillion—100,000,000,000,000— only has 15 digits!

Our discussion of factorials would not be complete without a couple more pieces of the puzzle.

First, let's talk about 0!. Although it is very tempting to think that $0! = 0$, that is incorrect. 0! is actually equal to 1. Some authors will make this claim "out of convenience" and others will claim it "as a definition." If you wish to accept $0! = 1$ without condition, so be it. If you would like a little proof, think of the following.

$$n! = n \times (n-1) \times (n-2) \times (n-3) \times ... \times 3 \times 2 \times 1$$

and

$$(n-1)! = (n-1) \times (n-2) \times (n-3) \times ... \times 3 \times 2 \times 1$$

Then, substituting $(n-1)!$ into the equivalent part of the first equation, we have

$$n! = n \times (n-1)!$$

Dividing both sides of the equation by n gives us

$$n!/n = (n-1)!$$

Next, if we let $n = 1$, the equation becomes

$$1!/1 = (1-1)!$$

And some minor simplification on both sides gives us

$$1 = 0!, \text{ which is the same as } 0! = 1.$$

Finally, since we have covered factorials for 0 and the positive integers (i.e., the Whole Numbers), one might be tempted to ask about factorials for fractions, decimals, or even negative numbers. Well, the good news is, for our purposes, we will only work with factorials involving Whole Numbers.

Permutations

A **permutation** is an arrangement of objects that are placed in a distinct order. Just like in our class photo discussion from earlier in the section, if the order changes, then we have a new permutation. We worked with this idea in our photograph example, which helped to explain factorials. The photo RGYBIV is different from the photo BIVGYR. The letters are the same, but the order has changed, creating a different photograph. Since changing the order makes the photo different, we are dealing with a permutation. **For a permutation, the order matters**.

As long as individual items are not being duplicated, the formula for finding the number of permutations is shown below. In this formula n is the total number of objects, and r is the number of objects being used. The phrase "being used" might not make sense yet, but it will as we continue to practice.

$$_nP_r = \frac{n!}{(n-r)!}$$

Although many people resort to memorizing that formula, it will make a bit more sense if we take a few moments to understand it.

Permutations are all the possible ways of doing something. Let's take another look at our discussion about the class photo. What if we wanted only four of the six students in the picture? How many different ways could it be done? Formally, this is called a "Permutation of six things, taken four at a time," or $_6P_4$.

Using the Fundamental Counting Principle, we have 6 choices for the first person in the photo, 5 for the second, 4 for the third, and 3 choices for the last position. That makes $6 \times 5 \times 4 \times 3 = 360$ different photos.

Alternatively, if we begin by considering all the possible arrangements with six students, we have 6!. Then, because we have two students left out of the photo, we would need to cancel the possible arrangements of those students. Using numbers, this looks like 6!/2!. Then, the 2×1 would cancel, leaving $6 \times 5 \times 4 \times 3$ in the numerator.

Relating that process to the formula, the $n!$ in the numerator refers to all possible arrangements. For the denominator, if we have n items and only want to count r of them, then there are $(n - r)$ of them we don't want to count. The $(n - r)!$ in the denominator refers to the arrangements that are not counted.

Now, going back to the class picture example,

$$_6P_4 = 6!/(6 - 4)! = 6!/2! = (6 \times 5 \times 4 \times 3 \times 2 \times 1)/(2 \times 1) = 6 \times 5 \times 4 \times 3 = 360$$

There are 360 different ways to take a photo using four of the six different students.

Combinations

A **combination** is a collection of distinct objects in which the order makes no difference. Distinguishing between combinations and permutations is often challenging, but remember, for combinations, order does not matter.

Let's suppose, for example, of the six students in a class, four of them will be chosen to go on a field trip. Here, we are making a collection of four students, and the order in which they are selected makes no difference. Each student is either chosen, or not, but it doesn't matter which one is chosen first. While RGBY would make a different *photo* than GBRY (which indicates a **permutation**), having RGBY go on the field trip is exactly the same as having GBRY go on the field trip (which indicates a **combination**). Making the distinction between permutations and combinations can be tricky. Try to decide if the order would make a difference in the specific situation. If not, then we have a combination.

In terms of combinations, RGBY is the same as GBRY, and these are both the same as YGRB. In fact, any group of those four students is the same. They are all redundant, because order does not matter. Furthermore, in this situation, there are $4! = 24$ redundancies.

Finding the number of combinations starts with finding the number of permutations and then involves cancelling out the number of redundancies.

Just like in the formula for permutations, as long as individual items are not reused, the formula for determining the number of combinations is shown below. And, just like with the formula for permutations, in this formula, n is the total number of objects, and r is the number of objects being used.

$$_nC_r = \frac{n!}{(n-r)!r!}$$

Let's think about that formula for a minute. Just like with the formula for permutations, $n!$ represents the total number of all possible arrangements and $(n - r)!$ has us cancelling out the unused arrangements. Then, $r!$ has us cancelling out the redundancies. It may also be helpful to remember, since we cancel out the redundancies, the number of combinations for a situation can never be more than the number of permutations for the same situation.

Going back to our example, let's say we want to pick four out of six students to take on the field trip. Here, we have six students, but only four of them will be chosen. Formally, this is called a "Combination of six things, taken four at a time," or $_6C_4$.

Using the combinations formula, we have:

$$_6C_4 = \frac{6!}{(6-4)!4!} = \frac{6!}{2!4!} = \frac{6 \cdot 5 \cdot 4 \cdot 3 \cdot 2 \cdot 1}{(2 \cdot 1)(4 \cdot 3 \cdot 2 \cdot 1)} = \frac{6 \cdot 5}{2 \cdot 1} = \frac{30}{2} = 15$$

Notice that we were able to cancel the $(4 \cdot 3 \cdot 2 \cdot 1)$ during the simplification. Although not necessary, this kept the numbers smaller and easier to work with. In the end, we see there are 15 different ways to pick four of the six students to take on the field trip.

A key thing to notice when working with the formula for combinations is that the factorials in the denominator are not multiplied together to form a single factorial. Combining the 4! and the 2! to make 8! would be incorrect. Don't do that.

Notice that the numbers used in the combination example about the field trip are the same as those used in the example for the permutation about the photograph, but the answers are *very* different.

Finally, in regard to the notations, we indicate permutations and combinations by subscripting the *n* and the *r* in $_nP_r$ and $_nC_r$. As an alternative, we could write nPr and nCr without subscripting the *n* and *r*. Also, in some texts, you may see these written as P(n, r) and C(n, r), respectively. In all cases, though, the P and C are capital letters. In the formula the n and r are always lowercase letters but are replaced with numbers for the actual computations.

> ## common mistake:
> When finding the product of two or more factorial expressions, such as $2! \cdot 4!$, do not merge them into a single factorial before expanding the multiplication. That is, $2! \cdot 4!$ is not 8!. It is $(2 \cdot 1) \cdot (4 \cdot 3 \cdot 2 \cdot 1)$.

One More Hint

Often, the hardest part about working with permutations and combinations is determining which one to use—based on the description of the situation. Sometimes, certain key words can help us decide if we have a permutation or a combination. Not always, but usually …

- Permutations are indicated by the terms "arrangement" and "order."

- Combinations are indicated by the terms "choose," "select," and "pick."

In general, *always* ask yourself, "Does order matter?" If so, we have a permutation. If not, it is a combination.

Also think about the logistics of the situation. If we have a box of 50 photographs, and we want to pick 15 of them to put into an album, we are working with a combination because it does not matter in what order we choose them—it doesn't matter if that picture of crazy Uncle Frank is picked first or sixth. If, however, we are actually putting the photos into the photo album, the order does matter. Putting that picture of Uncle Frank on the first page as opposed to the tenth page definitely makes a difference. If the order matters, we have a permutation.

Our discussion about the fundamental difference between permutations and combinations would be remiss if we neglected to address what is

Image 4.2.2: Combination Lock

commonly referred to as a "combination lock." From our personal experiences with the lockers found in gyms and high school hallways, to the wall safes we entrust with our valuables, we all know that to open the lock, we enter a sequence of three or four numbers by spinning a dial in alternating directions. We also know the combination of 17-34-29 is different from 34-17-29. Thus, since the order of the numbers matters, these locks are actually misnamed. They should be called "permutation locks." ☺

Using Your Calculator

If you have a scientific calculator, you probably have a factorial key on it. Type in the number and look for a button labeled "x!" or "n!." On some calculators, once you hit the factorial button, the computation will happen right away, without even having to hit the = key. On other calculators, you may have to hit = before seeing the result.

If your calculator can perform permutations and combinations, the keys will be labeled "nPr" and "nCr," respectively. The usage of these functions varies from calculator to calculator. In most cases, you type in the value for n, hit the nPr (or nCr) key, then enter in the value for r, and press the = key. If this sequence of entries does not work on your calculator, consult the calculator's owner's manual.

Do keep in mind: Even if your calculator performs factorials, permutations, and combinations, you still need to be able to recognize which of those functions applies to a given situation. Remember, the calculator is only as accurate as the person using it.

SECTION 4.2 EXERCISES

1. A fraternity is to elect a president and then a treasurer from the group of 40 members. How many ways can those two officers be elected?

2. Sandra has nine shirts and five pairs of pants. Assuming that everything goes together, how many different outfits can she make?

3. Area codes are made up of three-digit numbers.

   a. If all numbers can be used for each digit, how many area codes are possible?

   b. How many area codes would be possible if repetition is not allowed?

4. A school gymnasium has six different doors. How many ways can a person enter the gymnasium through one door and leave through a different door?

5. A license plate consists of three letters followed by three numbers.

   a. How many of these license plates are possible?

   b. How many plates are possible if repetition is not allowed?

Image 4.2.3

Evaluate:

6. 4!   7. 7!   8. 11!   9. 9!/5!

10. $_7P_3$ 11. $_5P_5$ 12. $_5P_1$ 13. $_9P_5$

11. You have eight books to place on a shelf, but you only have room for five of them. How many different ways can you arrange books on this shelf?

12. Sam has five favorite football teams, and every week, he puts their flags on his flagpole in different order.

    a. In a given week, how many different ways can he arrange the flags?

    b. If he only has room for three of the flags on his flagpole, how many different ways can they be arranged?

13. A baseball batting order is made up of nine players. How many different batting orders are possible?

14. Ten runners are in a race. How many different ways can they finish in 1st, 2nd, and 3rd place?

Evaluate:

18. $_7C_4$ 19. $_8C_3$ 20. $_5C_5$ 21. $_6C_0$

22. Of seven students in a class, two will be chosen to go on a field trip. How many different ways can they be selected?

23. Of the 15 players at an awards dinner, 3 of them will be given identical trophies. How many different ways can the trophies be given out?

24. A teacher chooses 5 of her 12 students to help clean the room after school. In how many ways can the students be chosen?

25. A student must answer five of the nine essay questions that are on an exam. How many ways can the student select five questions?

26. What is the difference between a permutation and a combination? Give an example of each.

ANSWERS TO SECTION 4.2 EXERCISES

1. 1560

2. 45

3. a. 1000,   b. 720

4. 30

5. a. 17,576,000,   b. 11,232,000

6. 24

7. 5040

8. 39,916,800

9. 3024

10. 210

11. 120

12. 5

13. 15,120

14. 6720

15. a. 120,   b. 60

16. 362,880

17. 720

18. 35

19. 56

20. 1

21. 1

22. 21

23. 455

24. 792

25. 126

26. When the order of the items matters, you have a permutation. When the order does not matter, you have a combination.

4.3 | What Happens in Vegas: Simple Probability and Odds

Review: Equivalent Fractions

Equivalent Fractions

Fractions are equivalent when they have the same value. For example, 2/3 and 4/6 are equivalent. Knowing how to recognize and create **equivalent fractions** is very important when fractions are to be added or subtracted, because when we perform those operations, it is necessary for the fractions to have a **common denominator**.

EXAMPLE 1:

Add 3/8 + 2/5.

SOLUTION: We first need to get a common denominator. To do this, we need to create fractions that are equivalent to the ones we are given so that they have the same denominator as one another.

We will start by identifying a common denominator, which is a number that both denominators will divide into evenly. For this problem, a number that 8 and 5 will both divide into evenly is 40.

In order to change the denominator of the first fraction to 40, we will need to multiply the denominator of the given fraction by 5. So that the new fraction we create is equivalent to the original, we must also multiply the numerator of that fraction by 5. After multiplying the numerator and the denominator of our first fraction by 5, we have changed 3/8 to the equivalent fraction.

$$\frac{3}{8} = \frac{15}{40}$$

Next, we will convert 2/5 to an equivalent fraction that has a denominator of 40. To do this, we will multiply the numerator and the denominator by 8.

$$\frac{2}{5} = \frac{16}{40}$$

At this point we have found fractions that are equivalent to those that we were given in the original problem, and now they have a common denominator. We have changed the format (but not the meaning) of the original problem to:

$$\frac{3}{8} + \frac{2}{5} = \frac{15}{40} + \frac{16}{40}$$

Now that our two fractions have a common denominator, they can be added.

$$\frac{3}{8} + \frac{2}{5} = \frac{15}{40} + \frac{16}{40} = \frac{31}{40}$$

Without being able to find equivalent fractions, we would not have been able to add these fractions very easily.

The Basics of Probability

A **sample space** is the list of everything that could possibly happen during an experiment, such as flipping a coin. It is common to list the sample space as a set, and the sample space for flipping a coin would be relatively short: {heads, tails}, or to abbreviate: {H, T}. Each possible result of the experiment is called an **outcome,** and outcomes can be listed individually or collectively as **events**.

If we are rolling a single six-sided die and are interested in the number of dots appearing on the top side, our sample space, which contains six different outcomes, would be: {1, 2, 3, 4, 5, 6}.

An example of an event would be rolling a three, which would correspond to the set: {3}. Another example of an event would be rolling an even number, which would correspond to the set: {2, 4, 6}.

There are two different kinds of probability. More formal definitions are out there, but what it boils down to is two different situations: Making predictions on what *should happen* and making predictions based on what *has already happened.*

Theoretical Probability

This is what *should happen.* Flipping a coin, we would expect heads to occur half of the time. That is, if we flipped a coin 100 times, we would expect to get about 50 heads. **Theoretical probability** (or just **probability**) is calculated as the likelihood of obtaining a specific event.

Relative Frequency

This is what *has already happened,* and we often see this referred to as "empirical probability," "estimated probability," or even "experimental probability." To avoid confusing it with theoretical probability, we will avoid the word "probability" and refer to it as **relative frequency** (or just **frequency**). To determine the relative frequency of an event, we must conduct an experiment or a study. Then, those results can be used to predict future results. If we flipped a coin 100 times and got 97 heads, we might suspect that this coin wasn't fair, and we could use those results to predict that we are much more likely to get a head on the next flip.

Image 4.3.1

Disclaimers

If it is impossible to predict all possible outcomes or the outcomes are not equally likely, then probabilities can only be determined from the result of an experiment, which means they are actually frequencies. For example, in baseball, it is impossible to predict whether or not a player will get a hit (the outcomes are not equally likely). However, based on all of his previous at bats, a fair prediction can be made. The player's batting average is, essentially, a relative frequency being used to make a prediction. Thus, based on previous at bats, a player with a batting average of .315 has a 31.5% chance of getting a hit on his next at bat.

Because some entities use the term "probability" in describing both theoretical probability and relative frequency, it can sometimes be difficult to distinguish between the two. In an ideal case, the two will be equal, and it would not matter. After an experiment, if the two are very different, it is usually an indication of an unusual occurrence.

In general, the problems that we will be working on will ask you to find a theoretical probability. Also, unless otherwise noted, we will assume each outcome has an equal chance of occurring.

Next, if you remember only one thing about probability, remember this:

$$\text{Probability of an Event} = \frac{\text{Number of Successes}}{\text{Total Number of Outcomes}}$$

A key thing to note here is that the term "success" is not necessarily something that corresponds to winning. We have a "success" if the event for which we are interested in finding the probability actually occurs. Also, for a compact notation, we will shorten the "Probability of an Event" to **P(Event)**. Yes, since parentheses typically imply multiplication, this looks like the product of P and Event, but it is not. To help distinguish the difference, it is customary to use a capital P for probability statements.

EXAMPLE 2:

A single six-sided die is to be rolled. What is the probability of rolling a four? Alternatively, using shorter notation, find P(4). Also, find the probability of rolling an even number, or P(even).

SOLUTIONS: In both cases, the sample space is {1, 2, 3, 4, 5, 6}. Since there are exactly six possible outcomes, that will be the denominator of our answer.

For P(4), the number of successes (notice, we don't *win* anything), or fours, on the dice is one. That will be the numerator of our answer. So, the probability of rolling a four is P(4) = 1/6.

For P(even), we succeed when the roll yields a two, four, or six. Since there are three "successes" and six "outcomes," the probability of rolling an even number is P(even) = 3/6.

This answer can be reduced to 1/2, but that is not necessary when working probability problems. The reason for leaving the fraction unreduced is because an answer can provide us information about the raw number of successes and outcomes for the situation we are considering. With P(even) = 3/6, we can tell there were three successes and six possible outcomes. If the fraction were reduced to P(even) = 1/2, we would not be able see the original number of successes or outcomes.

We could also represent this answer 0.50 or even 50%. These are not incorrect, but it is more common to write probabilities as fractions, instead of decimals or percents.

EXAMPLE 3:

If a coin is flipped and a die is rolled, find the probability of getting heads on the coin and a one on the die.

SOLUTION: With two possible events for the coin flip and six events for the die, the sample space consists of twelve unique outcomes: {H1, H2, H3, H4, H5, H6, T1, T2, T3, T4, T5, T6}.

Exactly one of those outcomes is H1. So, P(H1) = 1/12.

Rolling a Pair of Dice

It is very common to examine problems that involve rolling a pair of standard dice and taking the sum of the faces that are showing. There are 6 different outcomes on each die, and we can use the counting principle to determine that there will be $6 \times 6 = 36$ different outcomes.

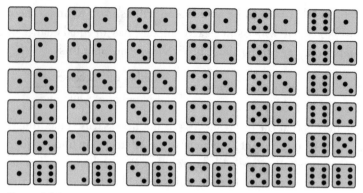

Figure 4.3.1 Dice Outcomes

Taking a close look at the possible outcomes for a pair of dice, we can see there are five ways to get a total of six: (1, 5), (2, 4), (3, 3), (4, 2) and (5, 1). Keep in mind, a 2 on the first die is different from a 2 on the second die.

EXAMPLE 4:

Two dice are rolled, and the sum of the faces is obtained. Find the probability that the sum is nine.

Solution: The number of outcomes when rolling a pair of dice is 36. That will be the denominator of our answer.

The number of successes, or ways to roll a nine, in our list of outcomes is four. That will be the numerator of our answer.

So, the probability of getting a sum of nine is P(9) = 4/36. This can be reduced to 1/9, but this reduction is not necessary.

Deck of Cards

Most people are familiar with the structure of a standard deck of 52 cards. There are two suits made up of red cards, hearts (♥) and diamonds (♦), and two suits made up of black cards, clubs (♣) and spades (♠). In each suit there are thirteen ranks—Ace (A), 2, 3, 4, 5, 6, 7, 8, 9, 10, Jack (J), Queen (Q), and King (K). Additionally, since the Jack, Queen, and King of each suit have pictures of people on them, they are often referred to as "face cards" or "picture cards."

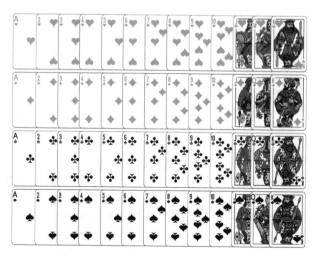

Figure 4.3.2 Complete Playing Card Set

EXAMPLE 5:

In selecting one card from a standard deck, find the probability of selecting a diamond.

SOLUTION: The number of outcomes when picking a card is 52. That will be the denominator of our answer. The number of successes, or diamonds, in the deck is 13. That will be the numerator of our answer.

So, the probability of picking a diamond is P(♦) = 13/52. As before, this can be reduced to 1/4, but this is not necessary.

EXAMPLE 6:

In selecting one card from a standard deck, find the probability of selecting a five, or a heart.

SOLUTION: The new idea here is the presence of the word "or," which tells us that *both* fives and hearts are now to be considered successes.

The number of outcomes when picking a card is 52. That will be the denominator of our answer. The number of fives in the deck is four, but these are not our only successes. When figuring out our numerator, we also must consider the hearts. There are 13 of them, but we have already counted the five of hearts, so there are 12 other hearts still to be counted as successes. Adding all our successes together, we have 16 of them, and that will be the numerator of our answer.

So, the probability of picking a five or a heart is P(5 or ♥) = 16/52. Once again, this can be reduced to 4/13, but this is not necessary.

EXAMPLE 7:

In selecting one card from a standard deck, find the probability of selecting an ace and a spade.

SOLUTION: The new idea here is the presence of the word "and," which tells us that a card must be an ace *and* a spade to be considered a success.

The number of outcomes when picking a card is 52. That will be the denominator of our answer. The number of successes, or cards that meet *both* conditions of being both an ace and a spade at the same time, is 1. That will be the numerator of our answer.

So, the probability of picking an ace and a spade, or P(A and ♠) = 1/52.

Image 4.3.2

A Couple of Important Observations

On a roll of a single six-sided die, find P(20). It can't happen, right? There is no way to roll a 20 on a single six-sided die. So, let's see what that would look like as a probability.

The number of outcomes is six, and the number of successes is zero, so **P(20) = 0/6 = 0**.

Something that can never happen has a probability of 0.

On a roll of a single die, find P(number less than 10).

Well, all of the numbers are less than 10, so this will happen 100% of the time. Remembering that 100% is equal to 1.00 = 1 in its decimal form,

The number of outcomes is six, and the number of successes is six, so **P(number < 10) = 6/6 = 1**.

> Something that will definitely happen has a probability of 1.

The two previous examples lead us to a very important conclusion:

> All probabilities are between zero and one, inclusive.

The good news here is that we can use this fact to check our answers. The bad news is that if we are asked to find a probability and give an answer that does not fall between 0 and 1, it shows that we may not have a very good understanding of probability, at all.

Odds

The "odds" a of particular event are a relatively simple idea, but be aware, they can occur in two ways: odds in favor and odds against. The **odds in favor** of an event are computed as the ratio of the *chance of successes* to *chance of failures*. The **odds against** a particular event are computed as the ratio of the *chance of failures* to *chance of successes*. Thus, if we know the odds against an event are 10 to 1, in 11 identical attempts, we should expect 10 failures and 1 success of the event in question. When considering odds, we *must* be sure of the situation with which we are being presented! For example, in almost all racetracks, casinos, and sportsbooks, the stated "odds" are always given as odds against. Also, odds statements can be expressed using the word "to," as a ratio using a colon to separate the two numbers, or even a fraction. To emphasize the difference between odds statements and probability statements, we will state odds as a ratio using a colon to separate the two numbers.

> Express odds statements as a ratio using a colon to separate the two numbers.

Be aware: The "odds" stated in racetracks, casinos and sportsbooks are not actually true odds statements. In reality, they are just **pay schedules**. That is, if a casino lists the odds of a team winning a game as 20/1 (read "20 to 1"), that means if the team wins, they will pay $20 for every $1 bet.

Furthermore, the pay schedules offered in sportsbooks are not necessarily representative of the projected outcomes for an event. Oddsmakers create these "odds" statements based on their knowledge, experience, and even inside information, but the statements they produce are actually an attempt to control the flow of money bet on a specific game or event. If a sportsbook sees a large amount of money being bet on one team in a game, they will adjust the payout so future wagers on that team do not pay as much.

Image 4.3.3

Also, although it is possible for sportsbooks to predict the likelihood of one team winning, they cannot be certain. For this reason, they would prefer to have an equal amount of money bet on both teams. Then, they make their money by taking a small percentage of the total amount that has been wagered.

For table games like Blackjack, the so-called odds statements given to gamblers are not true odds, either. Some casinos pay 2 to 1 for a Blackjack (being dealt an Ace along with a King, Queen, Jack, or 10) and others may pay 6 to 5, with otherwise identical rules. These payouts are always a bit less than they would be if they were based on the true odds in the game. That way, the casino will make money.

For our purposes, however, we are going to assume the statements are reflective of the true odds of an event.

EXAMPLE 8:

The probability of an event is 21/38. What are the odds in favor of the event? What are the odds against?

Solutions: Since the P(success) = 21/38, there would 21 successes out of 38 outcomes. This means there would be 38 − 21 = 17 failures.

The odds in favor of an event are expressed as the ratio of successes to failures, so the odds in favor of the event in this example are 21:17. Similarly, since the odds against an event are expressed as the ratio of failures to successes, the odds against the event in this example would be 17:21.

EXAMPLE 9:

If the odds against an event are 3:11, what is the probability of success for the event in question?

Solutions: From the odds statement, we can see that there are 3 failures and 11 successes. This means there must be 3 + 11 = 14 outcomes. Remember, probability = successes/outcomes.

Thus, P(success) = 11/14.

SECTION 4.3 EXERCISES

For Exercises #1 through #11, a dime is flipped, and a single die is rolled.

1. Use the counting principle to determine the total number of outcomes.

2. List the sample space of all possible outcomes.

3. Find the probability of getting heads and a three.

4. Find the probability of getting tails and a seven.

5. Find the probability of getting heads and an odd number.

6. Find the probability of getting heads and a number greater than six.

7. Find the probability of getting tails or a seven.

8. Find the probability of getting tails or a number less than nine.

9. Find the odds against obtaining a head.

10. Find the odds against obtaining a six.

11. Find the odds in favor of obtaining an even number.

For Exercises #12 through #16, a quarter is flipped, and a penny is flipped.

12. Use the counting principle to determine the total number of outcomes.

13. List the sample space of all possible outcomes.

14. Find the probability of getting tails on the quarter and tails on the penny.

15. Find the probability of getting exactly one tail.

16. Find the probability of getting no tails.

For Exercises #17 through #21, the letters of the word TOWEL are written on slips of paper and placed into a hat. Two of these letters will be pulled out of the hat, without replacement, one after the other.

17. Use the counting principle to determine the total number of outcomes.

18. List the sample space of all possible outcomes.

19. Find the probability that the first letter is a vowel.

20. Find the probability that both letters are vowels.

21. Find the probability that neither letter is a vowel.

For Exercises #22 through #26, a pair of dice is rolled, and the sum of the faces is obtained.

22. Find the probability that the sum is six.

23. Find the probability that the sum is odd.

24. Find the probability that the sum is divisible by three.

25. Find the odds against the sum being 11.

26. Find the odds in favor of the sum being five.

For Exercises #27 through #31, data regarding the transportation of children to school is given in the table.

Children	Bus	Car
Boys	9	5
Girls	3	8

Use the information in the table to find:

27. The probability that a student chosen at random is a girl.

28. The probability that a student chosen at random rides the bus.

29. The probability that a student chosen at random rides in a car.

30. The probability that a student chosen at random is a girl who rides the bus.

31. The probability that a student chosen at random is a boy who rides in a car.

For Exercises #32 through #36, a bag contains 24 jellybeans. 5 are red, 3 are blue, 7 are orange, 4 are green, 2 are yellow, and the last 3 are purple.

32. Find the probability that a jellybean selected at random is orange.

33. Find the probability that a jellybean selected at random is green or yellow.

34. Find the probability that a jellybean selected at random is neither red nor purple.

35. Find the probability that a jellybean selected at random is anything but yellow.

36. Find the probability that a jellybean selected at random is black.

For Exercises #37 through #45, a single card is drawn from a standard deck of 52 cards.

37. Find the probability that the card is the queen of hearts.

38. Find the probability that the card is a six.

39. Find the probability that the card is a black card.

40. Find the probability that the card is a red nine.

41. Find the probability that the card is an ace or a heart.

42. Find the probability that the card is an ace and a heart.

43. Find the probability that the card is a face card.

44. Find the odds against drawing a king.

Find the odds in favor of drawing a queen or a diamond.

46. The odds against an event are given below. Find the probability of each event.

   a. 5:2

   b. 3:7

47. What is the difference between theoretical probability and the relative frequency of an event?

ANSWERS TO SECTION 4.3 EXERCISES

Fractional answers that are reduced are acceptable, but the fractional answers given here have not been reduced.

1. 12

2. {H1, H2, H3, H4, H5, H6, T1, T2, T3, T4, T5, T6}

3. 1/12

4. 0

5. 1/4

6. 0

7. 6/12

8. 1

9. 6:6

10. 10:2

11. 6:6

12. 4

13. {HH, HT, TH, TT}

14. 1/4

15. 2/4

16. 1/4

17. 20

18. {TO, TW, TE, TL, OT, OW, OE, OL, WT, WO, WE, WL, ET, EO, EW, EL, LT, LO, LW, LE}

19. $8/20 = 2/5$

20. 2/20

21. 6/20

22. 5/36

23. 18/36

24. 12/36

25. 34:2

26. 4:32

27. 11/25

28. 12/25

29. 13/25

30. 3/25

31. 5/25

32. 7/24

33. 6/24

34. 16/24

35. 22/24

36. 0

37. 1/52

38. 4/52

39. 26/52

40. 2/52

41. 16/52

42. 1/52

43. 12/52

44. 48:4

45. 16:36

46. a. 2/7   b. 7/10

47. Experimental probability is the result of performing trials, and theoretical probability is calculated.

4.4 Stays in Vegas: Compound Probability and Tree Diagrams

Addition and Multiplication with Fractions

If two fractions have the same denominator, they can be added by simply adding the numerators and retaining the existing denominator. Then, if necessary, we can reduce the sum. For example, 5/9 + 3/9 = 8/9.

Equivalent fractions are needed to **add fractions** with different denominators. For example, to add 2/9 + 3/4, we need to start by rewriting each of the fractions as equivalent fractions that have the same denominator. Once that is done, we add the numerators, but keep the **common denominator**.

EXAMPLE 1:

Add 2/9 + 3/4

SOLUTION:

$$\frac{2}{9} + \frac{3}{4} = \frac{8}{36} + \frac{27}{36} = \frac{35}{36}$$

Unlike adding fractions, **multiplying fractions** does not require a common denominator. Instead multiply the numerators together, multiply the denominators together, and then reduce (if necessary).

EXAMPLE 2:

Multiply 5/9 × 3/4

SOLUTION:

$$\frac{5}{9} \times \frac{3}{4} = \frac{15}{36}$$

Since our answer here is not in simplest form, we could reduce it. In this case we can divide both the numerator and the denominator by 3, so that our answer could be 5/12.

Compound Probability

Events that occur one after the other, or in conjunction, are called **successive events**. When a series of successive events is necessary to arrive at an outcome, the individual probabilities are multiplied together to obtain the probability of that outcome. This is called **compound probability,** and it sounds a lot more confusing than it really is. Let's take a look.

EXAMPLE 3:

An urn contains 13 balls. 6 are red, 3 are white, and 4 are blue balls. One ball is selected and then replaced, and then another ball is selected. Find the probability that the first ball is white, and the second ball is blue.

SOLUTION: First, we find the individual probabilities:

P(first ball is white) = 3/13
P(second ball is blue) = 4/13

Since we need *both* of these events to happen to have a success, we multiply the probabilities together:

P(W, then B) = (3/13) × (4/13) = 12/169

EXAMPLE 4:

Using the same urn from the previous example, but this time once the first ball is selected it is *not* placed back into the urn. Find the probability that the first ball is white, and the second ball is blue. In this example, we are drawing **without replacement**.

SOLUTION: First, we find the individual probabilities:

P(first ball is white) = 3/13

After taking one ball out, there are only 12 balls left in the urn, so ...

P(second ball is blue) = 4/12

Since we need *both* of these events to happen to have a success, we multiply the probabilities together:

P(W, then B) = (3/13) × (4/12) = 12/156

We can reduce this answer to 1/13 if we want to, but it is not necessary.

EXAMPLE 5:

Ten of the 25 players on the Yankees make over a million dollars per year. Eleven of the 12 players on the Lakers make over a million dollars per year. If one player is selected at random from each of the teams, what is the probability that they will *both* make over a million dollars a year?

SOLUTION: We find the two individual probabilities:

P(Yankee makes over a million per year) = 10/25
P(Laker makes over a million per year) = 11/12

Since we need them *both* to make over a million per year to have a successful outcome, we need both events to happen, so we multiply the probabilities together:

P(both players chosen make over a million per year) = (10/25) × (11/12) = 110/300, which means *both* players will make over a million dollars per year about 1/3 of the times we try this activity.

The vast majority of our successive events problems will follow the setup of those listed above, in which we are able to simply multiply the probabilities together to arrive at the result. When the problems become more complex, a tree diagram can be used to illustrate the situation.

Tree Diagrams

A **tree diagram** is a graphical representation of all the possible outcomes of an activity. It literally looks like a tree turned onto its side or upside-down. To create a tree diagram, start with a single point. Then, draw and label a branch for each possible outcome of the first event. If branches for a second event are to be drawn, the results of the second event must be drawn from *every* outcome of the first event. With multiple events, tree diagrams can get very big very quickly, but they can be helpful in determining the sample space or probabilities associated with an experiment.

Here is a very simple tree diagram showing the possible events when a single coin is flipped.

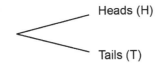

Heads (H)

Tails (T)

Figure 4.4.1 Tree Diagram for Flipping a Coin

Tree diagrams can also be used to represent multi-stage events.

EXAMPLE 6:

Create a tree diagram for flipping a coin two times.

SOLUTION:

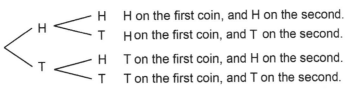

			Meaning
H		H	H on the first coin, and H on the second.
		T	H on the first coin, and T on the second.
T		H	T on the first coin, and H on the second.
		T	T on the first coin, and T on the second.

Figure 4.4.2 Tree Diagram for Flipping Two Coins

Tree diagrams are read left to right, one event at a time. What we will call a "path" is any route that you can take to get from the beginning point on the tree to an endpoint of the tree—and going backwards is not allowed. The diagram that describes a single coin flip has two different paths, one that goes to H, and one that goes to T. The diagram that describes two different coin flips is more complicated and has four different paths.

The number of endpoints we have will be the same as the number of paths, and this corresponds to the number of elements in the sample space. For the experiment of flipping two coins, the sample space is {HH, HT, TH, TT}.

Tree Diagrams and Probabilities

Finding a probability using a tree diagram, at this point, is a matter of putting the number of successes over the number of outcomes.

EXAMPLE 7:

When flipping two coins, what is the probability that both coins are tails?

SOLUTION: The number of outcomes shown in the tree (and in our sample space) is 4. That will be the denominator of our answer.

The number of successes (find the endpoints that have both flips as tails) is 1. That will be the numerator of our answer.

So, the probability of getting two tails is P(TT) = 1/4.

EXAMPLE 8:

When flipping two coins, what is the probability that at least one of the coins is heads?

SOLUTION: The number of outcomes shown in the tree is 4. That will be the denominator of our answer.

The number of successes—the endpoints that have at least one occurrence of heads—is 3. That will be the numerator of our answer.

So, the probability of getting at least one head is P(at least one H) = 3/4

As the problems get more complicated, the probabilities of the individual events can be written directly on the tree diagram. Since the tree is a picture of successive events, the probabilities are multiplied together as we move along a path.

EXAMPLE 9:

If we flip a coin two times, what is the probability of getting two heads?

SOLUTION: To solve this problem, we will draw a tree diagram and include the probability of each event.

```
              1/2   H
       1/2  H
1/2  H        1/2   T
              1/2   H
1/2  T
              1/2   T
```

Figure 4.4.3   Two Stage Tree Diagram with Probabilities

To arrive at the outcome of two heads, we must get heads on the first flip (in bold) *and* heads on the second flip (also in bold). Since these are successive events in our tree, we will multiply their probabilities together to find the probability of getting two heads. P(2 heads) = (1/2) × (1/2) = 1/4

Sometimes the problems will be even more complicated, and a tree diagram will become extremely useful. In the following example, it is the combination of the "at least" condition and the fact that experiment is done *without replacement* that causes the need for the tree. Let's go ahead and take a look at a problem that is fairly complicated ...

EXAMPLE 10:

We are going to buy two gumballs from a machine that contains 7 gumballs: 5 are white and 2 are red. What is the probability that we get *at least* one red gumball?

SOLUTION: First, we draw the tree diagram for the situation. The first gumball will either be red (R) or white (W). The second gumball will either be red (R) or white (W).

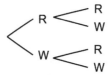

Figure 4.4.4a   Gumball Tree Diagram, Part 1

Next, we put the probabilities for the first event on the diagram. Since there are seven total gumballs, five white, and two red, the probabilities go on as follows:

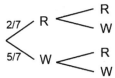

Figure 4.4.4b   Gumball Tree Diagram, Part 2

Since buying gumballs is done *without replacement*, we have to think carefully before placing the next probabilities on the diagram. If the first ball is red (following the 2/7 path), there are six gumballs left, and five of them are white, but only one of them is red (we bought one of the red ones already).

If the first ball is white (following the 5/7 path), there are six gumballs left, but now two red ones and only four of the whites are left (we bought a white one). Now we insert those probabilities onto the diagram:

Figure 4.4.4c   Gumball Tree Diagram, Part 3

Since these are successive events, we multiply the probabilities along each path to arrive at the probability of each outcome:

Figure 4.4.4d   Gumball Tree Diagram, Part 4

Now we are ready to answer the original question. We were asked for the probability of getting *at least* one red gumball, so we have to count each of the outcomes that satisfies this condition.

Figure 4.4.4e   Gumball Tree Diagram, Part 5

We have three different outcomes that satisfy the condition of the problem (getting at least one red gumball), which are the outcomes RR, RW, and WR. Each of these outcomes represents a way to have a success, so we want to include them in the result. The way we do this is by adding the probabilities of each outcome together. Thus, the probability of getting at least one red gumball is:

$$P(\text{at least one red}) = P(RR) + P(RW) + P(WR) = 2/42 + 10/42 + 10/42 = 22/42$$

This means, a little over half the time, we would get at least one red gumball.

The gumball example is not difficult, but there are a lot of steps. If you are comfortable with that one, however, you should be just fine with all of the tree diagram problems in this course.

Finally, we will look at a tree diagram that is read from top to bottom. Either method of drawing tree diagrams (left-to-right or top-to-bottom) is acceptable.

EXAMPLE 11:

Create a tree diagram, which will allow us to determine the sample space (list of all possible outcomes) for a pair of six-sided dice that are rolled.

Solution: This is what our diagram should look like:

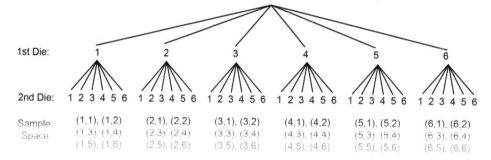

NOTE: (1,3) is the outcome of rolling a 1 on the first die and a 3 on the second die.

Figure 4.4.5   Tree Diagram for a Pair of Dice

What Are Tree Diagrams Good For?

Tree diagrams are a nice way to determine a sample space, and also, the theoretical probability of each outcome.

EXAMPLE 12:

Two normal, six-sided dice are rolled, with the outcome being the sum of the top-facing numbers. Find the following.

   a.   How many outcomes create a total of 7? What is the probability of rolling a 7?
   b.   How many outcomes create a total of 5? What is the probability of rolling a 5?
   c.   How many outcomes create a total of 3? What is the probability of rolling a 3?
   d.   How many outcomes create a total of 2? What is the probability of rolling a 1?
   e.   How many outcomes create a total of 1? What is the probability of rolling a 1?

Solutions: Keep in mind, there are $6 \times 6 = 36$ outcomes for this experiment.

   a.   There are six ways to roll a 7: (1, 6), (2, 5), (3, 4), (4, 3), (5, 2), and (6, 1). So, P(7) = 6/36, which can be reduced to 1/6.
   b.   There are four ways to roll a 5: (1, 4), (2, 3), (3, 2), and (4, 1). So, P(5) = 4/36 = 1/9.
   c.   There are two ways to roll a 3: (1, 2) and (2, 1). That makes P(3) = 2/36 = 1/18.
   d.   There is only one way to roll a 2: (1, 1). So, P(2) = 1/36.
   e.   With a pair of dice, it is impossible to roll any total less than 2. Thus, P(1) = 0/36 = 0.

SECTION 4.4 EXERCISES

1. A jar of jellybeans contains seven red, two orange, and three green jellybeans. One jellybean is selected and replaced, and then, another is selected. Find the probability that:

   a. The first jellybean is orange and the second is green.

   b. The first jellybean is red and the second is orange.

   c. The first jellybean is green and the second is red.

   d. Both jellybeans are orange.

   e. Both jellybeans are red.

   f. Both jellybeans are green.

Image 4.4.1

2. A card is selected from a standard 52-card deck, and then another card is selected without replacement. Find the probability that:

   a. The first card is a jack, and the second card is an ace.

   b. The first card is the jack of hearts, and the second card is an ace.

   c. The first card is a queen, and the second card is also a queen.

   d. The first card is a spade, and the second card is also a spade.

3. The teachers who will have bus duty are drawn randomly each week. Mr. Art, Mrs. Biology, Ms. Chemistry, Mr. Drama, and Mrs. English have their names put into a hat. Three names will be drawn out, without replacement. Find the probability that:

   a. Ms. Chemistry is chosen first.

   b. Mrs. Biology or Mr. Drama is chosen first.

   c. Ms. Chemistry is chosen first, Mr. Art is chosen second, and Mrs. English is chosen third.

   d. Mr. Drama is chosen first and second.

4. A bag contains 11 blue, 7 white, 4 red, and 6 purple marbles.

   a. Find the probability that a single draw results in a white marble.

   b. Find the probability of getting two blue marbles on two draws, with replacement.

   c. Find the probability of getting two blue marbles on two draws, if replacement is not allowed.

   d. Find the probability of getting two red marbles on two draws, if replacement is not allowed.

   e. Find the probability of getting a white marble and then a purple marble, if replacement is not allowed.

5. A family will decide where they should have dinner randomly, and has the options shown below. Use a tree diagram to show all the possible outcomes and use your tree diagram to answer the questions.

   Location: City, Suburbs, Rural
   Style: Buffet, Casual Dining, Fast Food, Fine Dining

   a. What is the probability that they will eat in the city?

   b. What is the probability that they will eat at a buffet?

   c. What is the probability that they will eat at a fine dining restaurant in the suburbs?

   d. What is the probability that will eat at rural restaurant that is either casual dining or fast food?

6. A nickel is flipped and then it is flipped again.

   a. Use a tree diagram to show the sample space and associated probabilities.

   b. Find the probability that both flips result in heads.

   c. Find the probability that both flips result in tails.

   Find the probability that the first flip is heads and the second flip is tails.

   e. Find the probability that at least one heads is obtained.

   f. Find the probability that neither coin results in heads.

7. A family consists of four boys and two girls. Two of them will be picked, at random, to do yard work this weekend.

   a. Use a tree diagram to show the sample space and associated probabilities.

   b. Find the probability that both people that will be doing yard work are girls.

   c. Find the probability that none of the people doing yard work are girls.

   d. Find the probability that exactly one of the people doing yard work is a girl.

8. A gumball machine contains six red and four blue gumballs. Two of them are purchased (without replacement).

   a. Use a tree diagram to show the sample space and associated probabilities.

   b. Find the probability that at least one of the gumballs is red.

   c. Find the probability that exactly one of the gumballs is red.

   d. Find the probability that at least one of the gumballs is blue.

   e. Find the probability that exactly one of the gumballs is blue.

   f. Find the probability that the second gumball is red.

9. What is the difference between with and without replacement?

ANSWERS TO SECTION 4.4 EXERCISES

Fractional answers that are reduced are acceptable, but the fractional answers given here have not been reduced.

1. a. 6/144   b. 14/144   c. 21/144   d. 4/144   e. 49/144   f. 9/144

2. a. 16/2652   b. 4/2652   c. 12/2652   d. 156/2652

3. a. 1/5   b. 2/5   c. 1/60   d. 0

4. a. 7/28   b. 121/784   c. 110/756   d. 12/756   e. 42/756

5. a. 4/12 = 1/3   b. 3/12 = 1/4   c. 1/12   d. 2/12 = 1/6

6. a. Tree Diagram:

$$1/2 \nearrow H \begin{cases} 1/2 \rightarrow H \quad P(HH) = 1/4 \\ 1/2 \rightarrow T \quad P(HT) = 1/4 \end{cases}$$
$$1/2 \searrow T \begin{cases} 1/2 \rightarrow H \quad P(TH) = 1/4 \\ 1/2 \rightarrow T \quad P(TT) = 1/4 \end{cases}$$

   b. 1/4   c. 1/4   d. 1/4   e. 3/4   f. 1/4

7. a. Tree Diagram:

$$4/6 \nearrow B \begin{cases} 3/5 \rightarrow B \quad P(BB) = 12/30 \\ 2/5 \rightarrow G \quad P(BG) = 8/30 \end{cases}$$
$$2/6 \searrow G \begin{cases} 4/5 \rightarrow B \quad P(GB) = 8/30 \\ 1/5 \rightarrow G \quad P(GG) = 2/30 \end{cases}$$

   b. 2/30   c. 12/30   d. 16/30

8. a. Tree Diagram:

$$6/10 \nearrow R \begin{cases} 5/9 \rightarrow R \quad P(RR) = 30/90 \\ 4/9 \rightarrow B \quad P(RB) = 24/90 \end{cases}$$
$$4/10 \searrow B \begin{cases} 6/9 \rightarrow R \quad P(BR) = 24/90 \\ 3/9 \rightarrow B \quad P(BB) = 12/90 \end{cases}$$

   b. 78/90   c. 48/90   d. 60/90   e. 48/90   f. 54/90

9. When we sample "with replacement," the two sample values are independent. This means the result of the first event does not affect the second event. For "without replacement," the two sample values are not independent. This means what we get for the first event does affect what we can get for the second one.

4.5 What It's Worth: Expected Value

Review: Order of Operations

If several people are asked to simplify the same multi-step arithmetic **expression**, a standard set of rules must be established for the order in which the operations are performed. Otherwise, different people may get different answers. For example, let's say Bill and Ted are asked to simplify the expression $3 + 4 \times 5$. Bill adds the $3 + 4$, and then multiplies that result by 5 to get a total of 35. Ted performs the multiplication first, and then adds 3 to get a total of 23. Who is right? In case you aren't sure yet … it is Ted.

Arithmetic started with addition (and subtraction). Repeated addition led to multiplication (and division), and repeated multiplication led to the use of exponents. In addition to those procedures, parentheses or other grouping symbols can also be used in an expression. Let's consolidate all of these processes into a single list, known as the "order of operations."

Arithmetic **Order of Operations:**

1.   All operations contained within parentheses ( ) or other grouping symbols, such as brackets [ ], or braces { }, should be done first.

2.   Secondly, simplify all expressions containing exponents.

3.   Multiplication and division are done next, as we come to them going from left to right.

4.   Addition and subtraction are done last, again, as we come to them going from left to right.

To help remember this order, many students like to memorize the acronym **PEMDAS** (Parentheses, Exponents, Multiplication, Division, Addition, Subtraction). This can be really helpful, but be careful! If you do not realize multiplication and division are done as we come to them going from the left to the right, you may fall into the trap of thinking multiplication always precedes division—it does not. The same holds true for addition and subtraction.

EXAMPLE 1:

Simplify: $5 + 6 \times 3$

SOLUTION: Since multiplication is performed before addition, start by multiplying 6×3. Then, add 5 to that result.

$5 + 6 \times 3$
$= 5 + 18$
$= 23$

EXAMPLE 2:

Simplify: $13 - 5 + 6$

SOLUTION: Remember, perform addition and subtraction as we come to them going from left to right. Here, that means the subtraction must be done first.

$13 - 5 + 6$
$= 8 + 6$
$= 14$

EXAMPLE 3:

Simplify: $13 - (5 + 6)$

SOLUTION: Since $(5 + 6)$ is inside parentheses, that operation is performed first.

$13 - (5 + 6)$
$= 13 - 11$
$= 2$

EXAMPLE 4:

Simplify: $(1/3) \times (-8) + (1/6) \times (4) + (1/2) \times (3)$

SOLUTION: There are parentheses in this expression, but take note that there is no operation to perform inside these parentheses. We have multiplication and addition to perform here, so we will perform the multiplications first, and the additions afterward. And, remember, to add fractions, we must have a common denominator.

$(1/3) \times (-8) + (1/6) \times (4) + (1/2) \times (3)$
$= -8/3 + 4/6 + 3/2$
$= -16/6 + 4/6 + 9/6$
$= -3/6$
$= -1/2$

EXAMPLE 5:

Simplify: $5 \times (2 + 3)^2 - (6 - 4) + 1$

SOLUTION: Here, we start with the operations that are inside the parentheses. Then, perform the operation using the exponent. After that, the multiplication is done. Finally, we have addition and subtraction, which are performed as we come to them going from left to right.

$5 \times (2 + 3)^2 - (6 - 4) + 1$
$= 5 \times (5)^2 - 2 + 1$
$= 5 \times 25 - 2 + 1$
$= 125 - 2 + 1$
$= 123 + 1$
$= 124$

In the Long Run ...

Remember that phrase: "In the long run ..." Although probabilities are used to make a prediction regarding what should happen for one particular event, the expected value calculations are all based on the long-term expectations of an event. While we expect one out of every two flips of a coin to be heads, sometimes we might get five tails in a row. Unusual things can happen in the short term, and a small sample space does not always give us results that are meaningful. What a probability value does tell us is that while a small number of flips might give strange results, if we flip that coin 1,000 times, it is very likely that the number of heads we end up with will be fairly close to 500. This idea is known as **The Law of Large Numbers**.

Expected Value

The **expected value** calculation is used to determine the value of a business venture or a game over the long run.

> Expected value is *not* the value of a particular event.
> It is the long run average value if the event was repeated many times.

EXAMPLE 6:

Let's look at a game in which we either win $40 or lose $1, and we play the game 20 times, winning twice. How much money can we expect to have won or lost at the end of those 20 turns?

SOLUTION: 2 wins $\times$ $40 + 18 losses $\times$ (−$1) = $80 + (−$18) = $62

In the previous example, since we played the game 20 times, the average amount we won per turn was $62/20 = $3.10. In other words, the long run results are the same as if we had won $3.10 each time we played. So, $3.10 is the expected value of each turn for that game.

We have a formula that is used to calculate the expected value (EV) of these types of events, which uses the possible results and the probability of each of those results:

$$EV = (\text{prob \#1}) \times (\text{result \#1}) + (\text{prob \#2}) \times (\text{result \#2}) + ... + (\text{last prob}) \times (\text{last result})$$

The game discussed above had two results, win $40 or lose $1. We played 20 times and won twice, which makes the probability of winning 2/20 and the probability of losing 18/20. To find the expected value, we will use the following information:

- Result #1 = win $40 and P(result #1) = 2/20
- Result #2 = lose $1 and P(result #2) = 18/20

Plugging these values into our expected value formula, we have:

$$EV = (\text{prob \#1}) \times (\text{result \#1}) + (\text{prob \#2}) \times (\text{result \#2})$$
$$EV = (2/20) \times (\$40) + (18/20) \times (−\$1) = \$4 − \$0.90 = \$3.10$$

Now, let's find the expected value of that same game, with one small change. This time, when we win, we only win $10. When we lose, we still lose $1, and the probabilities of winning and losing will stay the same. Also, this time, to show it can be done either way, we will use decimal values for the probabilities, instead of fractions. That is, $2/20 = 0.1$, and $18/20 = 0.9$.

$$EV = (\text{prob \#1}) \times (\text{result \#1}) + (\text{prob \#2}) \times (\text{result \#2})$$
$$EV = (0.1) \times (\$10) + (0.9) \times (-\$1) = \$1 - \$0.90 = \$0.10 = 10¢$$

Changing the payout for a win made this result quite a bit different from the original set up. In this later version of the game, over the long run, we will only win 10 cents per play.

Let's find the expected value of this same game one more time. This time, when we win, we only win $5:

$$EV = (\text{prob \#1}) \times (\text{result \#1}) + (\text{prob \#2}) \times (\text{result \#2})$$
$$EV = (0.1) \times (\$5) + (0.9) \times (-\$1) = \$0.50 - \$0.90 = -\$0.40 = -40¢$$

Notice the version with a $5 prize has a *negative* expected value. That means we would expect to *lose* an average of 40 cents per play. If we were to play this game 20 times, we would expect to lose a total of $20 \times (-\$0.40) = -\$8$.

Expected Value, Revisited

EXAMPLE 7:

Find the expected value of a game that involves a single spin on the following spinner.

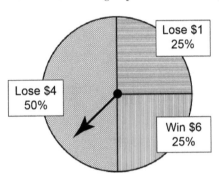

Figure 4.5.1

SOLUTION: In this game, we have three possible results; lose $1, win $6, or lose $4. To find the expected value, we will use the following:

- Result #1 = lose $1 and P(result #1) = 1/4

- Result #2 = win $6 and P(result #2) = 1/4

- Result #3 = lose $4 and P(result #3) = 1/2

Using the formula for expected value, we have:

$$EV = (\text{prob \#1}) \times (\text{result \#1}) + (\text{prob \#2}) \times (\text{result \#2}) + ... + (\text{last prob}) \times (\text{last result})$$
$$EV = (1/4)(-\$1) + (1/4)(+\$6) + (1/2)(-\$4)$$
$$EV = (-\$1/4) + (\$6/4) + (-\$4/2) = (-\$1 + \$6 - \$8)/4 = -\$0.75$$

The negative expected value tells us that we should expect to lose money in this game if we played it multiple times.

Keep in mind that this does *not* mean we will play one time and lose 75 cents. What this expected value means is, over the long term, we will lose an *average* of 75 cents per play.

EXAMPLE 8:

Find the expected value of a game that involves a single spin on the following spinner.

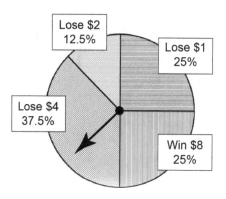

SOLUTION: We begin by finding each of our results, and the probabilities of each of those results. While we could find this expected value by using decimals, here, we will use fractions:

- Result #1 = lose $1 and P(result #1) = 0.25

- Result #2 = win $8 and P(result #2) = 0.25

- Result #3 = lose $4 and P(result #3) = 0.375

- Result #4 = lose $2 and P(result #4) = 0.125

From there, we can use the formula for expected value:

$$EV = (0.25)(-\$1) + (0.25)(+\$8) + (0.375)(-\$4) + (0.125)(-\$2)$$
$$EV = -\$0.25 + \$2 + (-\$1.50) + (-\$0.25) = \$0$$

Since a player would neither lose nor win playing this game over the long term, this game is considered "fair." Later in this section, the idea of fair games will be explored further.

Raffles

In a **raffle**, the player must pay up-front for the opportunity to take part. The money paid for a raffle ticket is not added to the prize money, and that has to be considered when calculating the expected value of a raffle. For example, if a player pays $5 for a raffle ticket and the prize is $100, the actual winnings would be $95, not $100. Raffles typically have a negative expected value for the player, which means a positive expectation for the organizing group. That is how the group makes money and is typically the goal of a raffle.

image 4.5.1

EXAMPLE 9:

One thousand raffle tickets are sold for $1 each. One first prize of $500 and two second prizes of $100 will be awarded. Consider the following questions.

a. If we buy one ticket and win the first prize, what is our *net* profit? (It is not $500!)

Answer: $499

b. What is the probability of winning the first prize?

Answer: 1/1000 or 0.001

c. If we buy one ticket and win one of the second prizes, what is our *net* profit?

Answer: $99

d. What is the probability of winning $100?

Answer: 2/1000 or 0.002

e. If we buy one ticket and win nothing, what is our *net* profit?

Answer: −$1 (You lose $1)

f. What is the probability of winning nothing at all?

Answer: 997/1000 or 0.997

g. What are the possible financial outcomes for us if we purchase one ticket?

Answer: Win $499, Win $99, or Lose $1

h. Use the above information to find the expected value of each $1 ticket.

Answer: EV = 0.001($499) + 0.002($99) + 0.997(−$1) = −$0.30 or −30¢

Fair Price

The **fair price** to pay for playing a game can be found by calculating the expected winnings. Our formula here is nearly identical to the one used to find expected value, as we are looking for the amount we would expect to win from playing this game.

$$EV = (\text{prob \#1}) \times (\text{result \#1}) + (\text{prob \#2}) \times (\text{result \#2}) + \ldots + (\text{last prob}) \times (\text{last result})$$

EXAMPLE 10:

A high school is selling 500 raffle tickets for a free dinner for two, valued at $75. What would be a fair price to pay for one ticket?

SOLUTION: EV = (1/500) × ($75) = $0.15, so the fair price to pay for a ticket would be 15 cents. Naturally, the school would not sell them for 15 cents each, but likely for $1 each, so that they can make a profit on the raffle.

EXAMPLE 11:

A carnival game allows a player to draw a card out of a hat. There are three cards inside the hat that correspond to the prizes listed below.

- Ace of spades = Win $10

- King of diamonds = Win $5

- Queen of hearts = Win $1

What is a fair price to pay for playing this game?

SOLUTION: As we did when calculating expected values, we must determine the possible results and the corresponding probabilities. Then, we can determine the amount we would expect to win when playing this game.

- Result #1 = win $10 and P(result #1) = 1/3

- Result #2 = win $5 and P(result #2) = 1/3

- Result #3 = win $1 and P(result #3) = 1/3

Expected Winnings = (1/3) × ($10) + (1/3) × ($5) + (1/3) × ($1)

Expected Winnings = ($10/3) + ($5/3) + ($1/3) = $16/3 = $5.33

Since the expected winnings is $5.33, the fair price to pay to play this game would be $5.33. Of course, if the carnival wants to make a profit, they will charge more than this.

Fair Games

Let's take a generic look at a simple game in order to further examine the cost to play a game. Assume we have a bag with 3 red balls and 1 white ball in it. If we randomly draw 1 ball from the bag and it is white, we will win $100. If, however, we draw a red one, we don't win anything. If the game is free to play, our expected winnings would be the Expected Value, EV:

$$EV = \left(\frac{1}{4}\right)(\$100) + \left(\frac{3}{4}\right)(\$0) = \frac{\$100}{4} = \$25$$

Now let's assume the game costs c dollars to play. The revised EV is

$$EV = \left(\frac{1}{4}\right)(\$100 - c) + \left(\frac{3}{4}\right)(\$0 - c) = \frac{\$100}{4} - \frac{c}{4} - \frac{3c}{4} = \$25 - \frac{4c}{4} = \$25 - c$$

This shows us if the game costs $10 to play, the EV would be $25 − $10 = $15. This means the average profit *per game* would be $15. We would never win or lose $15; we would just have a long-run average of winning $15 per game. So, if we played this game 1,000 times, we should be $15,000 ahead by the time we were done.

If, instead, this game costs $30 to play, the EV would then be −$5. The negative EV means we would lose an average of $5 for every time we played. If we played this game 1,000 times, when we were done, we should expect to have lost $5,000.

Looking at one more scenario, if the game costs $25 to play, the EV would be 0. Sometimes we would win $75 ($100 minus the $25 cost to play), and other times we would lose the $25 we paid to play.

If, however, we played the game 1,000 times, since the long-run average is $0, in the end, we could expect a $0 profit, which is commonly referred to as **breaking even**.

A game is considered "fair"—in the mathematical sense—when the expected value is equal to zero. This means we should break even over the long run, and there is no advantage for either player. The spinner from Example 8 is an example of a fair game.

Review: Solving Equations

An **equation** is a mathematical statement indicating that two expressions are equal. A **solution** is a value of the variable that makes the equation true. When **solving an equation**, steps are taken to determine all the values of the variable that will make the equation a true statement.

One of the steps available for use is known as the **addition property of equality**. This property states, "if the same quantity is added to both sides of an equation, the solution remains the same." Since any quantity can be added to both sides of an equation, a quantity is chosen that will isolate the variable.

EXAMPLE 12:

Solve: $x - 8 = 24$

SOLUTION: To solve this equation, we want to isolate the variable (x). To do that here, we will add 8 to both sides of the equation. This will cause the (-8) and the $(+8)$ on the left side of the equation to cancel each other out. We also simplify the right side of the equation, giving us our solution.

$x - 8 = 24$
$x - 8 + 8 = 24 + 8$
$x = 32$

As you might expect, we can add either positive numbers (like we did in Example 6), or negative numbers to both sides of an equation.

EXAMPLE 13:

Solve: $x + 7 = -8$

SOLUTION: Here, we will add (-7) to both sides of the equation.

$x + 7 = -8$
$x + 7 + (-7) = -8 + (-7)$
$x = -15$

Note: It is perfectly fine to think of the process as "subtracting 7 from both sides."

Another approach that may be used when solving an equation involves the **multiplication property of equality**, which states that "if both sides of an equation are multiplied (or divided) by the same non-zero quantity, the solution remains the same." Just as it is with the addition property of equality, since any quantity can be used, a quantity is chosen that will isolate the variable.

EXAMPLE 14:

Solve: 6x = 24

SOLUTION: To solve this equation, we want to isolate the variable (x). To do that here, we will divide both sides of the equation by 6.

6x = 24
6x/6 = 24/6
x = 4

You may be thinking, "if we *divide* by a number, why is this called the "multiplication" property of equality?" Instead of dividing by 6, we could have multiplied by (1/6) and had the same outcome. In the same way that the addition property of equality applies to both addition and subtraction, the multiplication property of equality applies to both multiplication and division. This streamlines our processes into just two properties that we use when trying to isolate a variable.

Some of the equations we solve will make use of *both* the addition and multiplication properties of equality. In some equations, we will use the distributive property to remove any parentheses, and some equations will require us to simplify each side of the equation as much as possible by combining like terms. That being the case, some equations will require several steps in the solving process.

If the variable exists on both sides of the equation, use the addition principle to remove it from one side. Try not to think of moving terms from one side of an equation to the other. Instead, focus on removing unwanted terms by adding their opposite. Then, remember, whatever we have done to one side of the equation, we must also do the same thing to the other side to keep the equation balanced. Once the term containing the variable has been isolated, then apply the multiplication property to remove any unwanted multiplication—just be sure to do it to both sides of the equation.

common mistake:

When faced with 6x = 24, some students attempt to isolate the x by subtracting 6 from both sides of the equation. Remember, the 6 and x are linked by multiplication, and multiplication is undone by division, not subtraction.

EXAMPLE 15:

Solve: 5x + 13 = 38

SOLUTION: To solve this equation, we want to isolate the variable (x). Here, we first need to isolate the term containing the variable. To do so, we begin by subtracting 13 from both sides of the equation. Then, we will divide both sides of the equation by 5.

5x + 13 = 38
5x + 13 − 13 = 38 − 13
5x = 25
x = 5

EXAMPLE 16:

Solve: $(1/4)(-6) + (3/8)(2) + (3/8)(x) = 0$

SOLUTION: In this problem, we start by simplifying as much as possible. We have terms that can be multiplied together, so we will start there. Next, we will find a common denominator and add the fractions together. Then, to make sure the variable exists on only one side of the equation, we can add 6/8 to both sides. Finally, to get the variable by itself, we will multiply both sides by 8/3.

$(1/4)(-6) + (3/8)(2) + (3/8)(x) = 0$
$-6/4 + 6/8 + (3/8)(x) = 0$
$-12/8 + 6/8 + (3/8)(x) = 0$
$-6/8 + (3/8)(x) = 0$
$(3/8)(x) = 6/8$
$(8/3) \times (3/8)(x) = (8/3) \times (6/8)$
$x = 48/24$
$x = 2$

There are times when we will be asked to determine the amount that should be won or lost in order to create a fair game. Let's take a look at that type of situation.

EXAMPLE 17:

A game involves a player drawing a single card from a standard deck. If the card is a face card, the player wins $10. If any other card is drawn, the player loses. In order for this to be a fair game, when a player loses, how much should they lose?

SOLUTION: There are 12 face cards in the deck, so the probability of winning is 12/52. This means that the probability of losing is 40/52. Using those values, we can set up an equation using the formula for expected value. At this point we don't know the amount of a loss, so we will use the variable "x" in that spot:

$EV = (12/52) \times (\$10) + (40/52) \times (x)$

In order for a game to be "fair", the expected value must be equal to zero. Plugging in that value, we know have an equation that we can solve for x:

$0 = (12/52) \times (\$10) + (40/52) \times (x)$
$0 = 120/52 + (40/52)x$
$-120/52 = (40/52)x$

Multiplying both sides by 52/40, we have:

$(52/40) \times (-120/52) = x$

Here we can cancel the 52 in the numerator with the 52 in the denominator, leaving:

$-120/40 = x$
$-3 = x$

Remember that we used "x" to represent the amount of a loss that would result in a fair game. So, in order to make this a fair game, a player should lose $3 when they lose.

Life Insurance

Buying life insurance is an important step in the lives of many people. If the policyholder passes away during the term of the insurance policy, the amount of the policy is paid to the beneficiaries.

In order to establish the cost of a life insurance policy, insurance companies do research to determine the likelihood of death at different ages for both males and females. A table of these probabilities is created to determine the rates and can be used to calculate the expected value of purchasing a policy. Finding the expected value of a life insurance policy will share one similarity with raffles. Since the cost of the policy is not returned to the policyholder, that cost must be subtracted from the payout.

EXAMPLE 18:

A 47-year old woman has a 0.248% chance of passing away during the next year. An insurance company charges $300 for a life insurance policy that pays a $110,000 death benefit. What is the expected value for the person buying the insurance?

SOLUTION: To find this expected value, we will list the possible results and corresponding probabilities.

Keep in mind, if the probability of the policyholder passing away is 0.248% (which is 0.00248), then the probability of the policyholder *not* passing away is $1 - 0.00248 = 0.99752$. Also, the cost of a life insurance policy is paid at the beginning of the term. So, when determining the result if the policyholder passes away, the cost of the policy is subtracted from the amount of the payout.

- Result #1 = If the policyholder does not pass away, they are out the cost of the policy, which is $300. In other words, Result #1 = −$300. And, P(Result #1) = 0.99752

- Result #2 = If the policyholder does pass away, their beneficiary will profit by $110,000 − $300 = $109,700. Thus, Result #2 = $109,700. And, P(Result #1) = 0.00248

Using the formula for expected value,

$$EV = (prob\ \#1) \times (result\ \#1) + (prob\ \#2) \times (result\ \#2)$$
$$EV = (0.99752)(-\$300) + (0.00248)(\$109,700)$$
$$EV = -\$299.256 + \$272.056$$
$$EV = -\$27.20$$

As would be the case with auto insurance, it isn't really a surprise that the expected value of a life insurance policy is negative. After all, the insurance company can only afford to stay open (and offer insurance) if it is making a profit. When it is in the position to pay out a benefit, the large number of policies that it carries offsets the cost of this payment.

For those who purchase life insurance, even though there is a negative expected value, this cost is acceptable given the security that comes along with having the life insurance policy in place.

SECTION 4.5 EXERCISES

1. Given the spinner:

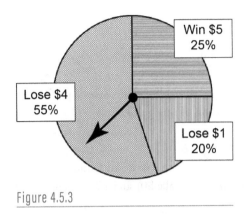

Figure 4.5.3

   a. Find the expected value of a game that involves one spin.

   b. What does this expected value mean?

2. Given the spinner:

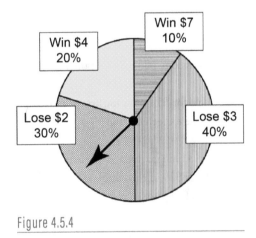

Figure 4.5.4

   a. Find the expected value of a game that involves one spin.

   b. What does this expected value mean?

3. A game consists of a player drawing a single card from a standard deck. If the card is a spade, the player wins $5; if the card is a club, the player wins $2; and if the card is red, the player loses $4.

   a. What is the expected value for someone who plays this game?

   b. What does this expected value mean?

   c. If someone played this game 100 times, how much money should he or she expect to win or lose?

4. An American roulette wheel contains slots with numbers from 1 through 36 and slots marked 0 and 00. Eighteen numbers are colored red, and eighteen numbers are colored black. The 0 and 00 are colored green.

You place a $1 bet on a roulette wheel betting that the result of the spin will be green. If you lose, you lose your $1 bet. If you win, you keep the $1 that was your bet, and collect winnings of $17.

a. What is the expected value of this bet? Round your answer to the nearest hundredth.

b. What does this expected value mean?

c. If someone made this bet 100 times, how much money should he or she expect to win or lose?

5. On a day when the weather is good, a golf course makes a profit of $900. When the weather is bad, the course loses $250. In the location of this golf course, bad weather happens 20% of the time. Find the expected value for the profit or loss of this golf course on a single day.

6. Scott is considering investing in a stock that he heard about. There is a 35% chance that he will lose $6,000, a 45% chance that he will break even (make $0), and a 20% chance that he will make $11,000.

a. What is the expected value of this investment?

b. Should Scott invest in this stock?

7. At the local library, the probabilities of a patron checking out no books, one book, two books, and three books are 0.1, 0.4, 0.3, and 0.2, respectively. Find the expected number of books that will be checked out by a single patron.

8. Five hundred tickets will be sold for a raffle, at a cost of $2 each. The prize for the winner is $750. What is the expected value of a ticket for someone playing this raffle?

9. Eight hundred raffle tickets will be sold for $5 each. One first prize of $500 will be awarded, along with five second prizes of $100, each. What is the expected value for a person who buys a single ticket for this raffle?

10. An urn contains 7 red, 10 white, and 3 blue marbles. A game involves drawing one marble from the urn, and if the marble is red, the player wins $20. If the marble is white, the player loses $10, and if the marble is blue, the player wins $40. What is a fair price to pay for playing this game?

11. A player rolls a single die, and if the result is a multiple of 3, the player wins $26. If the result of the roll is not a multiple of 3, the player loses $10. What is a fair price for playing this game?

12. Four baseball caps are on a table. One cap has a $1 bill under it, another has a $5 bill, another has a $50 bill, and the last one has a $100 bill. You can select one cap and keep the amount of money that is underneath. What is the fair price for playing this game?

Image 4.5.2

13. A game involves a player flipping 2 coins at the same time. If both coins land on heads, the player wins. Otherwise, the player loses $5. In order for this to be a fair game, when the player wins, how much should they win?

14. A game involves a player drawing a single card from a standard deck. If the card has an even number on it, the player wins $4. If the card is a face card, the player wins $5. If any other card is drawn, the player loses. In order for this to be a fair game, when a player loses, how much should he lose?

15. According to the tables used by insurance companies, a 36-year-old man has a 0.166% chance of passing away during the coming year. An insurance company charges $260 for a life insurance policy that pays a $150,000 death benefit. What is the expected value for the person buying the insurance?

16. According to the tables used by insurance companies, a 55-year-old woman has a 0.452% chance of passing away during the coming year. An insurance company charges $590 for a life insurance policy that pays a $125,000 death benefit. What is the expected value for the person buying the insurance?

ANSWERS TO SECTION 4.5 EXERCISES

1. a. −$1.15   b. That, over the long term, you can expect to lose $1.15 for each spin.

2. a. −$0.30   b. That, over the long term, you can expect to lose 30 cents for each spin.

3. a. −$0.25   b. Lose 25¢ per play   c. Lose $25

4. a. −$0.05   b. That, over the long term, you can expect to lose 5 cents for each spin.   c. Lose $5

5. $670

6. a. Make $100   b. Yes, based upon expected value.

7. 1.6 books

8. −$0.50

9. −$3.75

10. $8

11. $2

12. $39

13. $15

14. $7

15. −$11

16. −$25

CHAPTER 4 CREDITLINES

GEOMETRY

Let No One Ignorant of Geometry Enter

Legend has it, that phrase was inscribed over the door to **Plato's Academy** in Athens. The ancient Greeks were the pioneers of geometry. Before them, the Egyptians and the Babylonians used many geometric principles in practical applications, but the Greeks studied its philosophical properties.

In many high school geometry classes, students are frequently subjected to numerous two-column proofs, which are not the most fun or interesting things in the world. While there is merit in learning those proofs and techniques, the beauty and extreme usefulness of geometry often gets lost. Whether we are looking at the circular wheels on a bicycle or the straight lines and right angles of walls, ceilings, and doorways, our world would be a very different place without a basic understanding of geometry.

Image 5.0.1

5.1 On the Shoulders of Giants: Biographies and Historical References

For Geometry ...

The ancient Greeks were pioneers in the study of geometry. Even though many of the writings that exist today were originally collaborative efforts, a fair number of individuals stood out more prominently than the rest. Geometry, like all mathematics, progressed over time.

Pythagoras of Samos and the Pythagoreans

Pythagoras of Samos (569–475 BC) was a Greek philosopher, mathematician, and founder of the religious movement called Pythagoreanism. Most of the information about Pythagoras was written down centuries after he lived, so very little reliable information is known about him. We do know he was born on the island of Samos, and might have travelled widely in his youth, visiting Egypt and other places seeking knowledge. Around 530 BC, he established a religious sect. His followers pursued the religious rites and practices developed by Pythagoras and studied his philosophical theories.

Image 5.1.1: Pythagoras of Samos

Many mathematical and scientific discoveries were attributed to Pythagoras, including his famous theorem, as well as discoveries in the field of music, astronomy, and medicine. But it was the religious element that made the most profound impression on his contemporaries. He attained extensive influence, and many people began to follow him. Biographers tell fantastic stories of his eloquent speeches that led people to abandon their luxurious and corrupt way of life, and instead devote themselves to a "purer" system that he came to introduce. His followers established a select brotherhood for the purpose of pursuing the religious and ascetic practices developed by their master. What was done and taught among the members was kept a guarded secret, but the teachings most likely concerned science and mathematics.

The organization set up by Pythagoras was in some ways a school, in some ways a brotherhood, and in some ways a monastery. It was based upon the religious teachings of Pythagoras and was very secretive, as the members were bound to Pythagoras and each other by strict vows. **Pythagoreans** lived on a strict plant-based diet and were even prohibited from eating beans. Considerable importance seems to have been attached to the music and gymnastics that were a part of the daily exercises of the disciples. There were secret symbols by which members of the sect could recognize each other, even if they had never met before. The society took an active role in politics, which eventually led to their downfall.

Candidates for membership had to pass through a period of probation in which their powers of maintaining silence were especially tested, along with their general temper, disposition, and mental capacity. There were also gradations among the members themselves; it was an old Pythagorean maxim that everything was not to be told to every person. Thus, the Pythagoreans were divided into an inner circle called the **mathematikoi** ("learners") and an outer circle called the **akousmatikoi** ("listeners").

Pythagoras made influential contributions to philosophy and religion in the late sixth century BC. He is often revered as a great mathematician, mystic, and scientist. However, because legend and secrecy cloud his work, some have questioned whether he personally contributed much to mathematics or natural philosophy. Since the achievements of any of the Pythagoreans are attributed to Pythagoras himself, it is possible that many of the accomplishments credited to Pythagoras may actually have been those of his colleagues and successors. Accurate facts about the life of Pythagoras are so few that it is nearly impossible to provide more than a vague outline of his life.

Euclid of Alexandria and the *Elements*

Image 5.1.2: Euclid of Alexandria

Very few original references to **Euclid of Alexandria** survive, so little is known about his life. The date, place, and circumstances of both his birth and death are unknown and may only be estimated relative to other figures mentioned alongside him. The few historical references to Euclid were written centuries after he lived, and he is rarely mentioned by other Greek mathematicians after the time of Archimedes.

Because this lack of biographical information is unusual for ancient Greek mathematicians, some researchers have proposed that Euclid was not, in fact, an actual historical figure, and that his works were written by a team of mathematicians who took the name Euclid from the Greek philosopher Euclid of Megara. That being said, this hypothesis is not well accepted by scholars and there is little evidence in its favor.

Elements is a series of 13 books attributed to Euclid, written around 300 BC. It is a collection of definitions, postulates, propositions, and mathematical proofs. The thirteen books cover the geometry that bears his name (Euclidean geometry), and the ancient Greek version of elementary number theory. The work also includes an algebraic system that has become known as geometric algebra, which is powerful enough to solve many algebraic problems, including the problem of finding the square root of a number (remember, this was written in 300 BC!). *Elements* has proven instrumental in the development of logic and modern science, so much so that the theorems in it should be seen as having the same significance to geometry as an alphabet does to language.

Euclid's *Elements* has been referred to as the most successful and influential textbook ever written. Being first set in type in 1482, it is one of the very earliest mathematical works to be printed after the invention of the printing press and was estimated to be second only to the Bible in the number of editions published. For centuries, knowledge of at least part of Euclid's *Elements* was required of all students. Not until the 20th century, by which time its content was universally taught through other school textbooks, did it cease to be considered something that must be read by all educated people.

Hypatia of Alexandria

The mathematician and philosopher **Hypatia of Alexandria** (370–415) was the daughter of the philosopher Theon. She was educated at Athens, and around 400 AD, became head of the Platonist school at Alexandria. Admired for her dignity and virtue, she imparted the knowledge of Plato and Aristotle to students including pagans, Christians, and foreigners. Unfortunately, being an intelligent, dignified, and forthright woman just before the beginning of the Dark Ages led some fanatical Christian sects to consider her teachings to be paganism.

Image 5.1.3: Hypatia of Alexandria

Hypatia became a focal point of conflict between Christians and non-Christians, which eventually led her to a violent death. Threatened by her knowledge, a Christian mob claimed that she beguiled many people through magic and satanic wiles, attacked her, dragged her from her carriage, tore off all her clothes and burned her to death. Many scholars believe her murder marked the beginning of the downfall of intellectual life in Alexandria.

No written work widely recognized by scholars as Hypatia's own has survived to the present time. Many of the works commonly attributed to her are believed to have been collaborative efforts between her and her father. This kind of authorial uncertainty is typical for female philosophers in antiquity.

Indiana House Bill #246

In 1897, **Indiana House Bill No. 246** attempted to set the value of π to an incorrect rational approximation. The bill, written by amateur mathematician and medical doctor **Edwin Goodwin**, was so poorly crafted it even contradicted itself, implying three different values for π. Nevertheless, Dr. Goodwin succeeded in getting his state representative, Taylor Record, to introduce the bill, under the agreement that the state of **Indiana** could use the information free of charge, but the rest of the country would have to pay royalties for its usage.

The bill, which apparently no representative understood, passed through the Indiana House of Representatives unanimously (67–0), and was sent to the State Senate for approval. Fortunately, during the House's debate on the bill, **Purdue University** Mathematics Professor **Clarence Waldo** was present and became appalled. After the debate, a representative offered to introduce Professor Waldo to Dr. Goodwin. Professor Waldo declined by stating that he was already acquainted with as many crazy people as he cared to know. Later that evening, Professor Waldo informed the members of the Indiana Senate of the "merits" of the bill. The next day, after some good-natured ridicule at the expense of their colleagues in the House, the Senate moved the bill to an obscure committee and let it die a painless death.

References

Encyclopedia Britannica Online, s.v. "Hypatia." Last modified March 2, 2016. https://www.britannica.com/biography/Hypatia.

"Euclid." (1944). In *The Lincoln Library of Essential Information*, vol. 2, 1802. Buffalo, NY: The Frontier Press Company, 1944.

Eves, H. *An Introduction to the History of Mathematics*. Philadelphia, PA: Saunders College Publishing, 1990.

"Hypatia." In *The Lincoln Library of Essential Information*, vol. 2, 1869. Buffalo, NY: The Frontier Press Company, 1944.

Mueller, I., L. S. Grinstein, and P. J. Campbell. *Women of Mathematics: A Biobibliographic Sourcebook*. Westport, CT: Greenwood Press, 1987.

"Pythagoras." In *The Lincoln Library of Essential Information*, vol. 2, 1955–1956. Buffalo, NY: The Frontier Press Company, 1944.

World Book Encyclopedia, 1978 ed., s.v. "Euclid."

World Book Encyclopedia, 1978 ed., s.v. "Pythagoras."

5.2 Getting into Shape: Polygons and Tilings

A **closed broken line** is made up of line segments and begins and ends at the same point. A **simple closed broken line** is one that does not intersect itself, and is known as a **polygon**.

Common (and Some Not-So-Common) Polygons

TABLE 15.2.1 POLYGONS

NAME	NUMBER OF SIDES	PICTURE
Triangle	3	
Quadrilateral	4	
Pentagon	5	
Hexagon	6	
Octagon	8	
Nonagon	9	
Decagon	10	

Notice how, as the number of sides of the polygon increases, the figure looks more and more like a circle. A **dodecagon** has 12 sides, a **triskadecogon** has 13 sides, an **icosagon** has 20 sides, and a **hectogon** has 100 sides. Those figures, especially the hectogon, would look very similar to circles.

At the age of 19, **Carl Friedrich Gauss** proved it was possible to construct a regular **heptadecagon** (17 sides) using only a compass and a straightedge. He was so proud of the proof that he requested the shape be engraved onto his tombstone. The stonemason refused to perform the complicated task, stating the shape would have been indistinguishable from a circle.

The prefixes used in the polygon names define the number of sides. Tri- means three, quad- means four, penta- means five, and hexa-, octa-, and nona- mean six, eight, and nine, respectively. Deca- means 10, so a decagon has 10 sides. Can you recognize the prefixes for 12, 13, 20, and 100?

By the way, in the Roman Lunar Calendar, October was originally the eighth month, November (Novem- is an alternative prefix for nine) was originally the ninth month, and December was the tenth month. That original Roman calendar consisted of ten months and began with March. **Julius Caesar** eventually reformed the calendar to 12 months and renamed a couple of mid-year months to honor himself and his nephew Augustus, whom he later adopted.

Types of Triangles and Their Properties:

TABLE 15.2.2   TRIANGLES

TRIANGLE	PROPERTIES	PICTURE
Equilateral	All sides are equal, all angles are equal	
Isosceles	At least two sides are equal	
Scalene	No sides are the same length, no angles are equal	
Right	One of the angles measures 90°	
Acute	All angles measure less than 90°	
Obtuse	One angle measures greater than 90°	

You may have noticed the similarly shaped triangles appearing as an isosceles and an acute triangle. This does not mean all isosceles triangles are acute; it just means the pictured isosceles triangle is acute. An isosceles triangle can also be obtuse. Likewise, the pictured scalene triangle is also obtuse, but that does not mean all scalene triangles are obtuse. Yes, a triangle may fall into more than one of the categories, but be sure to treat each category according to its own properties.

Another subtle but important concept appears in the picture of the right triangle. Notice that there is a small square appearing in the right angle of the triangle. Since all the angles in a square measure 90°, that small square is there to indicate that angle measures 90°.

The Triangle Inequality

In order to construct a triangle from three line segments, the sum of the measures of any two of the segments must be greater than the measure of the third segment. For example, we cannot construct a triangle with segments lengths of 3 centimeters, 4 centimeters, and 9 centimeters, because the sum of 3 and 4 is *not* greater than 9. If you don't believe that, grab a ruler and try it!

Types of Quadrilaterals and Their Properties

TABLE 15.2.3   QUADRILATERALS

QUADRILATERAL	PROPERTIES	PICTURE
Trapezoid	*Exactly* one pair of opposite sides is parallel	
Parallelogram	*Both* pairs of opposite sides are parallel	
Rectangle	All angles measure 90°	
Rhombus	All sides are equal in length	
Square	All sides are equal in length, and all angles measure 90°	

Realize that many quadrilaterals may fall into more than one category. For example, a square satisfies the definition of a rhombus, a rectangle, and a parallelogram! To keep things simple, when we name a given quadrilateral, we should be as specific as possible. That is, even though all rectangles are parallelograms, if the angles all measure 90°, we should call it a rectangle—unless, of course, it is a square.

Are You Regular?

What does the word regular mean? In reference to a geometric figure, a **regular polygon** is a polygon whose sides are all the same length and whose interior angles all have the same measure. An **interior angle** is an angle measured on the inside of a given polygon.

Which of the following figures are regular polygons? (Hint: Only two of them are regular.)

Figure 5.2.1   Which are Regular?

A well-remembered fact from any geometry course is that the sum of the interior angles for any triangle is 180°. This fact does not tell us the individual measures of the three angles; it only tells us their sum. Unless they are given or measured, the exact angle measures can only be determined if the triangle is regular. The interior angles of a regular triangle—also known as an equilateral triangle—are 60°, because all three angles are equal and 180°/3 = 60°.

Whether regular or not, any polygon can be broken into a finite number of triangles by cutting the polygon along the lines connecting non-consecutive angles. For example, a hexagon (six sides) can be thought of as a composition of four triangles.

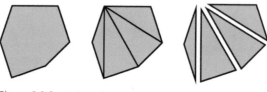

Figure 5.2.2   Split Polygon

Since each triangle has an interior angle sum of 180°, and a hexagon can be thought of as four triangles, the sum of the interior angle measures for any hexagon is 4(180°) = 720°. If the hexagon were a regular hexagon, then we could also say each of the six angles would be 120°.

In the example above, we saw that a 6-sided polygon was made up of 4 triangles. In fact, the number of triangles composing any polygon is always two less than the number of sides of the polygon. Thus, the sum of the interior angles of any polygon can be determined by the formula (n − 2)180°, where n is the number of sides for the polygon. Since, in a regular polygon, all the interior angles are equal, the total can then be divided by the number of angles to find the measure of each interior angle.

Keep in mind, this individual angle calculation can only be done with regular polygons.

EXAMPLE 1:

What is the measure of each of the interior angles of a STOP sign?

Solution: First, we need to recognize that a STOP sign is a regular octagon, which has eight sides. So, the sum of the eight interior angles is (8 − 2)(180°) = (6)(180°) = 1,080°

Since the STOP sign is a regular polygon, all eight angles are of equal measure, which means each one measures 1,080°/8 = 135°

Tilings

If done correctly, a tiling can be a beautiful creation. A **tiling** (also called a **tessellation**), is a space completely covered by geometric figures. A **regular tiling** is a tiling done exclusively with one particular regular polygon. The words "completely covered" are important, as a tiling cannot contain gaps between the figures. Tilings can be done with a single figure or multiple figures, but in every case, there are no gaps. Here are a few examples.

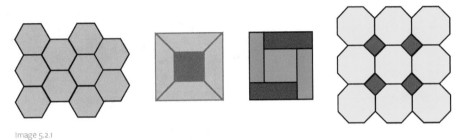

Image 5.2.1

In any tiling, the key to making the figures fit tightly lies in the interior angles of the polygons that are used. The polygons must be aligned in a way so that the sum of the adjacent angles is 360°. Here are a few examples.

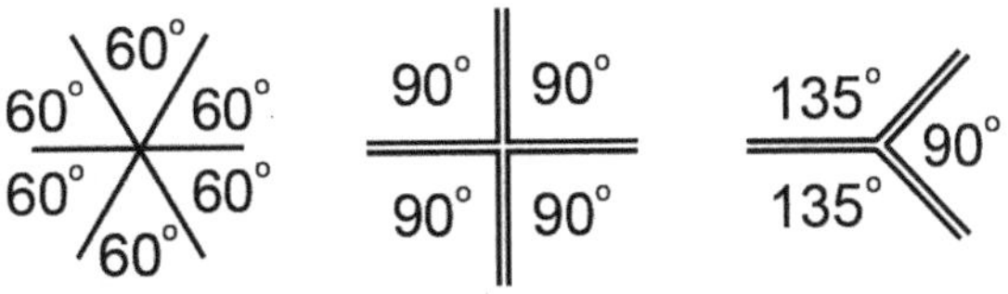

Figure 5.2.3 Tiling Angles

Why must the sum of the interior angles be 360°? In order to close all the gaps, imagine rotating around the point of intersection. Since there are 360° in a circle, we need the sum of the angles at that intersection to be 360°.

If the word "tiling" seems inappropriate to you, think of a tile floor in a house or a stone patio, which is often covered in square tiles.

Image 5.2.2a

Image 5.2.2b

Remember, tilings do not have to be made up of regular polygons. In many home stores, we can purchase bricks or oddly shaped stones that can be turned in different directions to form a tiling when placed together to make a patio or unique sidewalk.

For the sidewalk being made in the adjacent photograph, all the stones are the same rhombus shape—they are just turned in different directions. The rhombus-shaped stones have six 60° angles meeting in some areas and three 120° angles meeting in other areas. Either way, the total of all the angles at those points is 360°.

Image 5.2.3

SECTION 5.2 EXERCISES

1. Classify each of the following as simple or non-simple.

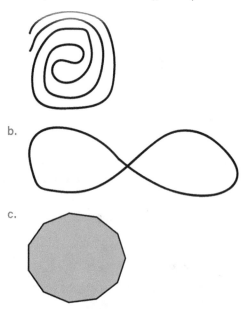

b.

c.

2. How many sides does a hexagon have?

3. What is the name for a 15-sided polygon?

4. Use the best term to classify the following triangles as equilateral, isosceles, or scalene.

a.

b.

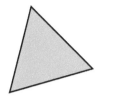

c.

5. Classify the following triangles as right, acute, or obtuse.

a.

b.

c.

6. Indicate whether the following statements are true or false. If false, correct the statement.

a. In a parallelogram, both pairs of opposite sides are parallel.

b. All squares are rectangles.

c. All rectangles are squares.

d. All rectangles are parallelograms.

e. All squares are parallelograms.

f. In a rectangle, exactly two angles measure 90°.

7. Consider the following street signs.

Image 5.2.4

a. Which of the signs are not shaped like a polygon?

b. Which of the signs are shaped like regular polygons?

c. What is the name of the shape used for the STOP sign?

8. What is the measure of each of the interior angles for a regular pentagon?

9. What is the measure of each of the interior angles for a regular hectogon (100 sides)?

10. Can you make a tiling with only regular pentagons? Why or why not?

11. A regular heptagon has seven sides. Can you list a practical use for something shaped like a regular heptagon?

12. The Pentagon is the headquarters for the US Department of Defense. Why is the name "Pentagon" appropriate?

Image 5.2.5

ANSWERS TO SECTION 5.2 EXERCISES

1. a. simple   b. non-simple   c. simple

2. six

3. pentadecagon

4. a. isosceles   b. equilateral   c. scalene

5. a. acute   b. acute   c. right

6. a. true

    b. true

    c. false — possible rewrite: Some rectangles are squares.

    d. true

    e. true

    f. false — possible rewrite: In a rectangle, all four angles measure 90°.

7. a. Railroad Crossing   b. Caution, Stop, and Yield   c. octagon

8. 108°

9. 176.4°

10. No. 108 is not a factor of 360. Three 108° angles add up to 324°, and four would be 432°.

11. Answers may vary, but one possible use is a daily pill container.

Image 5.2.6

12. The building is shaped like a pentagon.

5.3 How Tall Is That Tree?: Right and Similar Triangles

Square Roots

Given a quantity, the **principal square root** of that quantity is the positive number we must multiply by itself (square) to get that quantity. For our purposes, we will refer to the "principal square root" as just the "square root." For example, since $5 \times 5 = 25$, the square root of 25 is 5. Said another way, since $5^2 = 25$, the square root of 25 is 5. The notation we use for square roots is:

$$\sqrt{25} = 5$$

For numbers like 25, 36, 81, and 100, finding the square roots is easily done by inspection. These numbers are **perfect squares**. How do we find the square root of a number that is not a perfect square? Although there are ways to do this by hand, the fastest way is to just use a calculator. **Also, unless directed otherwise, we will round square roots to the nearest hundredth.**

Review: Order of Operations

If several people are asked to simplify the same multi-step arithmetic **expression**, a standard set of rules must be established for the order in which the operations are performed. Otherwise, different people may get different answers. For example, let's say Bill and Ted are asked to simplify the expression $3 + 4 \times 5$. Bill adds the $3 + 4$, and then multiplies that result by 5 to get a total of 35. Ted performs the multiplication first, and then adds 3 to get a total of 23. Who is right? In case you aren't sure yet ... it is Ted.

Arithmetic started with addition (and subtraction). Repeated addition led to multiplication (and division), and repeated multiplication led to the use of exponents. In addition to those procedures, parentheses or other grouping symbols can also be used in an expression. Let's consolidate all of these processes into a single list, known as the "order of operations."

Arithmetic **Order of Operations**:

1. All operations contained within parentheses ( ) or other grouping symbols, such as brackets [ ], or braces { }, should be done first.

2. Secondly, simplify all expressions containing exponents.

3. Multiplication and division are done next, as we come to them going from left to right.

4. Addition and subtraction are done last, again, as we come to them going from left to right.

To help remember this order, many students like to memorize the acronym **PEMDAS** (Parentheses, Exponents, Multiplication, Division, Addition, Subtraction). This can be really helpful, but be careful! If you do not realize multiplication and division are done as we come to them going from the left to the right, you may fall into the trap of thinking multiplication always precedes division—it does not. The same holds true for addition and subtraction.

EXAMPLE 1:

Simplify: $5 + 6 \times 3$

SOLUTION: Since multiplication is performed before addition, start by multiplying 6×3. Then, add 5 to that result.

$$5 + 6 \times 3$$
$$= 5 + 18$$
$$= 23$$

EXAMPLE 2:

Simplify: $13 - 5 + 6$

SOLUTION: Remember, perform addition and subtraction as we come to them going from left to right. Here, that means the subtraction must be done first.

$13 - 5 + 6$
$= 8 + 6$
$= 14$

EXAMPLE 3:

Simplify: $13 - (5 + 6)$

SOLUTION: Since $(5 + 6)$ is inside parentheses, that operation is performed first.

$13 - (5 + 6)$
$= 13 - 11$
$= 2$

EXAMPLE 4:

Simplify: $42 \div 3(2)$

SOLUTION: There are parentheses in this expression but take note that there is no operation to perform inside these parentheses. We have division and multiplication to perform here, and those are done going from left to right.

$42 \div 3(2)$
$= 14(2)$
$= 28$

EXAMPLE 5:

Simplify: $5 \times (2 + 3)^2 - (6 - 4) + 1$

SOLUTION: Here, we start with the operations that are inside the parentheses. Then, perform the operation using the exponent. After that, the multiplication is done. Finally, we have addition and subtraction, which are performed as we come to them going from left to right.

$5 \times (2 + 3)^2 - (6 - 4) + 1$
$= 5 \times (5)^2 - 2 + 1$
$= 5 \times 25 - 2 + 1$
$= 125 - 2 + 1$
$= 123 + 1$
$= 124$

Review: Solving Equations

An **equation** is a mathematical statement indicating that two expressions are equal. A **solution** is a value of the variable that makes the equation true.

When **solving an equation**, steps are taken to determine all the values of the variable that will make the equation a true statement.

One of the steps available for use is known as the **addition property of equality**. This property states, "if the same quantity is added to both sides of an equation, the solution remains the same." Since any quantity can be added to both sides of an equation, a quantity is chosen that will isolate the variable.

EXAMPLE 6:

Solve: $x - 8 = 24$

SOLUTION: To solve this equation, we want to isolate the variable (x). To do that here, we will add 8 to both sides of the equation. This will cause the (-8) and the $(+8)$ on the left side of the equation to cancel each other out. We also simplify the right side of the equation, giving us our solution.

$$x - 8 = 24$$
$$x - 8 + 8 = 24 + 8$$
$$x = 32$$

As you might expect, we can add either positive numbers (like we did in Example 6), or negative numbers to both sides of an equation.

EXAMPLE 7:

Solve: $x + 7 = -8$

SOLUTION: Here, we will add (-7) to both sides of the equation.

$$x + 7 = -8$$
$$x + 7 + (-7) = -8 + (-7)$$
$$x = -15$$

Note: It is perfectly fine to think of the process as "subtracting 7 from both sides."

Another approach that may be used when solving an equation involves the **multiplication property of equality**, which states that "if both sides of an equation are multiplied (or divided) by the same non-zero quantity, the solution remains the same." Just as it is with the addition property of equality, since any quantity can be used, a quantity is chosen that will isolate the variable.

EXAMPLE 8:

Solve: $6x = 24$

SOLUTION: To solve this equation, we want to isolate the variable (x). To do that here, we will divide both sides of the equation by 6.

$6x = 24$
$6x/6 = 24/6$
$x = 4$

You may be thinking, "if we *divide* by a number, why is this called the multiplication property of equality?" Instead of dividing by 6, we could have multiplied by (1/6) and had the same outcome. In the same way that the addition property of equality applies to both addition and subtraction, the multiplication property of equality applies to both multiplication and division. This streamlines our processes into just two properties that we use when trying to isolate a variable.

Some of the equations we solve will make use of *both* the addition and multiplication properties of equality. In some equations, we will use the distributive property to remove any parentheses, and some equations will require us to simplify each side of the equation as much as possible by combining like terms. That being the case, some equations will require several steps in the solving process.

If the variable exists on both sides of the equation, use the addition principle to remove it from one side. Try not to think of moving terms from one side of an equation to the other. Instead, focus on removing unwanted terms by adding their opposite. Then, remember, whatever we have done to one side of the equation, we must also do the same thing to the other side to keep the equation balanced. Once the term containing the variable has been isolated, then apply the multiplication property to remove any unwanted multiplication—just be sure to do it to both sides of the equation.

common mistake:

When faced with $6x = 24$, some students attempt to isolate the x by subtracting 6 from both sides of the equation. Remember, the 6 and x are linked by multiplication, and multiplication is undone by division, not subtraction.

EXAMPLE 9:

Solve: $x^2 = 10^2 + 6^2$

SOLUTION: To solve this equation, we start by simplifying the right side of the equation. Exponents and addition must be performed, so the exponents are simplified first, and then the addition is performed. Finally, to get the variable by itself, we take the square root of both sides.

$x^2 = 10^2 + 6^2$
$x^2 = 100 + 36$
$x^2 = 136$
$x = 11.661903789690601... \rightarrow 11.66$

EXAMPLE 10:

Solve: $29^2 = 20^2 + x^2$

SOLUTION: In this problem, we start by simplifying the exponents. Next, to isolate the variable on one side of the equation, we subtract 400 from each side. Finally, we take the square root of both sides.

$$29^2 = 20^2 + x^2$$
$$841 = 400 + x^2$$
$$441 = x^2$$
$$21 = x$$

The Pythagorean Theorem

As a reminder, a right triangle is a triangle that contains a 90° (right) angle. The longest side of a **right triangle** is always the side opposite the right angle, and this side is called the **hypotenuse**. The other two sides of the triangle are referred to as **legs**. The **Pythagorean Theorem** states:

common mistake:

Remember to follow the correct order of operations!

A common mistake is to add the leg lengths and then square the result.

Remember, the exponents must be dealt with BEFORE the addition.

In any right triangle, the square of the hypotenuse is equal to the sum of the squares of the legs. That is: $\text{hypotenuse}^2 = \text{leg}^2 + \text{leg}^2$

EXAMPLE 11:

Find the length of the hypotenuse in the following right triangle.

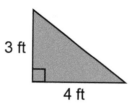

Figure 5.3.1

SOLUTION: Since the legs measure 3 feet and 4 feet, the Pythagorean Theorem states:

$$(\text{hypotenuse})^2 = 3^2 + 4^2$$
$$(\text{hypotenuse})^2 = 9 + 16$$
$$(\text{hypotenuse})^2 = 25$$

Taking the square root of both sides, we have:

$$\text{hypotenuse} = 5 \text{ ft}$$

Sometimes we are given the length of the hypotenuse and one of the leg lengths. To find the missing length in this case, we still use the Pythagorean theorem, but we will need to subtract after we square the given lengths.

EXAMPLE 12:

Find the length of the missing side in a right triangle if the hypotenuse is 6 feet long, and one of the sides is 2 feet long.

SOLUTION: Here we know one of the sides and the hypotenuse, so the solving process will be a little different:

$6^2 = 2^2 + (\text{side})^2$

$36 = 4 + (\text{side})^2$

Subtract 4 from both sides of the equation to get:

$32 = (\text{side})^2$

Taking the square root of both sides, we have:

$\text{side} = 5.6568... \approx 5.66 \text{ ft}$

What Good Is the Pythagorean Theorem, Anyway?

Carpenters still use a right triangle to square corners. Here's how.

First, think of a window frame and what happens to that frame if we anchor its bottom, and push the top to the left or the right.

In the figures on the right, a frame is shown in three states. The top frame is considered "square," because the angle X is a right angle.

In the middle frame, the top has been pushed to the left. Here the angle X is less than 90°, and the dotted line is shorter than the same line in the top frame.

In the bottom frame, the top has been pushed to the right. Here the angle X is greater than 90°, and the dotted line is longer than the same line in the top frame.

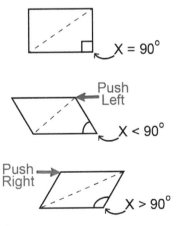

Figure 5.3.2   Window Frames

So, when the bottom of the window frame is nailed down, we can adjust the length of the dotted line by pushing the top of the frame to the left or right

We can be sure the window frame is "square" by a simple application of the Pythagorean Theorem. From one corner, we can make marks on the frame that are 3 inches in one direction and 4 inches in the other. Then, the whole frame can be adjusted until the straight-line distance between the two marks is 5 inches.

Essentially, since a triangle with a side ratio of 3-4-5 obeys the Pythagorean Theorem (that is, $3^2 + 4^2 = 5^2$), then that triangle *must* be a right triangle. In other words, if you force one of these 3-4-5 triangles into a corner of a frame, then, according to the Pythagorean Theorem, the angle across from the hypotenuse (the side of length 5) has to be a right angle.

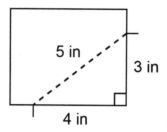

Figure 5.3.3   Frame with Right Angle

Review: Proportions

A **proportion** is a statement that two ratios (or rates) are equal. With the introduction of an equals sign, we can solve for a missing measure, provided we have the other three measures. This solution process involves **cross multiplication**, which is multiplying the quantities that are diagonal from each other across the = sign.

Then we set those two products equal to each other and solve the resultant equation using our algebra skills.

EXAMPLE 13:

Solve for x. $\dfrac{4}{8} = \dfrac{x}{12}$

SOLUTION: Cross-multiply to get:

8x = 4(12)
8x = 48
Divide by 8 to get x by itself:
x = 48/8 = 6

As it is not always convenient to type equations with fractions in a traditional vertical format (as shown in the previous example), we often see them written horizontally. When written horizontally, the two quantities appearing in the middle are called the **means**, and the quantities appearing at the beginning and end of the proportion are called the **extremes**.

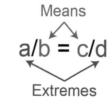

Figure 5.3.4   Means and Extremes

Then, the process for solving the proportion is the same, but, in this case, the equation we need to solve is determined by setting the product of the means equal to the product of the extremes (or the product of the extremes equal to the product of the means, if that is more convenient).

EXAMPLE 14:

Solve for x.

$x/35 = 9/12$

SOLUTION: Setting the product of the extremes equal to the product of the means:

$12x = 9(35)$
$12x = 315$
Divide by 12 to get x by itself:
$x = 315/12 = 26.25$

Similar Triangles

Similar triangles are triangles whose angles have the same measure, but their sides have different lengths. The triangles will look identical, but one will be smaller than the other. When two triangles are similar, their corresponding side lengths are proportional to each other.

Using the proportionality of the sides, similar triangles are a simple and very powerful problem-solving tool. Using the correspondence of the side lengths of similar triangles, we can find a missing side length.

When setting up a proportion, the first ratio is made up from the sides of the smaller triangle, while the second ratio has the side lengths from the larger triangle. The numerators are one pair of corresponding sides, and the denominators are also a pair of corresponding sides. Be sure to keep corresponding sides in the same positions in the respective ratios.

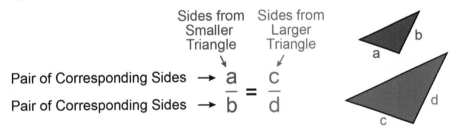

Figure 5.3.5 Proportion for Similar Triangles

EXAMPLE 15:

Given the following two triangles that are similar, we can see that side AB corresponds to side DE, side BC corresponds to side EF, and side AC corresponds to side DF. Find the lengths of BC and AC to the nearest hundredth.

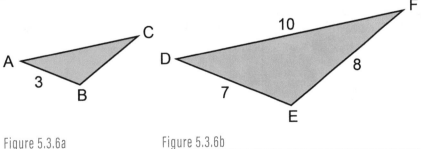

Figure 5.3.6a   Figure 5.3.6b

SOLUTION: We have two side lengths to find, and it doesn't matter which one we find first. So, using the side lengths that we know, we can set up a proportion to find side BC.

$$\frac{AB}{BC} = \frac{DE}{EF}$$

Plugging in the known values, we have:

$$\frac{3}{BC} = \frac{7}{8}$$

Cross-multiplying gives us: 7(BC) = 8(3), or 7(BC) = 24.
Dividing both sides by 7, we find: side BC = 24/7 = 3.428571... → 3.43

Similarly, we can set up a proportion to find side AC. For this one, let's work with the horizontal layout.
Our proportion is: AC/AB = DF/DE
Plugging in the known values, we have: AC/3 = 10/7
Using the means and extremes, we have: 7(AC) = 30
So, the side AC = 30/7 = 4.285714... → 4.29

Similar triangles can be extremely useful. For example, we can actually use our own shadow to determine the height of a tree.

EXAMPLE 16:

Let's say you are 6 feet tall, and at a certain time of day, you find your shadow to be 10 feet long. At the same time of day, you measure the shadow of a tree to be 38 feet long. How tall is the tree? Here's a picture:

image 5.3.1a

image 5.3.1b

Solution: Draw the corresponding triangles on the figure and label the sides we know.

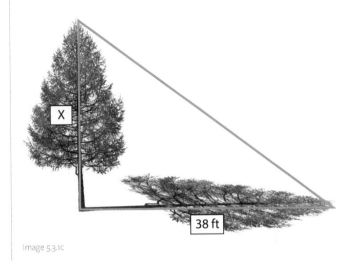

X

38 ft

Image 5.3.1c

6 ft

10 ft

Image 5.3.1d

Then, set up a proportion that looks like:

$$\frac{6 \text{ ft}}{10 \text{ ft}} = \frac{x}{38 \text{ ft}}$$

Cross-multiplying gives us: $(10 \text{ ft})(x) = (38 \text{ ft})(6 \text{ ft})$
Dividing both sides by 10 ft, we have:
$x = (38 \text{ ft})(6 \text{ ft})/(10 \text{ ft}) = 22.8 \text{ ft}$
So, the tree is 22.8 feet tall.

As an aside, this is not 22 feet 8 inches. The 0.8 here represents 8/10 of a foot.
Converting that to inches, we would have: $0.8 \times 12 = 9.6$, which is almost 10 inches.
To the nearest inch, the tree is 22 feet 10 inches tall.

Helpful Hint: To solve a problem involving similar triangles, a diagram is particularly helpful. If no diagram is provided in the question, it may be helpful to draw one.

SECTION 5.3 EXERCISES

1. Find the following. Round to the nearest hundredth, as necessary.

   a. $\sqrt{36}$

   b. $\sqrt{121}$

   c. $\sqrt{63}$

2. If a right triangle has legs measuring 6 feet and 8 feet, how long is the hypotenuse?

3. If a right triangle has one leg that measures 12 centimeters, and a hypotenuse that measures 13 centimeters, how long is the other side?

4. If both legs of a right triangle measure 6 inches, how long is the hypotenuse? Round your answer to the nearest tenth of an inch.

5. If a 10-foot ladder is leaning against the top of a 9-foot high wall, how far will the base of the ladder be from the bottom of the wall? Round your answer to the nearest tenth of a foot.

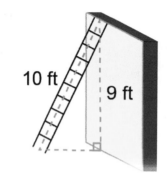

Figure 5.3.5   Ladder Leaning Against Wall

6. If you drive 12 miles north, make a right turn, and drive 9 miles east, how far are you, in a straight line, from your starting point?

7. On a baseball diamond, there are 90 feet between home plate and first base, and 90 feet between first base and second base. The base paths are at right angles. What is the straight-line distance from home plate to second base, to the nearest foot?

8. For a 25-inch television, the length of the screen's diagonal is 25 inches. If the screen's height is 15 inches, what is the width?

9. In the movie **The Wizard of Oz**, the Scarecrow, upon being presented with his ThD (Doctor of Thinkology), proudly exclaims, "The sum of the square roots of any two sides of an isosceles triangle is equal to the square root of the remaining side." What he said was incorrect. Name at least three mistakes in the Scarecrow's statement.

10. Given that the pictured triangles are similar, find the lengths sides DE and DF. Round your answers to the nearest tenth, as necessary.

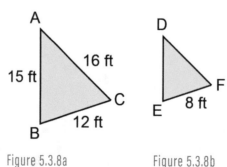

Figure 5.3.8a   Figure 5.3.8b

11. While standing 10 feet away from a light pole, Jim notices his shadow is 8 feet long. If Jim is 6 feet tall, how tall is the light pole?

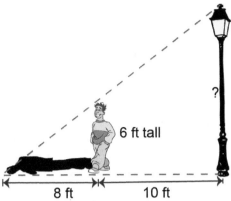

Figure 5.3.9 How Tall is the Lightpole?

12. In the given figure, triangle ABC is similar to triangle EBD (denoted △ABC ~ △EBD). What are the measures of BE and DE?

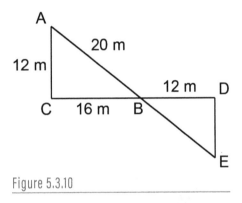

Figure 5.3.10

13. Mike wants to know the distance, **w**, across an east-to-west running river. He measures 120 feet along the southern bank of the river and then measures 16 feet south from the western edge of that measure (measure **a** in the figure). From that point, he cites a spot on the northern riverbank that is straight north from the place where he started the 120-foot measure, and that line of sight crosses the original 120-foot line 32 feet from the western edge (measure **b** in the figure). This process creates two similar triangles as shown in the figure below. What is the distance across the river? Round your answer to the nearest foot.

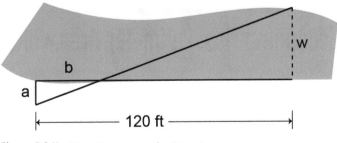

Figure 5.3.11 How Far Across the River?

14. Two poles are 20 feet tall and 30 feet tall, respectively. If they are 30 feet apart, how far is it from the top of one pole to the top of the other pole? Round your answer to the nearest tenth of a foot. (Hint: Draw a picture.)

ANSWERS TO SECTION 5.3 EXERCISES

1. a. 6   b. 11   c. 7.94

2. 10 ft

3. 5 cm

4. 8.5 in

5. 4.4 ft

6. 15 mi

7. 127 ft

8. 20 in

9. The Pythagorean Theorem is stated in squares, not square roots. The triangle must be a right triangle, not an isosceles triangle. You have to take the sum of the squares of the two shorter sides, not "any" two sides.

10. DE = 10 ft, DF = 10.7 ft

11. Be careful. The base of the larger triangle is 18 feet, not just 10 feet. The light pole is 13.5 feet high.

12. DE = 9 meters, BE = 15 meters

13. 44 ft

14. 31.6 ft

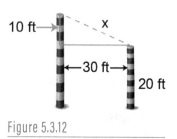

Figure 5.3.12

5.4 Redecorating Tips: Perimeter, Area, Volume, and Circles

Review: Order of Operations

If several people are asked to simplify the same multi-step arithmetic **expression**, a standard set of rules must be established for the order in which the operations are performed. Otherwise, different people may get different answers. For example, let's say Bill and Ted are asked to simplify the expression

$3 + 4 \times 5$. Bill adds the $3 + 4$, and then multiplies that result by 5 to get a total of 35. Ted performs the multiplication first, and then adds 3 to get a total of 23. Who is right? In case you aren't sure yet ... it is Ted.

Arithmetic started with addition (and subtraction). Repeated addition led to multiplication (and division), and repeated multiplication led to the use of exponents. In addition to those procedures, parentheses or other grouping symbols can also be used in an expression. Let's consolidate all of these processes into a single list, known as the "order of operations."

Arithmetic **Order of Operations:**

1. All operations contained within parentheses ( ) or other grouping symbols, such as brackets [ ], or braces { }, should be done first.

2. Secondly, simplify all expressions containing exponents.

3. Multiplication and division are done next, as we come to them going from left to right.

4. Addition and subtraction are done last, again, as we come to them going from left to right.

To help remember this order, many students like to memorize the acronym **PEMDAS** (Parentheses, Exponents, Multiplication, Division, Addition, Subtraction). This can be really helpful, but be careful! If you do not realize multiplication and division are done as we come to them going from the left to the right, you may fall into the trap of thinking multiplication always precedes division—it does not. The same holds true for addition and subtraction.

EXAMPLE 1:

Simplify: $5 + 6 \times 3$

SOLUTION: Since multiplication is performed before addition, start by multiplying 6×3. Then, add 5 to that result.

$5 + 6 \times 3$
$= 5 + 18$
$= 23$

EXAMPLE 2:

Simplify: $13 - 5 + 6$

SOLUTION: Remember, perform addition and subtraction as we come to them going from left to right. Here, that means the subtraction must be done first.

$13 - 5 + 6$
$= 8 + 6$
$= 14$

EXAMPLE 3:

Simplify: $3 \times (5) + 2 \times (4) + 4 \times (3)$

Solution: There are parentheses in this expression, but take note that there is no operation to perform inside these parentheses. We have multiplication and addition to perform here, so we will perform the multiplications first, and the additions afterward.

$$3 \times (5) + 2 \times (4) + 4 \times (3)$$
$$= 15 + 8 + 12$$
$$= 35$$

EXAMPLE 4:

Simplify: $(3.14) \times (12)^2$

Solution: There are parentheses in this expression, but take note that there is no operation to perform inside these parentheses. We have multiplication to perform and an exponent here, so we will simplify the exponent first, and then perform the multiplication.

$$(3.14) \times (12)^2$$
$$= (3.14) \times 144$$
$$= 452.16$$

EXAMPLE 5:

Simplify: $5 \times (2 + 3)^2 - (6 - 4) + 1$

Solution: Here, we start with the operations that are inside the parentheses. Then, perform the operation using the exponent. After that, the multiplication is done. Finally, we have addition and subtraction, which are performed as we come to them going from left to right.

$$5 \times (2 + 3)^2 - (6 - 4) + 1$$
$$= 5 \times (5)^2 - 2 + 1$$
$$= 5 \times 25 - 2 + 1$$
$$= 125 - 2 + 1$$
$$= 123 + 1$$
$$= 124$$

We have all seen squares and rectangles, and you probably remember some basic facts from previous studies. A **rectangle** is a flat, four-sided geometric figure in which both pairs of opposite sides are parallel and equal, and all four angles are right angles. A **square** is a rectangle in which all four sides are of equal length.

Perimeter and Area

Simply put, the **perimeter** of any flat geometric figure is defined as the distance around the figure. Although we may be presented with different formulas that get used for different figures, the perimeter of a given figure will still always be the distance around that figure.

The **area** of a flat geometric figure is defined as the amount of surface the figure covers. For rectangle and squares, this can be viewed as the number of square units that can be enclosed by the figure. In fact, for that very reason, area is always given in square units. For example, imagine a square that measures 1 inch on each side. How many of those 1-inch squares—also called "square inches"—can fit inside a rectangle that measures 2 inches wide by 5 inches long? If you're not sure, draw a picture.

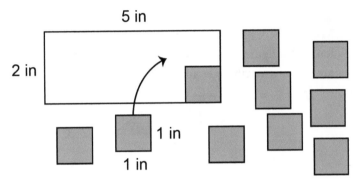

Figure 5.4.1 How Many Square Inches?

It would take 10 of these squares to cover the area inside this rectangle, so the area is 10 in².

When we are computing areas and perimeters, we need to pay attention to the units of measure. If no unit is stated, then only numeric answers should be given. If, however, a unit is stated—such as centimeters, feet, or inches—we must include the appropriate unit with our answers.

Linear units should accompany the linear measures of perimeter.

Areas should be stated in square units.

EXAMPLE 6:

A rectangular room measures 3 yards by 4 yards. How many square yards of carpet are needed to cover the floor? Also, how many yards of baseboard trim will be needed to go around the base of the room? Assume the door to the room is 1 yard wide.

SOLUTION: For the carpet, we need the number of square yards it would take to cover the floor (the area). A picture of a 3 yd by 4 yd rectangle can help us determine that we need 12 square yards of carpet.

For the baseboard trim, we need to find the perimeter of the room, less the width of the door.

3 yd + 4 yd + 3 yd + 4 yd − 1 yd (for the doorway) = 13 yd

We need 13 yards of baseboard trim.

Notice how we were able to perform the previous example without the use of formulas. In the case of a perimeter, whether we have a rectangle or not, all we need to do is add up the lengths of all the sides of the figure. When dealing with areas, we have already seen that the area of a rectangle is the product of the length and width. In formula form, if we use **l** for the length and **w** for the width, the formula is **A = lw**. Keep in mind, if we understand the origin of the formula, it is not necessary to memorize it.

At this point it is worth reviewing the Pythagorean Theorem discussion from a previous section. At times, we may be given the width of a rectangle along with the measure of the **diagonal**, which is the measure from one corner of the rectangle to the opposite corner. In such a case, we will need to use the Pythagorean Theorem to find the length of the rectangle. Do realize, however, in a rectangle, the length of the diagonal is not a part of the perimeter.

Parallelograms

A **parallelogram** is a four-sided figure in which both pairs of opposite sides are equal in length and parallel, but the angles are not necessarily right angles.

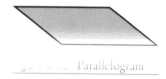

Parallelogram

Just like any flat geometric figure, the perimeter of a parallelogram is the distance around it. To find the area, we first need to identify the lengths of the base and height of the parallelogram. The **base**, b, of the parallelogram is the length of the bottom side. Actually, we can use any side, but, for simplicity, let's stick with the bottom. The **height**, h, of a parallelogram is the perpendicular distance from the base to the opposite side. This is usually represented by a dotted line drawn perpendicular to the base. Do not confuse the height with the length of a side. That is why we use a dotted line instead of a solid line.

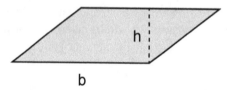

Figure 5.4.3   Base and Height of a Parallelogram

To determine the area of a parallelogram, imagine cutting off the triangular region on the right side and moving it to the left side as follows.

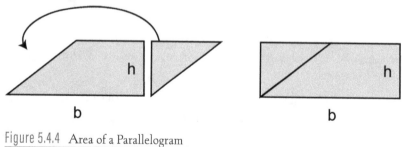

Figure 5.4.4   Area of a Parallelogram

The resulting figure would be a rectangle of dimensions b and h. Thus, the area of the parallelogram would be the product of the base and the height, or **A = bh**.

EXAMPLE 7:

Find the perimeter and area of the following parallelogram.

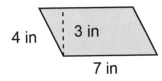

Figure 5.4.5

SOLUTION: The perimeter, P, is the sum of the four side lengths. Remember, the 3-inch measure is the height, not a side length.

P = 4 in + 7 in + 4 in + 7 in = 22 in

The area is the product of the base and the height. In this case, the base is 7 inches and the height is 3 inches.

A = (7 in)(3 in) = 21 in^2

Triangles

We all know what a triangle looks like, and once again, the **perimeter** of a triangle is just the sum of the three side lengths. For the **area**, we just need to recognize that a triangle is literally half of a parallelogram, when we cut it along the diagonal.

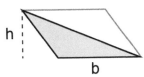

Figure 5.4.6   A Triangle is Half a Parallelogram

The height and base lengths are the same as with a parallelogram, but since we literally have half a parallelogram, the area of a triangle is half that of the parallelogram with the same base and height. That is, **A = (1/2)bh**.

EXAMPLE 8:

Find the perimeter and area of the following triangle.

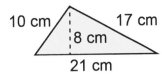

Figure 5.4.7

SOLUTION: The perimeter: P = 17 cm + 21 cm + 10 cm = 48 cm

The area: A = (1/2)(21 cm)(8 cm) = 84 cm^2

Composite Figures

A **composite figure** is made up of two or more smaller figures. Like always, the perimeter of such a figure is the distance around the figure. If the composite contains only right angles, we can cut the figure into squares and rectangles. Then we can find the areas of the smaller pieces and add them together to get the total area, which we will write as A_{Total}. Keep in mind, however, composite figures can be made of other shapes as well.

It is important to note, if we were asked to find the perimeter, we would add up *only* the sides that form the border of the composite figure. We should not try to break apart a figure to find the perimeter, but we may need to use some critical thinking skills to determine the lengths of unidentified sides.

EXAMPLE 9:

Find the area of the following composite figure.

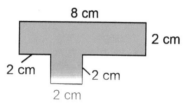

Figure 5.4.8a

SOLUTION: This figure can be viewed as a 2 cm by 8 cm rectangle on top of a 2 cm by 2 cm square, or as a 2 cm by 2 cm square next to two rectangles.

The figures below show two different ways this composite figure can be cut. The calculation below uses the split on the left, and you can use the split on the right for practice. The area you find should be exactly the same.

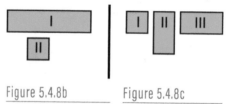

Figure 5.4.8b   Figure 5.4.8c

Using the option on the left, the total area of the composite figure is the sum of the rectangle (Region I), and the square (Region II).

$$A_{Total} = A_{Rectangle} + A_{Square} = 16 \text{ cm}^2 + 4 \text{ cm}^2 = 20 \text{ cm}^2$$

EXAMPLE 10:

Find the perimeter and area of the following figure.

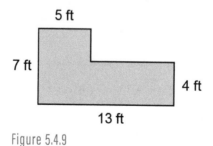

Figure 5.4.9

SOLUTION: Before we can accurately compute the perimeter or the area, we must first determine the lengths of the two unlabeled sides. For the missing horizontal measure, we need to notice the length of the bottom side is 13 feet, and the length of the top-most side is 5 feet. That means the missing horizontal measure must be 8 feet. Likewise, the missing vertical measure can be found to be 3 feet.

To find the perimeter, we add together the lengths of all six sides. Be careful not to forget the lengths of the sides that were originally unlabeled. Starting at the top and going clockwise, we find the perimeter, $P = 5 \text{ ft} + 3 \text{ ft} + 8 \text{ ft} + 4 \text{ ft} + 13 \text{ ft} + 7 \text{ ft} = 40 \text{ ft}$.

Next, for the area, we can imagine the composite as a 5-foot by 3-foot rectangle on top of a 13-foot by 4-foot rectangle. Thus, the total area, $A = (5 \text{ ft})(3 \text{ ft}) + (13 \text{ ft})(4 \text{ ft}) = 15 \text{ ft}^2 + 52 \text{ ft}^2 = 67 \text{ ft}^2$.

EXAMPLE 11:

Find the perimeter and area of the following figure.

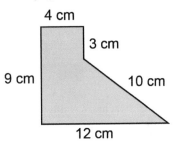

Figure 5.4.10a

SOLUTION: For the perimeter, start at the top and go clockwise around the figure.
$P = 4 \text{ cm} + 3 \text{ cm} + 10 \text{ cm} + 12 \text{ cm} + 9 \text{ cm} = 38 \text{ cm}$.

For the area, we should imagine the figure as a 4 cm by 9 cm rectangle with a triangular piece next to it. BE CAREFUL! The base length of that triangle part is not 12 cm; it is only 8 cm. Also, how do we find the height of the triangular piece?

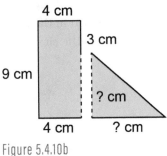

Figure 5.4.10b

Since the length of the bottom side for the entire composite figure is 12 cm, and 4 cm of that is composed of the rectangle, the triangle-shaped region has a base of 8 cm. For the height of the triangular region, we see the entire height of the composite figure is 9 cm, and the triangle height is 3 cm less than that. So, the height of the triangle is 6 cm.

Now, taking the entire composite figure in mind,

$A_{Total} = A_{Rectangle} + A_{Triangle}$
$A_{Total} = (4 \text{ cm})(9 \text{ cm}) + (1/2)(8 \text{ cm})(6 \text{ cm}) = 36 \text{ cm}^2 + 24 \text{ cm}^2 = 60 \text{ cm}^2$.

Volume

Linear distances—such as feet (ft), inches (in), and miles (mi)—are used quite frequently in our daily lives. Areas—such as square feet (ft²), square inches (in²), and square miles (mi²)—are pretty common, too. Additionally, there is another relatively common measure: **Volume**. Refrigerators have capacity stated in cubic feet (ft³), we pour concrete in cubic yards (yd³), and we buy gallons of milk, water, and gasoline. Volumes point to the third dimension in our three-dimensional world.

We can find the area of a rectangle by multiplying the length times the width. Expanding this formula into the third dimension, the volume of a **right rectangular parallelepiped** (a **box**) is found by multiplying the length by the width by the height, $V_{box} = l \times w \times h$.

Be sure to pay attention to the unit of measure. Many volumes are stated in imperial measures, like gallons and pints, or in metric measures like liters and milliliters. If, however, a volume is computed from the product of linear dimensions, it needs to have a cubic unit. That is, if we compute the volume by finding the product of a length, width, and height that were all measured in centimeters, the final unit of measure on the volume would be cm³. This is just like multiplying a × a × a to get a³, because cm × cm × cm = cm³.

EXAMPLE 12:

Find the volume of a box that has a length of 5 inches, a width of 8 inches, and a height of 4 inches.

SOLUTION: 5 in × 8 in × 4 in = 160 in³

Some students have trouble drawing boxes. If, however, we start with a rectangle, drawing a box in three steps is actually pretty easy. Once we have a rectangle, which will represent the front of our box, draw short upward slanted lines from the top two and lower right corners, being careful to keep the angle and length of each segment the same. Then, complete the box by connecting the tops of the slanted lines horizontally and vertically. As long as we keep the angle and length of the slanted lines the same, the horizontal and vertical segments added in the last step will be parallel to and the same length as the sides from our rectangle. With just a little bit of practice, you will be able to make nicely shaped boxes very quickly.

1.   2.   3.

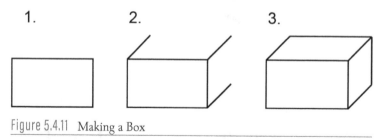

Figure 5.4.11   Making a Box

Beyond boxes, unfortunately, deriving the volume formulas for various three-dimensional figures can become quite complicated. Thus, in order to perform many of those calculations, we often have to resort to the memorization of formulas. If you are curious, you can see some of them at http://math.com/tables/geometry/volumes.htm.

Circles

All of us can identify a **circle** by sight, so we will focus on a few certain properties of circles. The **diameter** of a circle is the distance across a circle as measured through the circle's center, and is indicated with the letter **d**. The **radius, r,** is defined as half of the circle's diameter. Instead of using the word perimeter, the distance around a circle is called its **circumference**, and is indicated with the letter **C**.

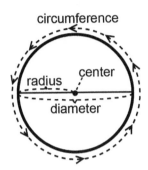

Figure 5.4.12   The Circumference, Radius, and Diameter of a Circle

Drawing a circle can be a little daunting when doing so by hand. To help create a more professional looking circle, we can trace a circular object or use a compass. If we don't have a compass, we can actually use a piece of string or a paperclip by anchoring one side with a pencil and then using a second pencil to rotate the opposite end.

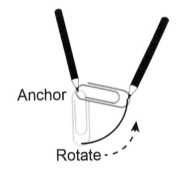

Figure 5.4.13   Making a Circle with a Paperclip

EXAMPLE 13:

Find the radius of a circle with a diameter of 12 centimeters.

Solution: The radius is half the diameter, so r = 6 cm.

EXAMPLE 14:

Find the diameter of a circle with a radius of 9 feet.

Solution: The diameter is twice the radius, so d = 18 ft.

Experiment

Select three circular objects and use a piece of string and a metric ruler to measure the circumference and diameter of each. Either print this sheet or make a list that looks like the one below. In each case, compute C/d (rounded to the nearest hundredth).

Object	C	d	C/d
_____	_____ cm	_____ cm	_____
_____	_____ cm	_____ cm	_____
_____	_____ cm	_____ cm	_____

Figure 5.4.14

Pi

For each of the circular objects you used, you should have found C/d to be close to 3.14. This value is so important that it is represented by the lowercase Greek letter **pi**, π.

Using Your Calculator

Scientific calculators have the value of pi built into them. Sometimes there is a key for pi, and other calculators require you to access the value in a sub-menu. If need be, look through your calculator's manual for help locating pi. Do, however, realize we will frequently be told to use 3.14 for pi. If we use the much more precise value of pi stored in our calculator, we will end up with answers that may not match what is presented in book and other course materials. Sure, the answers will be close, but they likely be off by a couple hundredths.

Area and Circumference Formulas for Circles

Using r for the radius, and d for the diameter, the **area** and **circumference** of a circle are defined as:

Area, $\mathbf{A = \pi r^2}$

Circumference, $C = \pi d$. Or, since $d = 2r$, we often see this as $\mathbf{C = 2\pi r}$.

To approximate the calculations, it is customary to use $\pi = 3.14$.

Use these formulas to find the area of the three circles you used in your experiment.

EXAMPLE 15:

Find the area and circumference of a circle with a radius of 3 inches. Be sure to label your answers. Use $\pi = 3.14$, and round your answers to the nearest hundredth.

SOLUTION: Area $= \pi r^2 = (3.14)(3 \text{ in.})^2 = (3.14)(9 \text{ in}^2) = 28.26 \text{ in}^2$

Circumference $= C = 2\pi r = 2(3.14)(3 \text{ in}) = 18.84 \text{ in}$

EXAMPLE 16:

Find the area and circumference of the following circle. Be sure to label your answers. Use $\pi = 3.14$, and round your answers to the nearest tenth.

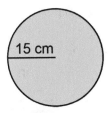

15 cm

Figure 5.4.15

SOLUTION: Area $= (3.14)(15 \text{ cm})^2 = (3.14)(225 \text{ cm}^2) = 706.5 \text{ cm}^2$

Circumference $= 2(3.14)(15 \text{ cm}) = 94.2 \text{ cm}$

SECTION 5.4 EXERCISES

NOTE: Figures provided with measurements may not be drawn to scale.

1. Find the perimeter and area of a square that has a side length of 5 inches.

2. Find the perimeter and area of a square with a side length of 3 miles.

3. Find the perimeter and area of a rectangle with a length of 2 meters and a width of 3 meters.

4. Find the perimeter and area of a rectangle with a length of 2 feet and a width of 9 feet.

5. Find the perimeter and area of a rectangle with a length of 5 cm and a diagonal of 13 cm.

6. Find the perimeter and area of a rectangle with a length of 6 ft and a diagonal of 10 ft.

7. Find the perimeter and area of the following parallelogram.

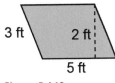

3 ft   2 ft
5 ft

Figure 5.4.16

8. Find the perimeter and area of the following parallelogram.

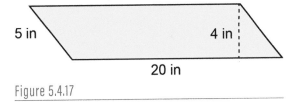

5 in   4 in

20 in

Figure 5.4.17

9. Find the area of a triangle with a base of 12 inches and a height of 3 inches.

10. Find the area of a triangle with a base of 7 meters and a height of 4 meters.

11. Find the perimeter and area of the following triangle.

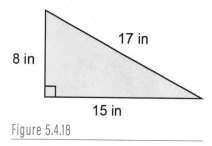

Figure 5.4.18

12. Find the perimeter and area of the following triangle.

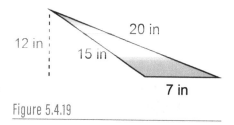

Figure 5.4.19

13. Find the perimeter and area for an isosceles triangle with two sides that measure 25 mm and a base that is 14 mm.

14. A rectangular room measures 10 feet by 12 feet. How many square feet of tile are needed to cover the floor?

15. John's kitchen is rectangular and measures 11 feet wide by 13 feet long, and he has a 3-ft by 4-ft island in the middle of the kitchen. Assuming no tiles are placed under the island, how many square feet of tile will John need to tile the floor?

16. A skirt is to be placed around a rectangular table that is 6 feet long and 2 feet wide. How long does the table skirt need to be to fit around the entire table (without overlapping)?

17. Find the perimeter and area of the following figure.

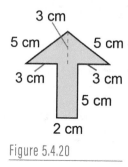

Figure 5.4.20

18. Find the perimeter and area of the following figure.

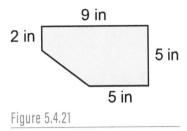

Figure 5.4.21

19. Find the perimeter and area of the following figure.

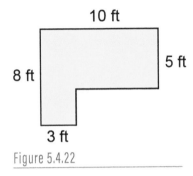

Figure 5.4.22

20. Find the perimeter and area of the following figure.

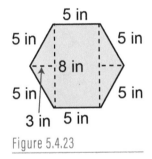

Figure 5.4.23

21. Find the perimeter and area of the following figure.

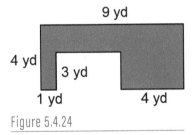

Figure 5.4.24

22. Find the area of the shaded region in the following figure.

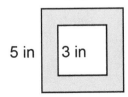

Figure 5.4.25

23. Draw two rectangles that have the same area but different perimeters.

24. Draw two rectangles that have the same perimeter but different areas.

25. If the area of a rectangle is 68 m² and the width is 4 m, what is the length?

26. If the area of a rectangle is 36 in² and the length is 12 in, what is the width?

27. Draw two different triangles that have the same area but different perimeters.

28. Draw two different triangles that have the same perimeter but different areas.

29. If the area of a triangle is 42 cm² and the height is 7 cm, what is the length of the base?

30. If the area of a triangle is 12 ft² and the base length is 3 ft, what is the height?

31. What is the volume of a box with a length of 3 cm, a width of 9 cm, and a height of 5 cm?

For Exercises #31 through #48, be sure to label your answers. Use $\pi = 3.14$, and round your answers to the nearest tenth.

32. Find the radius of a circle with a diameter of 12 inches.

33. Find the radius of a circle with a diameter of 25 feet.

34. Find the area and circumference of a circle with a radius of 10 centimeters.

35. Find the area and circumference of a circle with a radius of 20 centimeters.

36. Find the area and circumference of a circle with a radius of 12 meters.

37. Find the area and circumference of a circle with a radius of 15 millimeters.

38. Find the area and circumference of a circle with a radius of 0.25 inches.

39. Find the area and circumference of a circle with a radius of 0.75 miles.

40. Find the area and circumference of the following figures.

a.

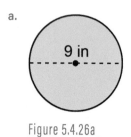

Figure 5.4.26a

b.

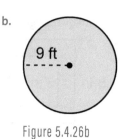

Figure 5.4.26b

41. Find the area of the following figures.

a.

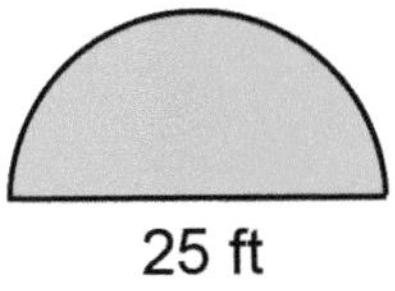

25 ft

Figure 5.4.27a

b.

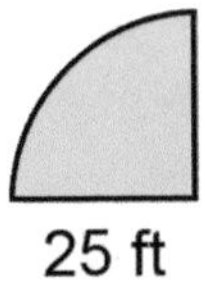

25 ft

Figure 5.4.27b

42. Find the area of the shaded region in the following figure.

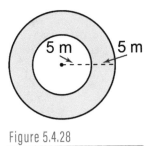

Figure 5.4.28

43. Imagine the surface of the earth to be circular at the equator. If a steel band with a circumference of 10 feet more than the circumference of the earth is placed around the equator and spaced equidistant away from the surface, which of the following animals could walk comfortably under the band?

a. A mouse.   b. A cat.   c. A dog.   d. An elephant.   e. A giraffe.

44. A fly lands on the tip of the minute hand of a circular clock. If the minute hand is 8 inches long, how far does the fly travel if it remains on the minute hand for 12 minutes?

Image 5.4.1

45. A table skirt is to be wrapped around a circular table with a diameter of 6 feet. How long does the skirt need to be?

46. If you double the circumference of a circle, by how much has the area changed?

47. If the area of a circle is doubled, by how much has the circumference changed?

48. A pizza company offers a single large 16-inch (diameter) pizza or a pair of medium 12-inch pizzas for the same price. Which option gives you more pizza?

ANSWERS TO SECTION 5.4 EXERCISES

1. $P = 20$ in, $A = 25$ in^2

2. $P = 12$ mi, $A = 9$ mi^2

3. $P = 10$ m, $A = 6$ m^2

4. $P = 22$ ft, $A = 18$ ft^2

5. $P = 34$ cm, $A = 60$ cm^2

6. $P = 28$ ft, $A = 48$ ft^2

7. $P = 16$ ft, $A = 10$ ft^2

8. $P = 50$ in, $A = 80$ in^2

9. $A = 18$ in^2

10. $A = 14$ m^2

11. $P = 40$ in, $A = 60$ in^2

12. $P = 42$ in, $A = 42$ in^2

13. $P = 64$ mm, $A = 168$ mm^2

14. 120 sq ft of tile are needed.

15. 131 sq ft of tile are needed.

16. The skirt must be 16 ft long.

17. $P = 28$ cm, $A = 22$ cm^2

18. $P = 26$ in, $A = 39$ in^2

19. $P = 36$ ft, $A = 59$ ft^2

20. $P = 30$ in, $A = 64$ in^2

21. $P = 32$ yd, $A = 24$ yd^2

22. 16 in^2

23. Answers can vary. One possible pair is a 6×2 rectangle and a 3×4 rectangle.

24. Answers can vary. One possible pair is a 5×2 rectangle and a 3×4 rectangle.

25. The length would be 17 meters.

26. The width would be 3 inches.

27. Answers can vary. For example, a triangle with a base of 6 in and a height of 2 in has the same area as a triangle with a base of 4 in and a height of 3 in. If you draw them carefully you will see the first one has a greater perimeter.

28. Answers can vary. For example, a triangle with side lengths of 15 in, 20 in, and 25 in has a perimeter of 60 in and an area of 150 in², while a triangle with side lengths of 10 in, 24 in, and 26 in has a perimeter of 60 in and an area of 120 in².

29. The base length is 12 cm.

30. The height is 8 ft.

31. 135 cm³

32. 6 in

33. 12.5 ft

34. A = 314 cm² & C = 62.8 cm

35. A = 1256 cm² & C = 125.6 cm

36. A = 452.2 m² & C = 75.4 m

37. A = 706.5 mm² & C = 94.2 mm

38. A = 0.2 in² & C = 1.6 in

39. A = 1.8 mi² & C = 4.7 mi

40. a. A = 63.6 in² & C = 28.3 in   b. A = 254.3 ft² & C = 56.5 ft

41. a. A = 245.3 ft²   b. A = 490.6 ft²

42. $A_{Total} = A_{Big\ Circle} - A_{Small\ Circle} = (3.14)(10\ m)^2 - (3.14)(5\ m)^2 = 235.5\ m^2$

43. To answer this, find the difference in the radii of the two circles. So, if r_1 is the radius of the earth, and r_2 is the radius of the steel band, we need to find $r_2 - r_1$. $2\pi r_2 = 2\pi r_1 + 10$. Subtract $2\pi r_1$ from both sides, and then factor out and divide by the 2π. You will find $r_2 - r_1 = 10/2\pi = 10/6.28 = 1.59$ ft, which is about 19 inches. So, with just 10 feet added to the circumference, the radius has increased by a little more than a foot and a half. That means the mouse and the cat can comfortably walk under the band. The dog could fit if it is a small-to-medium sized dog. A large dog could make it, but not comfortably. The elephant and giraffe won't fit.

44. In 12 minutes, the hand has traveled $12/60 = 1/5$ of an hour. Thus, the tip of the minute hand has traveled $1/5$ of the circumference of the circle or radius 8 in. $C = 2(3.14)(8 \text{ in}) = 50.24$ in. $50.24/5 = 10.048$ in. The fly has traveled a little over 10 inches.

45. 18.84 feet. By the way, the 0.84 is 84/100 of a foot, which is just over 10 inches. So, the skirt would need to be at least 18 feet 10 inches long.

46. In the formula $C = 2\pi r$, only the r can change. So, to double the circumference, the radius must be doubled. In the area formula $A = \pi r^2$, the radius is squared: $(2r)^2 = 4r^2$. Thus, the new area would be $\pi(4r^2)$, which would be written $4\pi r^2$. So, the area has been quadrupled.

47. In the formula $A = \pi r^2$, only the r can change. So, to double the area, the radius must be increased by a factor of the square root of 2. Thus, the circumference is also increased by a factor of the square root of 2.

48. The large pizza has an area of 201 square inches, and the pair of medium pizzas has an area of 226 square inches. You get more with the two medium pizzas.

5.5 It's Not Wrong: Right Triangle Trigonometry

Trigonometry. One of those things that sounds pretty darn complicated. Trigonometry (also known as "trig") is used in several areas including architecture, navigation, and engineering, but you know, if we break it down, it doesn't have to be mysterious. The word trigonometry, derived from the Greek words trigon (triangle) and metros (measure), literally means "triangle measurement." Measuring a triangle, heck, that's not scary at all.

Although the science of trigonometry includes triangles of any type, we will limit our study to problems involving only right triangles, that is, triangles that contain a 90° angle.

Triangle Notation

Any time the side of a triangle is being referenced, a lowercase letter will be used. To denote an angle, an uppercase letter will be used. Furthermore, "a" will represent the side of the triangle that is across from angle "A," and so on, as shown in the figure below.

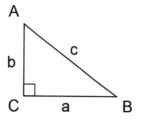

Figure 5.5.1 Triangle Notation

Opposite and Adjacent Sides of a Triangle

The terms **opposite** and **adjacent** play a very important role in right triangle trigonometry, so let's take a look at the meaning of those terms.

The three sides of a right triangle can be described in terms of each angle. For example, in the right triangle shown above, side "a" is across from, or **opposite**, angle A. Side "b" is next to, or **adjacent** to, angle A, and side "c" would be the hypotenuse.

Similarly, side "b" is **opposite** angle B, and side "a" is **adjacent** to angle B. Side "c" is still the hypotenuse.

The Trigonometric Ratios

There are three basic trigonometric functions, which are calculated by using the ratios of the lengths of the sides of the triangle. Those functions are:

Function	Pronunciation	Abbreviation
sine	sign	sin
cosine	co-sign	cos
tangent	tangent	tan

The sine of an angle is calculated using the following ratio:

sin A = (length of the side opposite angle A)/(length of the hypotenuse)

The cosine of an angle is calculated using the following ratio:

cos A = (length of the side adjacent to angle A)/(length of the hypotenuse)

The tangent of an angle is calculated using the following ratio:

tan A = (length of side opposite angle A)/(length of side adjacent to angle A)

This may seem like a lot to remember, but a really sharp teacher I had one time gave me a fancy word that I could use to help me remember it all. The "word" was: SOH CAH TOA.

SOH CAH TOA is shorthand for:

Sin = **O**pposite/**H**ypotenuse

Cos = **A**djacent/**H**ypotenuse

Tan = **O**pposite/**A**djacent

Let's put these functions into context by looking at an example:

EXAMPLE 1:

For the triangle below, find the sine, cosine, and tangent for angles A and B. State your answers as fractions:

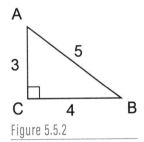

Figure 5.5.2

SOLUTION:

sin A = 4/5	sin B = 3/5
cos A = 3/5	cos B = 4/5
tan A = 4/3	tan B = 3/4

Using Your Calculator

On any scientific calculator, you should see buttons labeled "sin," "cos," and "tan." These buttons will allow you to find the values of sine, cosine, and tangent for any angle measure. Depending on the calculator, we may input the angle measure and then push the "sin," "cos," or "tan" button, or we may have to push the trig button, type the angle measure and then hit the "equals" button. **Also, it is very important to make sure the calculator is in degree mode, not radian mode**. If you are not sure which mode your calculator is in, check the calculator's manual.

Let's try a few:

EXAMPLE 2:

Use your calculator to find the following. Round your answers to four decimal places, if necessary:

a. sin 30°

b. sin 73°

c. cos 45°

d. cos 12°

e. tan 60°

f. tan 35°

SOLUTION:

a. sin 30° = 0.5000 (or just 0.5)

b. sin 73° = 0.9563

c. cos 45° = 0.7071

d. cos 12° = 0.9781

e. tan 60° = 1.7321

f. tan 35° = 0.7002

NOTE: If you tried to find sin 30° and got −0.9880, your calculator is in radian mode.

Much like we did with the Pythagorean Theorem, we can use these trig ratios to find missing side lengths of a triangle. Specifically, if we are given an angle measure and one of the side lengths, we can use that information to determine the length of the hypotenuse.

EXAMPLE 3:

Given the following right triangle, find the measure of side "c." In this example we will round the value of any trig function to four decimal places, and then round the final answer to the nearest hundredth.

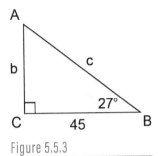

Figure 5.5.3

SOLUTION: We know the measure of angle B, and the length of the side that is adjacent to angle B. We are looking for the length of the hypotenuse. Thinking back to SOH CAH TOA, the trigonometric function that uses **adjacent** and **hypotenuse** is cosine. So, here we will use that function, and a little algebra, to solve this problem.

cos B = (length of side adjacent to angle B)/(length of the hypotenuse)

We can plug in the things we know, leaving only one variable, and then solve:

cos 27° = 45/c

Now, we can use our calculator to find cos 27° (rounded to four decimal places):

0.8910 = 45/c

Since our variable is in the denominator, it will take two steps to get the "c" by itself.

In algebra, multiplying both sides of an equation by zero would not be a legal step. Here, since "c" is a distance, it cannot be equal to zero, so our next step is completely fine.

That next step is to multiply both sides of the equation by "c," giving us:

0.8910(c) = 45

Finally, to get the "c" by itself, we divide both sides by 0.8910 to find:

c = 50.51

EXAMPLE 4:

Use right triangle ABC, where side "c" is the hypotenuse, for the following problems. Round the value of any trig function to four decimal places, and then round your final answer to the nearest hundredth.

a. Given B = 14° and c = 20, find a.

b. Given A = 15° and a = 600, find c.

SOLUTION: To solve each of these, begin by drawing a triangle with side "c" as the hypotenuse (just like the triangle under the *Triangle Notation* heading in this section).

In part (a), we are given angle B and side c. Label those in your diagram with the given numbers, and then, we need to find side a.

In relation to angle B, we are looking for the adjacent side and we know the length of the hypotenuse, so we should use cosine:

cos 14° = a/20

Using our calculator, cos 14 = 0.9703, giving us:

0.9703 = a/20

To get a by itself we multiply both sides by 20, giving us:

19.41 = a

In part (b), we are given angle A and side a. Again, label those parts of your diagram, and then, we need to find side c.

In relation to angle A, we know the length of the **opposite** side and we are looking for the **hypotenuse**, so we should use sine:

sin 15° = 600/c

Using our calculator, sin 15 = 0.2588, giving us:

0.2588 = 600/c

Multiplying both sides by c, we have:

0.2588c = 600

And finally, dividing both sides by 0.2588 gives us:

c = 2318.39

Let's put the usefulness of these trig functions into a more real-world context:

EXAMPLE 5:

A 15-foot ladder is leaning against the top of a wall so that it makes an angle of 62° with the wall. How tall is the wall? Round the value of any trig function to four decimal places, and then round your final answer to the nearest hundredth of a foot.

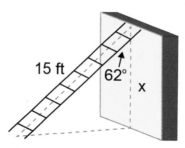

Figure 5.5.4   How Tall is the Wall?

Solution: Here, we are looking for the length of the side that is **adjacent** to the 62° angle, and we know the length of the ladder (which is the **hypotenuse** of the triangle).

The trig function that uses adjacent and hypotenuse is cosine, so we will use that function and a little algebra to find out how tall the wall is.

cos 62° = (side adjacent to the 62° angle)/(length of the hypotenuse)

We can plug in the length of the hypotenuse and use a variable to represent the length of the side that we are trying to find. You can use any variable you like, but here we will use "x."

cos 62° = x/15

Next, we can use our calculator to find cos 62° (rounded to four decimal places):

0.4695 = x/15

Finally, to get the "x" by itself we multiply both sides by 15, giving us:

7.04 = x

The wall is 7.04 feet tall.

Angle of Elevation and Angle of Depression

An angle of elevation is an upward angle made between the line of sight and a horizontal line. Similarly, an angle of depression is a downward angle made between the line of sight and a horizontal line.

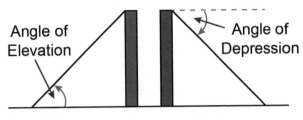

Figure 5.5.5 Angles of Elevation and Depression

EXAMPLE 6:

A 375-foot cable is attached to the top of a building, and the other end is anchored to the ground. The angle of elevation made by the cable, from ground level to the top of a building, is 29°. Find the height of the building. Round the value of any trig function to four decimal places, and then round your final answer to the nearest hundredth of a foot.

Solution: Remember, the angle of elevation is the upward angle from the observer to the object:

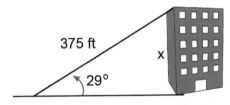

Figure 5.5.6 How Tall is the Building?

In this problem, we are looking for the height of the building (the length of the side that is **opposite** the 29° angle), and we know the length of the cable (the length of the **hypotenuse**). The trig function that uses opposite and hypotenuse is sine, so we will use that function to solve this problem.

sin 29° = (side opposite the 29° angle)/(length of the hypotenuse)

We can plug in the length of the hypotenuse, leaving only one variable. Then, we can use our calculator to find sin 29°, and round to four decimal places. Finally, to get the "x" by itself, we multiply both sides by 375.

sin 29° = x/375

0.4848 = x/375

181.80 = x

So, the building is 181.8 feet tall.

EXAMPLE 7:

A spot on the ground below an airplane is 24,000 feet from the base of the control tower, and the angle of depression from the plane to the base of the control tower is 16°. Find the altitude of the plane. Round the value of any trig function to four decimal places, and then round your final answer to the nearest whole foot.

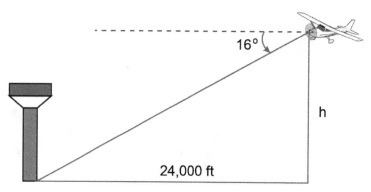

Figure 5.5.7   How High is the Plane?

Solution: In this problem, we are looking for the vertical distance from the plane to a spot on the ground below the plane. This side of the triangle has been labeled as "h," and it is the length of the side that is **adjacent** to angle P. We know the horizontal distance from a spot on the ground below the plane to the control tower to be 24,000 feet, and this is the length of the side **opposite** angle P.

In this particular situation, angle P is inside our triangle, and is the angle we will use to solve this problem. We are not given the measure of angle P, but we can find it. We were told that the angle of depression is 16°, and we know that the combination of angle P and the angle of depression makes a 90° angle. Using that information, we can determine that the measure of angle P is $(90° − 16°) = 74°$.

The trig function that uses opposite and adjacent is tangent, so we will use that function to solve this problem.

tan P = (side opposite angle P)/(side adjacent to angle P)

tan 74° = 24000/h

Now, we can use our calculator to find tan 74 and round to 4 decimal places:

3.4874 = 24000/h

Since the variable is in the denominator, it will take two steps to get the "h" by itself. First, we multiply both sides of the equation by "h," giving us:

3.4874(h) = 24000

Finally, we divide both sides by 3.4874, to get:

h = 24000/3.4874 = 6881.92

So, the altitude of the plane is 6,882 feet.

SECTION 5.5 EXERCISES

1.   For the triangle below, find the sine, cosine, and tangent for angles A and B. State your answers as fractions.

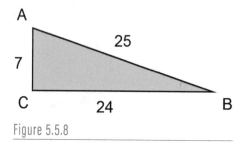

Figure 5.5.8

2. Use a calculator to find the following. Round your answers to four decimal places, if necessary.

   a. sin 38°

   b. sin 14°

   c. cos 71°

   d. cos 33°

   e. tan 17°

   f. tan 63°

3. For the following, use right triangle ABC, where side "c" is the hypotenuse. Do not round the values of the trig functions, but round your final answer to the nearest hundredth.

   a. Given A = 53° and c = 97, find a.

   b. Given A = 41° and c = 200, find b.

   c. Given B = 85° and b = 110, find a.

   d. Given B = 72° and c = 300, find a.

   e. Given A = 28° and a = 872, find c.

   f. Given A = 60° and b = 71, find a.

   f. Given A = 30° and c = 40, find a.

   h. Given B = 68° and a = 313, find c.

For Exercises #4 through #13, do not round the values of the trig functions, but round all answers to the nearest hundredth.

4. A plane takes off from the ground at a 14° angle. After flying in a straight line for 10,000 feet, what is the altitude of the plane?

5. A wire is tied to the top of a pole and attached to the ground at a spot 2 yards from the base of the pole. The wire makes a 64° angle with the ground. How long is the wire?

6. A security light is to be mounted on a building so that the angle of depression for the beam of light is 30°. How high must the light be mounted so that the light will shine on a spot that is 25 feet from the building?

7. A beetle is standing at a spot on the ground 22 feet from the base of a shed. If the angle of elevation from the beetle to the top of the shed is 27°, how tall is the shed? What is the straight-line distance from the beetle to the top of the shed?

8. Carl is standing on a platform built on the edge of a river that is 20 meters tall. The angle of depression from the top of the platform to the ground directly across the river is 53°. How wide is the river?

9. A 70-foot long rope is attached to the top of a building. Abigail is holding the rope to the ground so that the angle of elevation is 33°. How far is Abigail from the base of the building? How tall is the building?

10. The Stratosphere Tower is 350 meters tall. The angle of elevation from the spot where you are standing to the top of the Stratosphere Tower is 25°. How far from the base of the Stratosphere Tower are you?

11. The angle of depression from the top of a lighthouse to a ship is 17°. If the lighthouse is 140 feet tall, how far is the ship from the base of the lighthouse?

12. A ladder is leaning against a wall so that it makes an angle of 30° with the ground. The ladder touches the wall at a spot that is 8 feet from the ground. How long is the ladder?

13. A point on the edge of a canyon is 900 feet above the river below. The angle of depression to the middle of the canyon is 48°. What is the horizontal distance from the edge to a point directly above the middle of the canyon?

ANSWERS TO SECTION 5.5 EXERCISES

1. $\sin A = 24/25$ $\sin B = 7/25$ $\cos A = 7/25$
   $\cos B = 24/25$ $\tan A = 24/7$ $\tan B = 7/24$

2. a. 0.6157   b. 0.2419   c. 0.3256   d. 0.8387   e. 0.3057   f. 1.9626

3. a. $a = 77.47$ b. $b = 150.94$ c. $a = 9.62$ d. $a = 92.71$

   e. 1857.41   a. 122.98   a — 20.00   e. 835.54

4. The altitude is 2,419.22 feet.

5. The wire is 4.56 yards long.

6. The light should be mounted 14.43 feet above the ground.

7. The shed is 11.21 feet tall, and the distance from the beetle to the top of the shed is 24.69 feet.

8. The distance across the river is 15.07 meters.

9. Abigail is 58.71 feet away from the building that is 38.12 feet tall.

10. You are 750.58 meters from the base of the tower.

11. The ship is 457.92 feet from the base of the lighthouse.

12. The ladder is 16 feet long.

13. The horizontal distance to a point above the center of the canyon is 810.36 feet.

CHAPTER 5 CREDITLINES

IMG 5.0.1: Copyright © 2016 Depositphotos/ga_l_ka.

IMG 5.1.1: Copyright © 2016 Depositphotos/chatsimo.

IMG 5.1.2: Source: http://commons.wikimedia.org/wiki/File:Euklid-von-Alexandria_1.jpg.

IMG 5.1.3: Source: http://commons.wikimedia.org/wiki/File:Hypatia_portrait.png.

IMG 5.2.2a: Copyright © 2012 Depositphotos/Imphot.

IMG 5.2.2b: Copyright © 2013 Depositphotos/paulmaguire.

IMG 5.2.3: Copyright © 2017 Depositphotos/dechevm.

IMG 5.2.4a: Copyright © 2016 Depositphotos/smarques27.

IMG 5.2.4b: Copyright © 2016 Depositphotos/smarques27.

IMG 5.2.4c: Copyright © 2011 Depositphotos/nmarques.

IMG 5.2.4d: Copyright © 2011 Depositphotos/nmarques.

IMG 5.2.4e: Copyright © 2011 Depositphotos/nmarques.

IMG 5.2.4f: Copyright © 2013 Depositphotos/zager.

IMG 5.2.5: Copyright © 2015 Depositphotos/icholakov.

IMG 5.2.6: Copyright © 2014 Depositphotos/cbenjasuwan.

IMG Fig 5.3.1ab: Copyright © 2013 Depositphotos/Dr. Pas.

IMG Fig 5.3.1ab: Copyright © 2015 Depositphotos/juliarstudio.

Fig. 5.3.9a : Source: https://pixabay.com/vectors/street-lamp-lantern-old-lights-146295/.

Fig. 5.3.9b : Copyright © 2011 Depositphotos/Regisser_com.

IMG 5.4.1: Copyright © 2011 Depositphotos/smelnikovs.

Fig 5.4.13: Copyright © 2013 Depositphotos/Blankstock.

Fig 5.5.6: Source: https://pixabay.com/vectors/building-blue-building-building-567929/ .

Fig 5.5.7: Source: https://pixabay.com/vectors/airplane-plane-aircraft-vehicle-26563/.

VOTING AND APPORTIONMENT

6

Whether deciding the outcome of a political election, the best candidate to hire for a job opening, or simply where to go to dinner, it can sometimes be difficult to arrive at a satisfactory consensus decision. This is where voting comes in. A number of different approaches to voting exist, and there is no single voting method that is best in all situations. Since the voting method employed can have a significant impact on the outcome, it is critical that the voting method be determined prior to an election taking place.

Derived from the Latin *portio*, which means "share," the term **apportion** means to divide and give out in fair shares. In other words, it is a distribution according to some rule. Apportionment can be used to divide items among a group of people, and it is also one of the most important functions of the census that is conducted every ten years in the United States. While each state is guaranteed one seat in the House of Representatives, the accurate population of each state is needed so that the seats can be correctly apportioned.

Image 6.0.1

6.1 On the Shoulders of Giants: Biographies and Historical References

For Voting and Apportionment ...

Elections can get very nasty, but few were worse than the Presidential election of 1800. During that campaign, Federalist newspapers claimed the election of Thomas Jefferson would cause the "teaching of murder, robbery, rape, adultery, and incest." That election also saw Alexander Hamilton attempt to sabotage the efforts of his own Federalist party because of a personal dislike of its candidate, the incumbent President John Adams. Also, in that election, Hamilton ended up breaking a tie between Jefferson and Aaron Burr. Because he detested Burr, Hamilton lobbied aggressively against him.

The election of a United States president depends greatly on the population of the individual states. Despite his questionable influence in a couple of elections, Alexander Hamilton devised a system of determining the number of votes that were awarded to each state. Although originally vetoed by President **George Washington** (the very first exercise of veto power by the president of the United States), the **Hamilton Method of Apportionment** was later adopted by Congress and was used for many years.

In the United States, modern-day voters in presidential elections often think they are voting directly for a specific candidate. In actuality, they are indicating the way they want an official, called an **elector**, to vote. Additionally, even if the majority of a state's voters prefer a specific candidate, the identified electors in the **Electoral College** can actually vote for a different candidate.

The Presidential Election of 1800

In early presidential elections, electors voted for two candidates. The candidate with the most votes was named president, while the one with the second-highest vote total became the vice president. A typical strategy by political parties at that time was to have one elector abstain from casting a second vote, thereby allowing their intended presidential candidate to have one more vote than their intended vice-presidential candidate.

The presidential election of 1800 was one of the nastiest political campaigns of all time. One of the things that made it particularly interesting was the fact that it pitted the sitting president, Federalist **John Adams**, against the sitting vice president, Democratic-Republican **Thomas Jefferson**. The Federalists also had **Charles Cotesworth Pinckney** as a candidate, and the Democratic-Republican Party added **Aaron Burr** to the slate of candidates.

John Adams faced substantial opposition to his re-election from within his own Federalist party. Alexander Hamilton schemed to have Pinckney, the implied vice-presidential candidate, receive more electoral votes and, thus, become president. Unfortunately for the Federalists, the Democratic-Republican team of Jefferson and Burr got more votes. And, unfortunately for the Democratic-Republicans, Jefferson and Burr each got the *same number* of votes. Since no single candidate in the election had secured a majority of the votes, the election was turned over to the House of Representatives, which had a large number of Federalist members.

The House deliberated for seven days and voted 36 times. Many Federalist members of the House detested Jefferson, and hence, supported Burr for President. The Democratic-Republican members, on the other hand, wanted Jefferson to be President. Alexander Hamilton despised Aaron Burr even more than he hated Thomas Jefferson, and through his considerable influence (and back-stabbing), he succeeded in getting some Representatives to change their votes. On the 36th ballot, Jefferson was selected President, making Aaron Burr the Vice-President.

Alexander Hamilton

Alexander Hamilton (1755–1804) was born in Charlestown, the capital of Nevis in the British West Indies, and was raised in the Caribbean. He was one of the founding fathers of the United States, the first secretary of the treasury, and served as a military officer and confidant to **George Washington** during the American Revolutionary War. Hamilton was one

Image 6.1.1: Alexander Hamilton

of America's first lawyers, and he contributed to the development of many theories related to economics and political science. He is credited with writing the majority of the **Federalist Papers**, which were, and continue to be a leading source for interpretation of the US Constitution.

After coming to the colonies, Hamilton attended King's College (now Columbia University) in New York City. At the start of the American Revolutionary War, he studied military history and tactics, raised the New York Provincial Company of Artillery, and became a captain in the Continental Army. In March of 1777, when he reached the rank of Lieutenant Colonel, Hamilton joined George Washington's staff. He served Washington for four years and was involved in a wide variety of high-level duties including intelligence, diplomacy, and negotiation with senior army officers. The importance of these duties makes a statement about the high level of confidence Washington had in him.

Hamilton's intense rivalry with **Aaron Burr** would bring about a tragic ending to his life. Following an exchange of nasty letters, and despite the attempts of friends to avert a confrontation, a duel between the two men was scheduled for July 11, 1804. It was to be held along the west bank of the Hudson River in Weehawken, New Jersey. Ironically, this was the same dueling site where Hamilton's eldest son, Philip, was killed three years earlier. At dawn on the scheduled date, then Vice President Aaron Burr shot Hamilton, and the injuries sustained resulted in Hamilton's death the next afternoon.

The Electoral College

While the total number of votes for each candidate is made public, the popular vote is not the basis for determining the winner of a presidential election in the United States. The United States **Electoral College** is an example of an "indirect election," because rather than directly voting for the president, US citizens actually cast votes that instruct the 538 members of the college on how to elect the president.

Although there is nothing in the US Constitution requiring the winner of the popular vote within each state to be given *all* of the electoral votes from that state, this has been the tradition since the

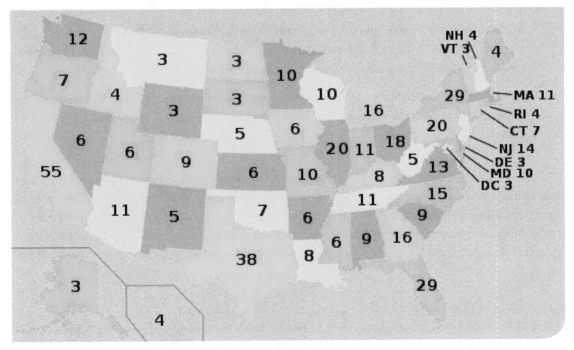

Image 6.1.2: The 2012-2021 Electoral College Map

founding of the country. At present, only **Maine** and **Nebraska** split their electoral votes among the candidates. These states give one of their votes to the candidate who wins each congressional district.

The number of **electoral votes** for a specific state is based on population and corresponds to the number of senators and representatives the state has in Congress. The states with the smallest populations have 2 senators and 1 representative, so they are assigned 3 electoral votes. California, which currently has the largest population of all the states, has 2 senators and 53 representatives for a total of 55 electoral votes. The image 6.1.2 shows the number of votes each state has in the Electoral College for the years from 2012 through 2021, which is based on the 2010 US **Census**. These numbers will likely change in 2022, when the results of the 2020 US Census are recorded and congressional districts are redrawn.

The constitutional theory behind the indirect election of the president of the United States is that, while the members of Congress are elected by popular vote, the president is considered to be the executive of a federation of independent states. Therefore, each state selects its preferred candidate and gives their electoral votes to that candidate. To win the election as president, a simple majority of the 538 electoral votes is needed. Since half-votes are not allowed, a candidate must obtain 270 electoral votes to win.

Although uncommon, there have actually been five presidential elections in which the winner did not receive the highest number of popular votes.

- In 1824, the Democratic-Republicans were the only dominant political party in the United States. They put four candidates on the ballot, which led to none of them receiving the majority of electoral votes. The House of Representatives awarded **John Quincy Adams** the presidency, even though he had finished second to **Andrew Jackson** in *both* the electoral and popular votes.

- In 1876, **Rutherford Hayes** had over 250,000 fewer popular votes than his rival, **Samuel Tilden**. The **Compromise of 1877** conceded 20 disputed electoral votes to Hayes, and he was declared the winner with 185 out of 369 electoral votes (Tilden got 184).

- In 1888, the incumbent, President **Grover Cleveland**, had nearly 100,000 more popular votes but lost the election to **Benjamin Harrison**. Harrison won the electoral vote 233–168.

- In 2000, **Al Gore** received over 500,000 more votes than **George W. Bush**, but conceded the election to his rival after a Supreme Court ruling halted recounts in Florida. The 25 electoral votes from Florida gave Bush 271, while Gore finished with 266.

- Most recently, despite having over 2.8 million more popular votes, **Hillary Clinton** lost the 2016 election to **Donald Trump** when Trump won enough electoral votes to surpass the 270-vote threshold in the Electoral College.

Critics of the Electoral College argue it is inherently undemocratic and gives certain swing states disproportionate clout in selecting the president. Proponents argue that the Electoral College is an important and distinguishing feature of federalism in the United States and protects the rights of smaller states. Numerous constitutional amendments have been introduced in Congress seeking a replacement of the Electoral College with a direct popular vote, but no proposal has ever been passed.

Dis-approval Voting

Voting is the foundation of any democracy. However, the way we vote and what we vote on varies greatly. An Ancient Greek politician, **Cleisthenes**, introduced one of the earliest forms of democracy in 508 BC. With a very large government representing millions of people, a voting process was employed that can be described as a negative election—what we might call *dis*-approval voting. In this system, every year, voters were asked to cast a vote for the politician they most wished to *have exiled* for 10 years. Votes were written on pieces of broken pots known as **ostraka** (ostraka is the plural of ostracon), which is the origin of the word "ostracize." If no politician received more than 6,000 votes, they all remained. If any one of them received more than 6,000 votes, the politician with the largest number of votes was exiled. Requiring someone to have over 6,000 votes before being ostracized was done to ensure politicians would only be exiled if they were unpopular with a large number of people.

Image 6.1.3: Ostracon

References

Bowling, K. R. and D. R. Kennon. *Establishing Congress: The Removal to Washington, D.C., and the Election of 1800.* Athens, OH: Ohio University Press, 2005.

Brookhiser, R. (2000). *Alexander Hamilton, American.* New York, NY: Simon & Schuster, 2000.

Dunn, S. *Jefferson's Second Revolution: The Election Crisis of 1800 and the Triumph of Republicanism.* Boston, MA: Houghton Mifflin Harcourt, 2004.

Edwards, G. C. *Why the Electoral College Is Bad for America.* New Haven, CT: Yale University Press, 2011.

"Electors, Presidential." In *The Lincoln Library of Essential Information*, vol. 2, 1474. Buffalo, NY: The Frontier Press Company, 1944.

"Hamilton, Alexander." In *The Lincoln Library of Essential Information*, vol. 2, 1842. Buffalo, NY: The Frontier Press Company, 1944.

The National Children's Book and Literacy Alliance. *Our White House.* http://ourwhitehouse.org/getting-the-votes-and-getting-elected-the-popular-vote-vs-the-electoral-college/.

Sharp, J. R. *The Deadlocked Election of 1800: Jefferson, Burr, and the Union in the Balance.* Lawrence, KS: University Press of Kansas, 2010.

Sisson, D. *The American Revolution of 1800: How Jefferson Rescued Democracy from Tyranny and Faction—and What This Means Today.* San Francisco, CA: Berrett-Koehler Publishers, 2014.

The World Book Dictionary, vol 1, 1980 ed.

World Book Encyclopedia, 1978 ed., s.v. "Electoral College."

World Book Encyclopedia, 1978 ed., s.v. "Hamilton, Alexander."

6.2 And the Winner Is ...: Basic Voting Methods

On the surface, voting seems rather simple. People identify their preference, and the votes are counted. But is it always as simple as saying that the choice with the most votes is the winner?

Suppose Alice, Bob, Carol, and Don are trying to decide where to go to dinner.

- Alice wants Chinese food, is willing to have Italian food, but hates Mexican food.

- Bob wants Mexican food, is willing to have Italian food, but hates Chinese food.

- Carol wants Mexican food, is willing to have Italian food, but hates Chinese food.

- Don loves Italian food, is willing to have Chinese food, but hates Mexican food.

If everyone stated only his or her main preference, Mexican food would get two votes, and each of the other two choices would get a single vote. Thus, the foursome would head to a Mexican restaurant. However, is that really the best choice here?

Let's think about it; half of the group hates Mexican food. And, since all four people are willing to have Italian food, perhaps it is the best choice. That way, no one in the group would be unhappy. Counting only everyone's favorite choice takes care of the likes, but completely ignores the dislikes. When we take the dislikes into account, the situation can turn out very differently.

Preference Lists

When there are several alternatives to choose from in a situation where voting will take place, it is possible to have each voter **rank** the alternatives. When this ranking is created, it is called a **preference list**.

Let's say ten people rank their favorite flavors of ice cream, with the choices being Chocolate, Vanilla, and Strawberry.

	SPECIFIC VOTERS									
	#1	#2	#3	#4	#5	#6	#7	#8	#9	#10
First Choice	C	S	V	S	S	C	V	S	C	S
Second Choice	S	V	S	C	C	S	S	C	S	C
Third Choice	V	C	C	V	V	V	C	V	V	V

As we look over the choices that were made, we can combine identical rankings and summarize this group of ballots into the following preference list.

	NUMBER OF VOTERS			
	4	3	2	1
First Choice	S	C	V	S
Second Choice	C	S	S	V
Third Choice	V	V	C	C

From this preference list, we can see four people ranked the flavors in the order S, C, V; three people ranked the flavors C, S, V; two people ranked the flavors V, S, C; and one person ranked the flavors S, V, C.

Also, pay attention to the top rows in each of the two previous tables. In the first table, we see an indication of how each voter indicated his or her preferences, while the second table represents a tally of all the votes. This is a subtle but very important difference.

EXAMPLE 1:

Use the information from the ice cream preference list (above) to answer the following:

a. How many voters had Strawberry as their favorite flavor?

b. How many people voted?

c. How many voters indicated Vanilla was their least favorite flavor?

Image 6.2.1

Solutions:

a. 5   b. 10   c. 7

Preference Voting Methods

There are many different ways to determine the winner in a situation where a voter ranks the candidates, and we will investigate several of them in this section.

Plurality

Many of us are familiar with a common type of political election used when voters are selecting their preferred choice from a list of multiple candidates. For our first technique, let's look at an election in which the voters rank their preferences, and the winner is decided by the **Plurality Method**.

While we will use preference list ballots as we study each different method of voting, in the Plurality Method, only the first-place votes are considered. **The candidate with the most first-place votes is the winner.**

Plurality Voting Method
The candidate or choice with the most first-place votes is the winner.

Don't confuse *plurality* with *majority*. Whereas a majority would constitute more than half of the first-place votes, in a plurality system the winner doesn't necessarily need to earn a majority of first-place votes; they just need more than the other candidates.

EXAMPLE 2:

Use the provided preference list and the Plurality Voting Method to determine the winner.

	NUMBER OF VOTERS			
RANK	5	3	3	2
First Choice	C	B	B	D
Second Choice	D	D	A	A
Third Choice	A	A	D	C
Fourth Choice	B	C	C	B

SOLUTION: In this preference list, Candidate A has zero first-place votes, Candidate B has six first-place votes, Candidate C has five first-place votes, and Candidate D has 2 first-place votes.

With more first-place votes than the other candidates, using the Plurality Method, Candidate B is the winner.

Borda Count

Named after a French military officer and mathematician, **Jean-Charles de Borda**, the **Borda Count Voting Method** assigns point values to each position within the preference list. In the Borda Count Method, if n candidates are ranked, a first-place ranking is worth n points, a second-place ranking is worth $(n-1)$ points, and so on, making a last-place ranking worth one point.

What we have referred to as the "Borda Count" method should really be called a "**Standard Borda Count**" method. In a "standard" version of the Borda Count method, we always assign one point to the item or candidate in last place, two points for the one in the second-to-last place, and so on up the chain. Unless stated otherwise, we will stick with a Standard Borda Count method.

In a Non-Standard Borda Count method, different weights can be assigned to the places, as long as the votes closer to first place are greater in value. For example, if there are three candidates, 10 points can be assigned to a first-place vote, 5 points to a second-place vote, and 2 points given for a third-place vote. This strategy gives a distinct advantage to the candidate with the highest number of first-place votes, especially if the weights are extreme. If first-place votes were worth 1,000 points, second-place votes earned a candidate 2 points, and last-place was worth 1 point, we would have something very close to a plurality system. The difference would be, in the event of a tie in the number of first-place votes, the points earned from second- and third-place votes would serve as the tiebreaker.

When the Borda Count is used, the weight of each place must be identified *before* any voting begins. If someone were to see all the votes before the results get tabulated, it would be possible for that person to manipulate the results by declaring an extreme weight for first-place votes. Keep in mind, if a Standard Borda Count Method is declared, specific point values don't need to be mentioned, as a first-place vote will have a value that is equal to the number of candidates.

Borda Count Voting Methods are used in a number of situations, including when polls are taken to rank collegiate sports teams.

Standard Borda Count Voting Method

Assign point values to each position within a preference list. With n candidates, a first-place vote is worth n points. A last-place vote is worth 1 point. The candidate with the highest weighted total is the winner.

EXAMPLE 3:

Use the provided preference list and the Standard Borda Count Voting Method to determine the winner.

	NUMBER OF VOTERS			
RANK	5	3	3	2
First Choice	C	B	B	D
Second Choice	D	D	A	A
Third Choice	A	A	D	C
Fourth Choice	B	C	C	B

SOLUTION: This election involves four candidates, so a first-place vote is worth four points, a second-place vote is worth three points, a third-place vote is worth two points, and a fourth-place vote is worth one point.

Be sure to read this preference list properly. Remember, the "5" at the top of the first column indicates that this column represents the rankings of **five voters**. That being the case, when we calculate the point totals for each candidate, the values of those rankings will get **multiplied by five.** The other columns will be treated similarly.

Let's take a look at the rankings for Candidate A.

Finding Candidate A in the first column of the preference list, we can see that five people ranked Candidate A as their third choice. In this election each third-place ranking is worth two points, so from this column, Candidate A will receive $5 \times 2 = 10$ points.

Finding Candidate A in the second column, we see that three people ranked Candidate A as their third choice. Here again, each third-place ranking is worth two points, so from the second column, Candidate A will receive $3 \times 2 = 6$ points.

In the third column, we see that three people ranked Candidate A as their second choice. Since each second-place ranking in this election is worth three points, Candidate A will receive $3 \times 3 = 9$ points from this column.

Finally, in the fourth column, we see that two people ranked Candidate A as their second choice. Again, each second-place ranking is worth three points, so Candidate A will receive $2 \times 3 = 6$ points from this column.

With that in mind, let's calculate the number of points for each candidate:

- Points for Candidate A: $(5 \times 2) + (3 \times 2) + (3 \times 3) + (2 \times 3) = 10 + 6 + 9 + 6 = 31$
- Points for Candidate B: $(5 \times 1) + (3 \times 4) + (3 \times 4) + (2 \times 1) = 5 + 12 + 12 + 2 = 31$
- Points for Candidate C: $(5 \times 4) + (3 \times 1) + (3 \times 1) + (2 \times 2) = 20 + 3 + 3 + 4 = 30$
- Points for Candidate D: $(5 \times 3) + (3 \times 3) + (3 \times 2) + (2 \times 4) = 15 + 9 + 6 + 8 = 38$

With the greatest weighted total, using the Standard Borda Count Method, Candidate D is the winner.

Hare System

Developed by **Thomas Hare** in 1861, and described by John Stuart Mill as "among the greatest improvements yet made in the theory of practice of government," if no one has a majority after the initial rankings, the **Hare Voting System** eliminates the candidate who receives the least number of first-place votes and then recounts the ballots. This process is repeated until a single candidate has obtained a majority of the first-place votes. This type of voting is used in elections in Australia, Ireland, and Northern Ireland, and when determining the winners of the Best Picture category for the **Academy Awards**.

image 6.2.2

Hare Voting System

Eliminate the candidate(s) with the least number of first-place votes, and recount the votes. Repeat this process until one candidate has a majority of first-place votes and is declared the winner.

The Hare System is also known as the **Instant Run-Off**, the **Single Transferable Vote (STV)**, or the **Plurality with Elimination** voting method.

EXAMPLE 4:

Use the provided preference list and the Hare Voting System to determine the winner.

	NUMBER OF VOTERS			
RANK	5	3	3	2
First Choice	C	B	B	D
Second Choice	D	D	A	A
Third Choice	A	A	D	C
Fourth Choice	B	C	C	B

SOLUTION: There are 13 voters, so a candidate will need at least seven first-place votes to be the winner. To use the Hare System, we determine the number of first-place votes for each candidate and eliminate the candidate who has the lowest number.

- Candidate A has zero first-place votes.
- Candidate B has six first-place votes.
- Candidate C has five first-place votes.
- Candidate D has two first-place votes.

No single candidate has more than half of the first-place votes, so we can't declare a winner yet. Continuing with the procedure prescribed by the Hare System, Candidate A has the fewest first-place votes and is eliminated.

With Candidate A removed, the preference list is now:

	NUMBER OF VOTERS			
RANK	5	3	3	2
First Choice	C	B	B	D
Second Choice	D	D		
Third Choice			D	C
Fourth Choice	B	C	C	B

None of the first-place votes changed, but it is still a good idea to get in the habit of condensing the table after removing one of the candidates. That is, in each column, leave the votes in the same order, but decrease the number of options by one and remove any blanks in the table.

The condensed version of the table will be:

	NUMBER OF VOTERS			
RANK	5	3	3	2
First Choice	C	B	B	D
Second Choice	D	D	D	C
Third Choice	B	C	C	B

Recounting the number of first-place votes for each remaining candidate, we have:

- Candidate B has six first-place votes.

- Candidate C has five first-place votes.

- Candidate D has two first-place votes.

Once again, no candidate has a majority, so we keep going. This time, Candidate D has the fewest number of first-place votes and needs to be eliminated.

Deleting Candidate D from the list gives us the following:

	NUMBER OF VOTERS			
RANK	5	3	3	2
First Choice	C	B	B	
Second Choice				C
Third Choice	B	C	C	B

Now, because Candidate C has become the top choice of the voters represented in the fourth column, those two first-place votes belong to Candidate C.

A condensed version of the preference list would now be:

	NUMBER OF VOTERS			
RANK	5	3	3	2
First Choice	C	B	B	C
Second Choice	B	C	C	B

There are now only two candidates remaining, and we recount the current number of first-place votes.

- Candidate B has six first-place votes
- Candidate C has seven first-place votes

Candidate C now has more than half of the first-place votes and is the winner.

Important Observation

So far, we have seen three different voting methods: Plurality, Borda Count, and Hare. You may not have noticed, but each one used the exact same preference list, and each method declared a different winner! If someone is allowed to view the ballots before a method of voting is declared, knowledge of the different systems could be used to manipulate the results.

Since that is the case, we always need to identify a voting system before any vote is cast. Voters need to know if they are to vote for a single candidate or multiple candidates. And, if they are voting for multiple candidates, they need to know whether their choices must be ranked in a preference list.

Always identify a voting method **before** any vote is cast.

EXAMPLE 5:

Use the provided preference list and the Hare System to determine the winner.

	NUMBER OF VOTERS			
RANK	7	5	3	2
First Choice	C	B	A	D
Second Choice	D	D	B	C
Third Choice	A	A	D	A
Fourth Choice	B	C	C	B

SOLUTION: This preference list contains a total of 17 voters. In order for a candidate to have a majority and be declared the winner, he or she will need to have nine first-place votes.

As of now, the number of first-place votes for each candidate is as follows:

- Candidate A has three first-place votes.
- Candidate B has five first-place votes.
- Candidate C has seven first-place votes.
- Candidate D has two first-place votes.

Since no single candidate has the necessary nine first-place votes, the candidate with the lowest number of first-place votes will be eliminated. Here, that is Candidate D.

Removing Candidate D, and condensing the preference list, we have:

	NUMBER OF VOTERS			
RANK	7	5	3	2
First Choice	C	B	A	C
Second Choice	A	A	B	A
Third Choice	B	C	C	B

The two voters who had Candidate D as their first choice now have Candidate C as their top choice. Now, the number of first-place votes are as follows:

- Candidate A has three first-place votes.
- Candidate B has five first-place votes.
- Candidate C has nine first-place votes.

Candidate C now has the required nine first-place votes and is declared the winner.

Pairwise Comparison

The **Pairwise Comparison Voting Method** examines only two candidates at a time, matching them up in head-to-head comparisons. The winning candidate from each head-to-head matchup gets one point. If there is a tie between two candidates, each of those candidates receives half a point. Every possible comparison must be made, and in the end, the candidate with the highest number of points is declared the winner.

Pairwise comparison is a technique that is used in round robin tournaments, such as the opening round of the **World Cup Soccer** tournament, where each country is placed into groups of four.

> **Pairwise Comparison Voting Method**
>
> Examine two candidates at a time, in a head-to-head matchup, and assign one point to the winner. The candidate with the highest point total is the winner.

Let's look at an example with four candidates: A, B, C, and D. Remember, we have to look at every possible comparison, so we will need to find the winner of each of the following matchups.

- A against B
- A against C
- A against D
- B against C
- B against D
- C against D

Image 6.2.3

EXAMPLE 6:

Use the provided preference list and the Pairwise Comparison Voting Method to determine the winner.

	NUMBER OF VOTERS			
RANK	7	5	3	2
First Choice	C	B	A	D
Second Choice	D	D	B	C
Third Choice	A	A	D	A
Fourth Choice	B	C	C	B

SOLUTION: For the matchup between Candidates A and B:

- From the first column, we see that seven voters prefer A over B.
- From the second column, we see that five voters prefer B over A.
- From the third column, three voters prefer A over B.
- From the last column, two voters have A ranked higher than B.

In this comparison, 12 of the 17 voters have A ranked higher than B. Therefore, from that matchup, A will get one point.

Evaluating all of the matchups, we have:

MATCHUP	VOTER PREFERENCE	ASSIGNED POINTS
A against B	12 of the 17 voters prefer A over B	A is given 1 point
A against C	9 of the 17 voters prefer C over A	C is given 1 point
A against D	14 of the 17 voters prefer D over A	D is given 1 point
B against C	9 of the 17 voters prefer C over B	C is given 1 point
B against D	9 of the 17 voters prefer D over B	D is given 1 point
C against D	10 of the 17 voters prefer D over C	D is given 1 point

Adding up all the points, find that:

- A has a total of one point.
- B has a total of zero points.
- C has a total of two points.
- D has a total of three points.

With the highest number of points, Candidate D is the winner.

When using the Pairwise Comparison Method, it is very important to make sure all possible head-to-head comparisons have been made. If we are familiar with the counting techniques used in Chapter 4, we can use the formula for combinations to determine the number of comparisons that will need to be made. In the previous example, we needed to find all of the combinations with four candidates, taken two at a time. Using the formula for combinations, with n = 4 and r = 2, we have:

$$_4C_2 = \frac{4!}{(4-2)!2!} = \frac{4!}{2!2!} = \frac{4 \times 3 \times 2 \times 1}{(2 \times 1)(2 \times 1)} = \frac{4 \times 3 \times 2 \times 1}{4} = 6$$

Remember, this doesn't tell us which two candidates to compare; it just tells us *the number of* comparisons that are needed.

To be sure that each candidate is compared with every other candidate on the ballot, make sure to use an organized approach.

Start with the first candidate and compare them with every other candidate. Then move on to the second candidate. Since the comparison between the first two candidates has already been done, start the comparison list for the second candidate with the third candidate in the list. Keep comparing each candidate with every candidate that comes after them. When the last candidate is reached, you should have all of the possible combinations.

Approval Voting

When the **Approval Voting Method** is used, each voter is allowed to cast a vote for as many candidates as they find acceptable. There is no limit to the number of candidates a voter can choose. The winner is the candidate who receives the highest number of votes.

> **Approval Voting Method**
>
> Each voter can vote for as many candidates as they find acceptable. The candidate with the most votes is the winner.

Since **a ranking of the candidates is not necessary,** we do not use a preference list with Approval Voting. Instead, we use a table showing the votes that were cast. Since this is not a preference list, the numbers under the heading of "Voters" do not indicate the number of people voting a certain way. They simply denote Voter #1, Voter #2, etc. Approval Voting is a **non-preferential voting method**.

EXAMPLE 7:

Use the provided table of votes and the Approval Voting Method to determine the winner.

In this particular election we have a total of eight voters, who are allowed to vote for up to four candidates.

	Voters							
	#1	#2	#3	#4	#5	#6	#7	#8
Candidate A	✓		✓		✓	✓	✓	✓
Candidate B	✓	✓	✓	✓		✓	✓	✓
Candidate C		✓			✓			✓
Candidate D	✓		✓		✓	✓		

SOLUTION: Counting the number of votes for each candidate, we see that:

- Candidate A has a total of six votes.

- Candidate B has a total of seven votes.

- Candidate C has a total of three votes.

- Candidate D has a total of four votes.

Using approval voting for this election, Candidate B is the winner.

It is also possible to use approval voting to declare several "winners." This is the approach used when selecting members of the **National Baseball Hall of Fame**. In order to qualify for induction into the Hall, a candidate needs to be selected by at least 70% of the voters. For example, if there were 8 voters, a candidate would have to receive at least 5.6 votes to be elected. Since fractional votes are not permitted, it would take at least six votes for a candidate to have the necessary 70% and be elected. In Example 7, both Candidate A and Candidate B were selected by at least 70% of the voters. Thus, if this ballot were for Hall of Fame voting, both of them would be declared "winners."

Image 6.2.4

EXAMPLE 8:

A city council is voting on locations where parks could be constructed. If a location gets 75% of the votes, then a park will be constructed in that location. Given the votes in the table below, at which locations will parks be constructed?

	VOTERS							
	#1	#2	#3	#4	#5	#6	#7	#8
Location A	✓		✓			✓	✓	✓
Location B	✓	✓	✓	✓		✓	✓	✓
Location C		✓			✓			✓
Location D	✓		✓		✓	✓	✓	✓

SOLUTION: There are eight voters, and approval by 75% of them is needed in order for a location to be given a park. This means that $(0.75 \times 8) = 6$ votes are needed for a location to be given a park. Counting the number of votes for each location, we see that:

- Location A has a total of five votes.

- Location B has a total of seven votes.

- Location C has a total of three votes.

- Location D has a total of six votes.

Since 75% approval is needed, Location B and Location D will be given parks.

Summary of Basic Voting Methods

Preferential Methods

- **Plurality**: The candidate or choice with the most first-place votes is the winner.

- **Borda Count**: Assign point values to each position within a preference list. The candidate with the highest weighted total is the winner.

- **Hare System**: Eliminate the candidate with the least number of first-place votes, and recount the votes. Repeat this process until one candidate has a majority of first-place votes and is declared the winner.

- **Pairwise Comparison**: Examine two candidates at a time in a head-to-head matchup and assign one point to the winner or, in the event of a tie, a half point to each candidate. The candidate with the highest point total is the winner.

Non-Preferential Method

- **Approval Voting**: Each voter can vote for as many candidates as they find acceptable. The candidate with the most votes is the winner.

SECTION 6.2 EXERCISES

1. Match each voting method (a.–e.) with the phrase (i.–v.) that best describes it:

    a. Plurality Voting

    b. Borda Count

    c. Hare System

    d. Pairwise Comparison

    e. Approval Voting

    i. Points are given to candidates based upon their ranking in preference list ballots

    ii. Uses preference list ballots to delete candidates who receive the lowest number of first-place votes until one of the candidates has a majority of the votes

    iii. Candidates are matched against each other in head-to-head comparisons

    iv. The winner is the candidate that receives the highest number of first-place votes

    v. Each voter casts votes for every candidate that they find to be acceptable

2. If there are three candidates in an election, how many pairwise comparisons need to be made to determine the winner?

3. If there are six candidates in an election, how many pairwise comparisons need to be made to determine the winner?

4. These candidates received the following number of votes:

    Albert = 375, Benny = 210, Carol = 411, Donna = 189

    Using the Plurality Method, which candidate is the winner?

5. Using the provided preference list, answer the questions that follow it.

	NUMBER OF VOTERS			
RANK	3	2	2	1
First Choice	D	C	B	A
Second Choice	B	B	C	C
Third Choice	C	A	A	B
Fourth Choice	A	D	D	D

    a. How many voters were there?

    b. How many voters have ranked the candidates in the order D, B, C, A?

    c. Who is the winner using Plurality Voting?

    d. Who is the winner using the Borda Count Method?

    e. Who is the winner using the Hare System?

    f. Who is the winner using Pairwise Comparison?

6. Using the provided preference list, answer the questions that follow it.

	NUMBER OF VOTERS			
RANK	4	2	2	1
First Choice	B	C	A	A
Second Choice	D	A	C	B
Third Choice	C	D	B	C
Fourth Choice	A	B	D	D

    a. How many voters were there?

    b. How many voters have ranked the candidates in the order A, B, C, D?

    c. Who is the winner using Plurality Voting?

    d. Who is the winner using the Borda Count Method?

    e. Who is the winner using the Hare System?

    f. Who is the winner using Pairwise Comparison?

7. Using the provided preference list, answer the questions that follow it.

	NUMBER OF VOTERS			
RANK	5	3	2	1
First Choice	C	B	D	B
Second Choice	B	A	C	A
Third Choice	D	D	B	D
Fourth Choice	A	C	A	C

a. How many voters were there?

b. How many voters have ranked the candidates in the order C, B, D, A?

c. Who is the winner using Plurality Voting?

d. Who is the winner using the Borda Count Method?

e. Who is the winner using the Hare System?

f. Who is the winner using Pairwise Comparison?

8. Using the provided preference list, answer the questions that follow it.

	NUMBER OF VOTERS			
RANK	4	3	2	1
First Choice	D	B	A	C
Second Choice	B	A	C	B
Third Choice	A	C	D	A
Fourth Choice	C	D	B	D

a. How many voters were there?

b. How many voters have ranked the candidates in the order A, C, D, B?

c. Who is the winner using Plurality Voting?

d. Who is the winner using the Borda Count Method?

e. Who is the winner using the Hare System?

f. Who is the winner using Pairwise Comparison?

9. Using the provided preference list, answer the questions that follow it.

	NUMBER OF VOTERS			
RANK	4	2	2	1
First Choice	B	C	A	A
Second Choice	A	B	C	B
Third Choice	C	A	B	C

a. How many voters were there?

b. How many voters have ranked the candidates in the order B, A, C?

c. Who is the winner using Plurality Voting?

d. Who is the winner using the Borda Count Method?

e. Who is the winner using the Hare System?

f. Who is the winner using Pairwise Comparison?

10. Using the provided preference list, answer the questions that follow it.

	NUMBER OF VOTERS			
RANK	4	4	2	1
First Choice	A	C	B	A
Second Choice	B	B	C	C
Third Choice	C	A	A	B

a. How many voters were there?

b. How many voters have ranked the candidates in the order C, A, B?

c. Who is the winner using Plurality Voting?

d. Who is the winner using the Borda Count Method?

e. Who is the winner using the Hare System?

f. Who is the winner using Pairwise Comparison?

11. In Major League Baseball, when deciding who won the 2019 National League (NL) Cy Young award (for the best pitcher in the NL for that season), the Baseball Writers' Association of America had 30 voters each vote for five pitchers. The system awarded 7 points for a first-place vote, 4 points for a second-place vote, 3 points for third place, 2 for fourth place and 1 point for a fifth-place vote.

a. What type of voting system is this?

b. Jacob deGrom from the New York Mets won the 2019 NL Cy Young award with 29 first-place votes and 1 second-place vote. How many total points did he receive?

12. Jack, Karen, and Nancy are all running for the open seat on the local HOA board, and each homeowner gets one vote. Jack gets 50 votes, Karen gets 62, and Nancy gets 39 votes. If Karen is declared the winner, what type of voting system is this?

13. In a 3-candidate approval voting election with 14 voters, if 7 approve of A and B, 5 approve of B and C, and 2 approve of A and C, who wins the election?

14. In a 4-candidate approval voting election with 15 voters, if 2 approve of A and C, 7 approve of B and C, and 6 approve of A and D, who wins the election?

15. Use the provided table of votes and the Approval Voting Method to answer the questions that follow it.

	SPECIFIC VOTERS									
	#1	#2	#3	#4	#5	#6	#7	#8	#9	#10
Candidate A	✓	✓			✓		✓		✓	✓
Candidate B	✓	✓	✓			✓	✓			
Candidate C		✓			✓				✓	
Candidate D	✓		✓	✓	✓		✓	✓		✓
Candidate E		✓	✓			✓			✓	
Candidate F				✓	✓		✓	✓		

a. Which candidate is chosen if only one person is to be elected Chairman of the Board?

b. Which candidates will be elected if three people are being elected to the Board?

c. Which candidates are chosen if 60% approval is needed to be elected?

ANSWERS TO SECTION 6.2 EXERCISES

1. a. iv   b. i   c. ii   d. iii   e. v

2. 3

3. 15

4. Carol

5. a. 8   b. 3   c. D   d. B   e. C   f. B

6. a. 9   b. 1   c. B   d. B   e. A
   f. There is no winner. (3-way tie between A, B, and C)

7. a. 11   b. 5   c. C   d. B   e. C
   f. There is no winner. (3-way tie between B, C, and D)

8. **a.** 10   **b.** 2   **c.** D   **d.** B   **e.** D   **f.** A

9. **a.** 9   **b.** 4   **c.** B   **d.** B   **e.** B   **f.** B

10. **a.** 11   **b.** 0   **c.** A   **d.** B   **e.** C   **f.** B

11. **a.** A Non-Standard Borda Count System   **b.** 207 points

12. Plurality

13. B

14. C

15. **a.** D   **b.** A, B, and D   **c.** A and D

6.3 Dummies and Dictators: Weighted Voting Systems

Weighted Voting

So far, in all the voting methods we have discussed, all voters were treated equally. However, not all voting systems operate that way. A common example is a situation where stockholders are given voting power based on the number of shares of stock they own. A system in which the voters are not treated equally is a **weighted voting system**.

In a weighted voting system, each participant has a number of votes which is called his or her weight. In order to determine whether the result of a vote is "pass" or "fail," a **quota** is established. The quota must be more than half of all the votes, and a common method for setting the quota is to use a **simple majority quota**. When a simple majority quota is used, the quota is the smallest whole number greater than half of the total weight of the voters.

If the sum of the weights of the voters who are in favor of a proposal is greater than or equal to the quota, then the proposal passes. When this is the case, the group of voters is called a **winning coalition**.

When the group of voters that support a proposal has a combined weight less than the quota, the proposal does not pass. This group of voters is called a **losing coalition**.

Notation for Weighted Voting Systems

When we describe a weighted voting system, the voting weight of each participant, as well as the quota, is specified using a specific type of notation. The quota is represented by q, and the weights of the individual voters are represented by $w_1, w_2, w_3, \ldots, w_n$. Also, the individual weights of all the voters are always listed in order, from highest to lowest. Remember, for a weighted voting system to work correctly, the quota must be greater than or equal to a simple majority of the votes—not the number of voters.

A weighted voting system is written as:

$$[q: w_1, w_2, w_3, \ldots, w_n]$$

EXAMPLE 1:

For the voting system [7: 5, 3, 2], identify the quota, the number of voters, and the weight of each voter.

SOLUTION: The quota is 7, and there are a total of three voters. The weight of the first voter is 5, the weight of the second voter is 3, and the weight of the third voter is 2.

Dummy Voters

A **dummy voter** is a voter whose vote does not matter. The system [12: 9, 3, 2] has a dummy voter. In this situation, the only way that a proposal can pass is if the nine-weight voter and the three-weight voter support it, and when that happens, the support of the two-weight voter is not necessary. Since the support of the two-weight voter is not needed in any winning coalition, and the two-weight voter cannot prevent the other voters from passing a proposal, this voter has no impact on the outcome of a vote.

> A dummy voter is one whose vote is never necessary for reaching the quota.

If any winning coalition exists that requires the inclusion of a specific voter, then that voter is not a dummy. When checking a system for dummy voters, check for a winning coalition using the lowest-weight voter first. If the lowest-weight voter is not a dummy, then there cannot be a dummy voter in the system.

EXAMPLE 2:

Given the weighted voting system [9: 6, 3, 1], is there a dummy voter?

SOLUTION: Yes. Since there is not a winning coalition that requires the 1-weight voter, that 1-weight voter is a dummy.

EXAMPLE 3:

Given the weighted voting system [10: 6, 3, 1], is there a dummy voter?

SOLUTION: No. Here, the only possible winning coalition includes *all three* voters. So, for all practical purposes, each voter in this system has equal power, and there is no dummy voter.

EXAMPLE 4:

Given the weighted voting system [40: 21, 20, 19, 4], is there a dummy voter?

SOLUTION: No. At first glance, we may think the 4-weight voter would not have much power. However, since a coalition including the 20-, 19-, and 4-weight voters can reach the quota, and the 4-weight voter is a necessary part of this winning coalition, the 4-weight voter is not a dummy.

There are certainly other winning coalitions that could be formed, but as long as there is at least one winning coalition that requires the 4-weight voter to be included, the 4-weight voter is not a dummy.

Dictators

A **dictator** is a voter who has enough power to determine the outcome of any vote, regardless of how the others cast their votes. The system [35: 40, 10, 5] has a dictator, because the 40-weight voter has enough weight to pass a proposal, and the other voters cannot pass a proposal without the support of the 40-weight voter. When there is a dictator, all of the other voters are dummy voters.

> A dictator has a voter weight that is greater than or equal to the quota. There can never be more than one dictator in a voting system.

Veto Power

A voter whose support is necessary to pass a proposal has **veto power**. The system [8: 5, 3, 1] actually includes two voters with veto power. Since a proposal cannot reach this quota without the support of the 5-weight voter and the 3-weight voter, both of these voters have veto power.

> Veto power is having enough weight to be necessary in every coalition that reaches the quota.

If every possible winning coalition includes a specific voter, then that voter has veto power. When checking to see whether a system includes a voter with veto power, check the highest-weight voter first. If the highest-weight voter does not have veto power, then none of the voters in the system have veto power.

Note the difference between a dictator and a voter with veto power. In order to be a dictator, the voter must have a weight greater than or equal to the quota. Since the quota must be greater than half of the total weight of the voters, there can never be more than one dictator, if one exists at all. On the other hand, a voter with veto power can prevent a proposal from passing, but if this voter is too weak to be a dictator, they cannot pass a proposal without the support of other voters.

EXAMPLE 5:

Given the weighted voting system [71: 40, 35, 31, 24, 3], answer the following.

- a. How many voters are in the system?
- b. What is the quota?
- c. Is there a dictator?
- d. Is there a dummy voter?
- e. How many voters have veto power?
- f. How many voting coalitions are there with exactly the quota required for the proposal to pass?

SOLUTIONS:

- a. Five
- b. 71
- c. No.
- d. Yes. The 3-weight voter is not a necessary part of any winning coalition and is therefore a dummy.
- e. None.
- f. One. The only way to get a total weight of exactly 71 is if the 40-weight and 31-weight voters are the only ones who support the proposal.

EXAMPLE 6:

Given the weighted voting system [36: 27, 15, 10, 6, 4], answer the following.

- a. How many voters are in the system?
- b. What is the quota?
- c. Is there a dictator?
- d. Is there a dummy voter?
- e. How many voters have veto power?
- f. How many voting coalitions are there with exactly the quota required for the proposal to pass?

SOLUTIONS:

- a. Five
- b. 36
- c. No.
- d. No. A coalition of the 27-, 6-, and 4-weight voters would reach the quota and be a winning coalition. Since the 4-weight voter is necessary for this coalition to reach the quota, the 4-weight voter is not a dummy.
- e. One. The 27-weight voter is needed in any winning coalition.
- f. None.

Important Note: The Making of a Dictator

In the examples provided in this section, the systems only had a few voters. In most weighted voting systems, however, there are a large number of voters. Typically, a company has thousands of voters, which are often weighted by the number of shares of company stock each voter owns. The same principles still exist, though; quotas must still consist of more than half of the weighted votes, and a dictator will have a weight greater than the quota. Even though it is not uncommon for single voters to be dummy voters, many coalitions are usually formed. Keep in mind, though, if a company has a total of a 50,000-weight voting system, a quota must consist of more than 25,000 votes. In such a case, we often see CEOs with weights in excess of 20,000 votes.

Another common practice is for members of a voting system to transfer their voting authority to a different member. This happens with many homeowner's associations—members who do not vote may have their votes conceded to the association president, which can turn the president into a dictator. If, indeed, this is an option, it will be spelled out in the by-laws of the association.

SECTION 6.3 EXERCISES

Determine the quota for a voting system that has the following number of votes and uses a simple majority quota.

   a. 26

   b. 66

   c. 83

   d. 44

2. For the weighted voting system [9: 9, 5, 2], indicate whether the following statements are true or false.

   a. There are four voters in this system.

   b. The nine-weight voter is a dictator.

   c. The two-weight voter is a dummy.

3. For the weighted voting system [11: 5, 5, 1, 1, 1], indicate whether the following statements are true or false.

   a. Three of these voters have equal weight.

   b. None of these voters have veto power.

   c. There is exactly one dummy voter.

4. For the weighted voting system [8: 8, 2, 2, 1], indicate whether the following statements are true or false.

   a. There is a dictator.

   b. There are exactly three dummy voters.

   c. Exactly one voter has veto power.

5. Given the weighted voting system [61: 35, 30, 25, 2]:

    a. How many voters are in the system?

    b. What is the quota?

    c. Is there a dictator?

    d. If there are any dummy voters, identify them.

    e. If there are any voters with veto power, identify them.

6. Given the weighted voting system [38: 27, 10, 5, 3, 1]:

    a. How many voters are in the system?

    b. What is the quota?

    c. Is there a dictator?

    d. If there are any dummy voters, identify them.

    e. If there are any voters with veto power, identify them.

7. Given the weighted voting system [6: 5, 3, 2, 1]:

    a. How many voters are in the system?

    b. What is the quota?

    c. Is there a dictator?

    d. If there are any dummy voters, identify them.

    e. If there are any voters with veto power, identify them.

8. Given the weighted voting system [4: 4, 2, 1]:

    a. How many voters are in the system?

    b. What is the quota?

    c. Is there a dictator?

    d. If there are any dummy voters, identify them.

    e. If there are any voters with veto power, identify them.

9. Given the weighted voting system [10: 9, 2, 2, 2, 2]:

    a. How many voters are in the system?

    b. What is the quota?

c. Is there a dictator?

d. If there are any dummy voters, identify them.

e. If there are any voters with veto power, identify them.

10. Given the weighted voting system [59: 35, 35, 25, 2]:

   a. How many voters are in the system?

   b. What is the quota?

   c. Is there a dictator?

   d. If there are any dummy voters, identify them.

   e. If there are any voters with veto power, identify them.

11. Given the weighted voting system [17: 7, 5, 3, 2]:

   a. How many voters are in the system?

      What is the quota?

   c. Is there a dictator?

   d. If there are any dummy voters, identify them.

   e. If there are any voters with veto power, identify them.

12. Given the weighted voting system [12: 6, 4, 4, 2], how many voting coalitions are there with exactly the quota required to win?

13. Given the weighted voting system [10: 6, 4, 4, 2], how many voting coalitions are there with exactly the quota required to win?

14. Given a system with four voters, having weights of 30, 29, 28, and 13, of which only one voter has veto power:

   a. Which voter has veto power?

   b. What is the quota?

   c. Is there a dummy voter?

15. If you hold 51% of the stock in a company, you have total control over the company. Why?

16. Why does having a dictator make all of the other voters dummies?

ANSWERS TO SECTION 6.3 EXERCISES

1. a. 14   b. 34   c. 42   d. 23

2. a. False   b. True   c. True

3. a. True   b. False   c. False

4. a. True   b. True   c. True

5. a. 4   b. 61   c. No   d. None
    e. The 35-weight voter has veto power.

6. a. 5   b. 38   c. No   d. None
    e. Both the 10- and the 27-weight voters have veto power.

7. a. 4   b. 6   c. No   d. None   e. None

8. a. 3   b. 4   c. Yes   d. The two- and one-weight voters.
    e. The four-weight voter.

9. a. 5   b. 10   c. No   d. None
    e. The nine-weight voter.

10. a. 4   b. 59   c. No   d. The two-weight voter.
    e. None.

11. a. 4   b. 17   c. No   d. None.
    e. All the voters have veto power.

12. 2

13. 3

14. a. The 30-weight voter.
    b. 71. With veto power, the 30-weight voter must be included in a winning coalition. Thus, the quota must be greater than $29 + 28 + 13 = 70$. And, if the quota was 72, both the 29- and 30-weight voters would have veto power.
    c. No.

15. Having 51% of the stock makes you equivalent to a 51-weight voter in a system with a quota of 51. This makes you a dictator.

16. The dictator can pass or reject a motion alone, which makes the votes of all of the other voters irrelevant.

6.4 Who Gets the Bigger Half?: Fair Division

Fair division is the concept of dividing something between two or more people in such a way that each person finds their share to be fair. There are a number of ways to achieve fair division, and some of them will be investigated in this section. Before we begin, however, we must clarify one very import-ant point. Divisions do not have to be equal; they just need to be fair in the eye of the beholder. Each party should get what they deem to be a fair share, and what happens to everyone else does not matter. Also, the parties involved in the division are expected to be reasonable. Otherwise, an independent arbitrator must oversee the procedure.

> Fair division *does not* necessarily mean equal division.

Discrete items, such as cash or a box full of books, can usually be split equally. Some **continuous items,** such as pets and cars, cannot be cut up, as they would lose their value and become worthless. Other continuous items, like pizza, can be split up without losing value. It is common for continuous items that cannot be split to be liquidated into money to perform a division.

Divider-Chooser Method

The **Divider-Chooser Method** is a practical (and simple!) approach to having two people share an object that can be cut into pieces. You may already be familiar with this process.

Let's say two children, a brother and sister, want to share a piece of cake. While this could result in a terrible argu-ment, there is a simple, yet fair way to divide that piece of cake.

Image 6.4.1

1. First, flip a coin to determine which child will be Player 1. The other will be Player 2.

2. Next, Player 1 gets to cut the piece of cake into two parts, wherever he or she wishes.

3. Then, Player 2 gets to choose the piece of cake he or she would like to have, leaving the other piece for Player 1.

In this system, one player gets to divide the cake and the other player gets to choose which piece to take.

Taking Turns

One of the most basic approaches to the fair division of items is **taking turns**. The process of taking turns has inherent flaws, since the person who goes first may have a tremendous advantage. However, when both parties know the preferences of the other, there is an interesting strategy that can be used to bring about a fair division. Developed by mathematicians D.A. Kohler and R. Chandrasekaran in 1969, the process is known as the bottom-up strategy, and it is an excellent way to divide items when a neutral arbitrator is used.

Bottom-Up Method

When two parties are going to divide items, simply taking turns can often leave an individual with an undesirable item. When each party knows the preferences of the other, mapping out the choices from the bottom-up can help both parties achieve satisfaction. This process is known as the **bottom-up method**. When this strategy is used, the individual identified with the *last* choice begins by putting the item from the *bottom* of the other person's list as their *bottom choice*. This process continues, with the parties taking turns in reverse order, until all of the choices have been mapped out.

For those who are new to this system, the most difficult part about using the bottom-up strategy is assigning the first item. Once that item is assigned, the rest of the choices will all fall into place.

When we say, "Bob gets to pick first," that means if Bob and Tom were to divide the items normally, Bob would begin the process by selecting one of the items to be his, and they would continue taking turns until all the items were gone. So, if there were four items, Bob would have the first pick, Tom would get the second pick, Bob would get the third pick, and Tom would take what was left with the fourth and final pick. To give a better idea of how this looks, we can literally map out these picks, providing a blank space for each item that will be selected.

1. Bob: _____

2. Tom: _____

3. Bob: _____

4. Tom: _____

Notice how we can make that "map" without actually knowing the items they are dividing. At this point we just know that there are four items, so there will be a total of four picks.

In order to use the bottom-up strategy, we need to know what the four items are, and how Bob and Tom rank these items. To continue with our example, let's say they provide the following rankings for a dog, an iPod, a couch and a set of books.

Tom	Bob
Dog	iPod
iPod	Couch
Couch	Dog
Books	Books

Now that we have their rankings, we can literally assign the picks by filling in our blank spaces in the map—from the bottom-up. That is, since Tom would be picking last, according to the bottom-up strategy, he places the *lowest* ranked item from *Bob's list* in that last spot. According to their lists, that pick will be the books.

1. Bob: _____

2. Tom: _____

3. Bob: _____

4. Tom: Books_____

To avoid accidentally selecting them again, since the books have been assigned to Tom, we will cross "Books" off of *both* lists.

TOM	BOB
Dog	iPod
iPod	~~Couch~~
Couch	Dog
~~Books~~	~~Books~~

Continuing from the bottom-up, the next step is to assign the next-to-last overall pick. In this case, that is the #3 pick. Since this pick belongs to Bob, he takes the *lowest* available item from *Tom's list*, which is the couch. So, we put the couch in the blank space for the #3 pick and cross it off of both lists.

1. Bob: _____

2. Tom: _____

3. Bob: Couch_____

4. Tom: Books_____

TOM	BOB
Dog	iPod
iPod	~~Couch~~
~~Couch~~	Dog
~~Books~~	~~Books~~

Continuing this process, Tom takes Bob's lowest ranked available item, so we fill in the #2 blank space with the dog. Finally, Bob will select the only item left, which is the iPod. In the end, Bob will get the iPod and the couch, while Tom takes home the dog and the books. By agreeing to use the bottom-up strategy, Tom ends up with his first and fourth ranked items (even though he picked second), which is a good result for him, and Bob gets his first and second choices, which is a great result for him.

EXAMPLE 1:

Ben and Jerry will use the bottom-up strategy to divide a TV, a desk, a refrigerator, and a bookcase. Ben gets to choose first. Each person ranks the items in order of preference, before the selection process begins, as follows:

BEN	JERRY
TV	Refrigerator
Desk	TV
Bookcase	Desk
Refrigerator	Bookcase

Image 6.4.2

How will the items be divided?

SOLUTION: Since Ben will choose first, the picks will go as follows:

1. Ben: _____

2. Jerry: _____

3. Ben: _____

4. Jerry: _____

Using the bottom-up strategy, we start by identifying the item that will be chosen last. With the fourth (and final) pick, Jerry indicates he will choose the item Ben wants the least. In other words, Jerry will choose the item from the *bottom* of Ben's list.

1. Ben: _____

2. Jerry: _____

3. Ben: _____

4. Jerry: Refrigerator _____

Next, with the #3 pick, Ben will choose the *lowest available item* from Jerry's list.

1. Ben: _____

2. Jerry: _____

3. Ben: Bookcase _____

4. Jerry: Refrigerator _____

Image 6.4.3

Moving up the list of blank spaces (going "bottom-up"), Jerry then chooses the lowest available item on Ben's list. Since the refrigerator and the bookcase have already been chosen, the lowest available item remaining on Ben's list is the desk.

1. Ben: _____

2. Jerry: Desk _____

3. Ben: Bookcase _____

4. Jerry: Refrigerator _____

Finally, Ben will slot in the #1 pick, which will be the lowest available item on Jerry's list.

1. Ben: TV _____

2. Jerry: Desk _____

3. Ben: Bookcase _____

4. Jerry: Refrigerator _____

Using the bottom-up strategy, Ben will end up with the TV and the bookcase. Jerry will end up with the desk and the refrigerator.

In the previous example both parties got their first and third choices, which is a fairer division than simply picking items 1-2-3-4. If they had simply taken turns from the beginning, Ben would have gotten his top two choices, but Jerry would have ended up with his top choice and his least desirable item.

It is important to note, however, that the party allowed to choose first definitely makes a difference in the way the items will be divided. Let's look at the previous example again, except this time, let's see what happens when Jerry goes first.

EXAMPLE 2:

Assume Ben and Jerry use the bottom-up strategy to divide an iPod, speakers, a DVD player, and a turntable. Jerry gets to choose first. Each person ranked the items, in order of preference, before the selection process began, as follows:

Ben	Jerry
TV	Refrigerator
Desk	TV
Bookcase	Desk
Refrigerator	Bookcase

How will the items be divided?

Solution: Jumping to the completed map of picks, we have:

1. Jerry: <u>TV</u>

2. Ben: <u>Desk</u>

3. Jerry: <u>Refrigerator</u>

4. Ben: <u>Bookcase</u>

This time, Ben will end up with the desk and the bookcase, while Jerry will get the TV and the refrigerator. With Jerry going first, Jerry was able to get his first and second choices, while Ben got his second and third choices. Since neither person was stuck receiving the fourth item on his list, this is likely a division that both parties can find to be agreeable.

Review: Solving Equations

An **equation** is a mathematical statement indicating that two expressions are equal. A **solution** is a value of the variable that makes the equation true.

When **solving an equation,** steps are taken to determine all the values of the variable that will make the equation a true statement.

One of the steps available for use is known as the **addition property of equality**. This property states, "if the same quantity is added to both sides of an equation, the solution remains the same." Since any quantity can be added to both sides of an equation, a quantity is chosen that will isolate the variable.

EXAMPLE 3:

Solve: $x - 8 = 24$

Solution: To solve this equation, we want to isolate the variable (x). To do that here, we will add 8 to both sides of the equation. This will cause the (-8) and the $(+8)$ on the left side of the equation to cancel each other out. We also simplify the right side of the equation, giving us our solution.

$$x - 8 = 24$$
$$x - 8 + 8 = 24 + 8$$
$$x = 32$$

As you might expect, we can add either positive numbers (like we did in Example 6), or negative numbers to both sides of an equation.

EXAMPLE 4:

Solve: $x + 7 = -8$

Solution: Here, we will add (-7) to both sides of the equation.

$$x + 7 = -8$$
$$x + 7 + (-7) = -8 + (-7)$$
$$x = -15$$

Note: It is perfectly fine to think of the process as "subtracting 7 from both sides."

Another approach that may be used when solving an equation involves the **multiplication property of equality**, which states that "if both sides of an equation are multiplied (or divided) by the same non-zero quantity, the solution remains the same." Just as it is with the addition property of equality, since any quantity can be used, a quantity is chosen that will isolate the variable.

EXAMPLE 5:

Solve: $6x = 24$

Solution: To solve this equation, we want to isolate the variable (x). To do that here, we will divide both sides of the equation by 6.

$6x = 24$
$6x/6 = 24/6$
$x = 4$

You may be thinking, "if we *divide* by a number, why is this called the multiplication property of equality?" Instead of dividing by 6, we could have multiplied by (1/6) and had the same outcome. In the same way that the addition property of equality applies to both addition and subtraction, the multiplication property of equality applies to both multiplication and division. This streamlines our processes into just two properties that we use when trying to isolate a variable.

Some of the equations we solve will make use of *both* the addition and multiplication properties of equality. In some equations, we will use the distributive property to remove any parentheses, and some equations will require us to simplify each side of the equation as much as possible by combining like terms. That being the case, some equations will require several steps in the solving process.

If the variable exists on both sides of the equation, use the addition principle to remove it from one side. Try not to think of moving terms from one side of an equation to the other. Instead, focus on removing unwanted terms by adding their opposite. Then, remember, whatever we have done to one side of the equation, we must also do the same thing to the other side to keep the equation balanced. Once the term containing the variable has been isolated, then apply the multiplication property to remove any unwanted multiplication—just be sure to do it to both sides of the equation.

common mistake

When faced with $6x = 24$, some students attempt to isolate the x by subtracting 6 from both sides of the equation. Remember, the 6 and x are linked by multiplication, and multiplication is undone by division, not subtraction.

EXAMPLE 6:

Solve: $5x + 13 = 38$

Solution: To solve this equation, we want to isolate the variable (x). Here, we first need to isolate the term containing the variable. To do so, we begin by subtracting 13 from both sides of the equation. Then, we will divide both sides of the equation by 5.

$5x + 13 = 38$
$5x + 13 - 13 = 38 - 13$
$5x = 25$
$x = 5$

EXAMPLE 7:

Solve: $27 + 5x = 22 + 30(1 - x)$

SOLUTION: In this problem, we first need to use the distributive property to remove the parentheses. Next, we need to simplify as much as possible by combining like terms. Then, to make sure the variable exists on only one side of the equation, we can add 30x to both sides. From here we follow the process shown in Example 6 to isolate the variable.

$$27 + 5x = 22 + 30(1 - x)$$
$$27 + 5x = 22 + 30 - 30x$$
$$27 + 5x = 52 - 30x$$
$$27 + 35x = 52$$
$$35x = 25$$
$$x = 25/35 = 5/7$$

The Adjusted Winner Procedure

The **Adjusted Winner Procedure** is a method by which two parties can divide a group of items in a fair manner, provided one of the items can be split apart.

This process uses the following steps:

1. Each party is allowed to assign a total of 100 points to the items that are being divided. The more important an item is to a party, the more points it should be given.

2. Initially, the party that assigns the highest point value to a specific item is given that item. (We will assume there are no ties in the point assignments.)

3. At this point, the number of points each party has received is determined.

4. Once this initial division is done, if the point values are equal, the process is complete. However, this is very unlikely. It is probable that one party has received more points than the other, and this will have to be rectified.

5. Let's call the party that has received more points "Party A," and the other "Party B." In order for this division to be fair, we will need to take some points away from Party A, and give them to Party B. To do so, we may have to transfer a fractional amount of an item from Party A to Party B. The item to be split either needs to be split without losing its value, or it must be liquidated to perform the division.

Disclaimers for the Adjusted Winner Procedure

In Step 2 of this process, as indicated in the parentheses, we are keeping the process simpler by assuming there are no ties in the point assignments. In the event of a tie that cannot be resolved by the parties involved, then an independent arbitrator can be used.

In the last step of this process, it is necessary for us to point out there are different methods that can be used to determine which item gets split apart in order to equalize the points. One method allows for the point leader to determine the item that gets divided, and typically, this party will split the item that was assigned the lowest number of points. If, however, there is an item that is easier to divide (such as cash), the division could be done by splitting that item.

EXAMPLE 8:

Champ and Monte have purchased the contents of an abandoned storage shed. They look inside and find some sporting goods, stuffed animals, and textbooks. They decide to create a fair division of these objects using the Adjusted Winner Procedure, and they assign their points as shown:

POINT ALLOCATIONS

Item	Champ	Monte
Sporting Goods	60	10
Stuffed Animals	10	70
Textbooks	30	20

Solution: Initially, because the parties assigned higher point values to these items, Champ is given the textbooks and the sporting goods, while Monte is given the stuffed animals.

At this point, Champ has been given items totaling 90 points, and Monte has been given items that he deemed to be worth 70 points.

Since the point values given to the parties are not equal, the process continues. Points will have to be taken from Champ and given to Monte. Of the items that have been given to Champ, he assigned the lowest number of points to the textbooks. So, he will balance this division by keeping part of the textbooks and giving the rest to Monte. That is, each party will get a *fraction* of the books. To calculate the appropriate fractions, let's start by saying Champ will get "x." Monte will get the fraction of the books that are not given to Champ. This amount will be represented by "$1 - x$."

In order to determine the number of points that Champ will get from the books, we will multiply the points Champ assigned to the books by "x." Similarly, to find the number of points Monte will receive from the books, we will multiply the number of points Monte assigned to the books by "$1 - x$."

Using the point values Champ and Monte assigned to each of the items, we can set up an expression that shows the total number of points each party will receive after the books are divided.

	Points from Sporting Goods	Points from Stuffed Animals	Points from Books	Total Points Received
Champ	60	0	30x	$60 + 30x$
Monte	0	70	$20(1 - x)$	$70 + 20(1 - x)$

To achieve fairness in this division, the total points received by each of the parties must be equal. So, we set the two expressions in the "Total Points Received" column equal to one another, and then solve for x. And remember, we called "x" the fraction of the 10 books that will be given to Champ.

$$60 + 30x = 70 + 20(1 - x)$$

Using the distributive property, we get:
$$60 + 30x = 70 + 20 - 20x$$

Image 6.4.4

Combining like terms gives us:

$60 + 30x = 90 - 20x$

Adding 20x to both sides, and subtracting 60 from both sides, we have:

$50x = 30$

Finally, dividing both sides by 50, we get:

$x = 3/5$

So, Champ will be given 3/5 of the textbooks.

The fraction of the books that Monte gets is "1 − x," which here is:

$1 - 3/5 = 5/5 - 3/5 = 2/5$

So, 2/5 of the books will be given to Monte.

To illustrate *how* this achieves a fair division, let's take a look at the final total number of points that are given to each party. Champ was given the sporting goods, which were worth 60 points. He was also given 3/5 of the textbooks, which to him is worth $(3/5)(30) = 18$ points. So, all together, Champ was given items that added to 78 points.

Monte was given the stuffed animals, which are worth 70 points. He was also given 2/5 of the textbooks, which to him is worth $(2/5)(20) = 8$ points. So, all together, Monte was given items that added to 78 points.

Since each party received the same number of points, this is a fair division of the items.

EXAMPLE 9:

Dave and Dan have to divide four items: a riding lawn mower, a pool table, a couch, and a baseball card collection. Using the Adjusted Winner procedure, Dave assigns his allotment of 100 points as follows: 40 to the mower, 10 to the pool table, 20 to the couch, and 30 to the baseball cards. Dan assigns his points as follows: 20 to the mower, 50 to the pool table, 10 to the couch, and 20 to the baseball cards. Indicate the way the items should be divided.

	Point Allocations	
Item	Dave	Dan
Lawn Mower	40	20
Pool Table	10	50
Couch	20	10
Baseball cards	30	20

Solution: Initially, Dan would get the pool table (50 points) and Dave would take the lawn mower (40) and the couch (20). Since allowing either party to take the entire baseball card collection would result in an unfair division, and the baseball card collection is the only item that can be split apart without being liquidated, we will divide the baseball card collection.

Letting "x" be the fraction of the baseball cards that Dave will get, we can use the point assignments to compute the total points that each party will receive.

	Points Before Baseball cards	Points from Baseball cards	Total Points Received
Dave	60	30x	60 + 30x
Dan	50	20(1 − x)	50 + 20(1 − x)

Dave has 60 points from the mower and couch and will get 30x points from the baseball cards. Dan has 50 points from the pool table and will get 20(1−x) points from the baseball cards. Setting these point totals equal to each other and solving for "x," we have:

$$60 + 30x = 50 + 20(1 − x)$$
$$60 + 30x = 50 + 20 − 20x$$
$$50x = 10$$
$$x = 1/5$$

We let "x" represent the fraction of the baseball cards that Dave would get, so Dave gets 1/5 of the baseball cards and Dan gets the remaining (1 − 1/5) = 4/5 of them.

Checking the final point totals,

Dave: 40 (lawn mower) + 20 (couch) + (30 × 1/5 = 6) (baseball cards) = 60 + 6 = 66
Dan: 50 (pool table) + (20 × 4/5 = 16) (baseball cards) = 50 + 16 = 66

The point totals are equal, so the division is fair.

Method of Sealed Bids

The previous methods are all ways to equitably divide things between two people. Unfortunately, when more than two people are involved, those methods become overly complicated or even logistically impossible. In 1945, Polish mathematician Bronislaw Knaster developed an alternative method of fair division that works well when two or more people are involved. The **Method of Sealed Bids**, also called the **Knaster Inheritance Procedure**, is completed using the following procedure:

1. Each person writes down the highest amount they would be willing to pay for each item—without knowing the amount that the other parties will bid for the same item(s). (We will assume there are no ties in the bids).

2. The highest bidder for each item will win it, and the other people will be compensated with money, paid to them by the person who won the item. Bidders, however, are not compensated directly. Instead, if there are *n* bidders, the winner will place (n−1)/n times the amount of the winning bid into a kitty. For example, if there are 4 bidders, the winner places 3/4 of his bid into the kitty.

3. Those who did not win the item will then take 1/nth of their individual bids from the kitty. For example, if four people are involved in the division, each person who did not win is entitled to 1/4 of the amount they bid for that item.

4. After each non-winner has taken the appropriate amount from the kitty, the remaining funds in the kitty are then divided equally among each bidder, including the person who won the item.

In this method, since all the bids are monetary, there is no need to worry about dividing or liquidating an item.

EXAMPLE 10:

Jenny and Amy are no longer going to be roommates, but they have to decide who will get to keep their dog. Obviously, they won't be able to "divide" the dog, and they do not want to sell it, either. So, they will use the method of sealed bids instead.

- Jenny bids $300 for the dog.
- Amy bids $400 for the dog.

Solution: Since this division involves two people, each of them is entitled to 1/2 of the value of their bid.

Amy, as the higher bidder, will get the dog, and she will have to put 1/2 of her bid into the kitty. Her bid was $400, so she puts $200 into the kitty.

Jenny did not get the dog, so she will take 1/2 of her bid from the kitty. Her bid was $300, so she takes $150 from the kitty.

This leaves $50 in the kitty, which is split evenly between the two people. At this point each person takes $25 from the kitty.

Amy put $200 into the kitty, and then took out $25.

Jenny took $150 out of the kitty, and then took out $25 more.

So, to complete this fair division, Amy gets the dog and has paid $175 to Jenny.

Image 6.4.5

EXAMPLE 11:

Apollo, Athena, and Artemis all claim joint ownership of a magic helmet used by their father, Zeus. Using the method of sealed bids, Apollo bids $6,000 for the helmet and Athena bids $3,000 for it, while Artemis only bids $900. Apollo will win the helmet and must pay cash to his siblings. According to the method of sealed bids, how much does he have to pay to each of them to make the division fair?

Solution: Each of the three children has a rightful claim to 1/3 of the helmet. In order to cover the two thirds that are owed to his siblings, Apollo must put 2/3 of his bid into the kitty. His bid was $6,000, so he will start the process by putting $(2/3 \times \$6,000) = \$4,000$ into the kitty.

Athena is entitled to 1/3 of her bid, which was $3,000, so she takes $1,000 from the kitty. Artemis is entitled to 1/3 of her bid, which was $900, so she takes $300 from the kitty. After those shares have been taken from the kitty, $2,700 remains. That residual amount is split equally among the three siblings, so each of them will get $900.

Athena will initially get $1,000 from the kitty and then $900 more when the residual is split, making a total of $1,900. Likewise, Artemis will initially take $300 from the kitty and then get $900 of the residual, giving her a total of $1,200. So, for the honor of taking his father's helmet, Apollo would put $4,000 into the kitty but get $900 of it back. That means he has to give a total of $3,100 to his siblings, which is split into $1,900 for Athena and $1,200 for Artemis.

EXAMPLE 12:

There are two items, a painting and a sculpture, to be divided fairly among three people using the method of sealed bids.

Each person puts forth a bid on each item, as follows:

Item	Audrey	Brian	Cindy
Painting	4,200	6,000	5,100
Sculpture	6,600	4,800	7,500

Solution: When using the method of sealed bids, each item is handled separately.

Starting with the painting ...

Brian is the high bidder, so he will get the painting.

There are three people involved in this division, so Brian must place 2/3 of his $6,000 bid into the kitty, which is (2/3) × $6,000 = $4,000.

Audrey and Cindy, since they did not get the painting, will take money from the kitty. Their fair shares of the painting are equal to 1/3 of the amount of their respective bids.

Audrey bid $4,200 on the painting, so she is entitled to 1/3 of $4,200, which is $1,400. So, she takes $1,400 from the kitty.

Image 6.4.6: A FRIEND IN NEED

Cindy bid $5,100 on the painting, so she is entitled to 1/3 of $5,100, which is $1,700. So, she takes $1,700 from the kitty.

The kitty originally contained $4,000. After Audrey and Cindy each removed their shares, $900 remained. That $900 is divided equally among all three people, so each of them receives $300.

At this point, the method of sealed bids has taken care of the division of the painting:

- Audrey's share: $1,400 + $300 = $1,700

- Brian's share: painting − $4,000 + $300 = painting − $3,700

- Cindy's share: $1,700 + $300 = $2,000

The same procedure will be used with the sculpture.

Cindy is the high bidder, so she will get the sculpture.

There are three people involved in this division, so Cindy must place 2/3 of her $7,500 bid into the kitty, which is $(2/3) \times \$7,500 = \$5,000$.

Audrey and Brian, since they did not get the sculpture, will take money from the kitty. Their fair shares of the painting are equal to 1/3 of the amount of their respective bids.

Image 6.4.7

Audrey bid $6,600 on the sculpture, so she is entitled to 1/3 of $6,600, which is $2,200. So, she takes $2,200 from the kitty.

Brian bid $4,800 on the sculpture, so he is entitled to 1/3 of $4,800, which is $1,600. So, he takes $1,600 from the kitty.

This leaves the kitty with $5,000 − $2,200 − $1,600 = $1,200, which is divided equally among the three people. So, each of them receives $400.

With regard to the sculpture:

- Audrey's share: $2,200 + $400 = $2,600
- Brian's share: $1,600 + $400 = $2,000
- Cindy's share: sculpture − $5,000 + $400 = sculpture − $4,600

Finally, we combine the results of dividing the two items to obtain the final distribution.

	PAINTING	SCULPTURE	TOTAL
Audrey	$1,700	$2,600	$4,300
Brian	Painting−$3,700	$2,000	Painting−$1,700
Cindy	$2,000	Sculpture−$4,600	Sculpture−$2,600

To complete the fair division of these items, Brian keeps the painting and pays $1,700 to Audrey, while Cindy gets the sculpture and pays $2,600 to Audrey.

SECTION 6.4 EXERCISES

1. Two friends want to share the last cookie. Describe how it may be divided using the divider-chooser method.

2. Assume Brian and Daryl use the bottom-up strategy to divide the different types of sports cards listed below, and Brian gets to choose first. What items will each person receive?

image 6.4.8

BRIAN	DARYL
Hockey	Football
Football	Baseball
Baseball	Basketball
Basketball	Hockey

3. Assume Brian and Daryl use the bottom-up strategy to divide the different types of sports cards listed below, and Daryl gets to choose first. What items will each person receive?

BRIAN	DARYL
Hockey	Football
Football	Baseball
Baseball	Basketball
Basketball	Hockey

4. Assume Alvin and Simon use the bottom-up strategy to divide the items listed below, and Alvin gets to choose first. What items will each person receive?

ALVIN	SIMON
Boat	Car
Truck	Truck
Car	Boat
Computer	TV
Furniture	Computer
TV	Furniture

5. Assume Alvin and Simon use the bottom-up strategy to divide the items listed below, and Simon gets to choose first. What items will each person receive?

Alvin	Simon
Boat	Car
Truck	Truck
Car	Boat
Computer	TV
Furniture	Computer
TV	Furniture

6. Butch and Droopy must make a fair division of the following objects using the Adjusted Winner Procedure, and they assign points as shown.

	Point Allocations	
Item	Butch	Droopy
Dynamite	50	10
Sports Car	30	60
Gold Coins	20	30

Butch will end up with the dynamite and a fraction of the gold coins. What fraction of the gold coins will he get?

7. Labor and management are negotiating the following items. Using the Adjusted Winner Procedure, they assign points as shown.

	Point Allocations	
Issue	Labor	Management
Benefits	45	50
Salary	35	40
Vacation	20	10

Labor will be awarded all of the vacation issues and a percentage of the salary issues. What percentage of the salary issues will Labor get?

8. Jack and Diane must make a fair division of the following possessions using the Adjusted Winner Procedure, and they assign points as shown.

	Point Allocations	
Item	Jack	Diane
Horse Farm	49	16
Urban Condo	16	63
Houseboat	35	21

Jack will end up with the Horse Farm and a percentage of the value of the Houseboat. What percentage of the Houseboat will he get?

9. In the process of a divorce, Jeff and Charlotte are going to use the method of sealed bids to determine who will get their car. Jeff bids $24,000 and Charlotte bids $21,500, so Jeff will get the car. How much will he have to pay Charlotte in order to keep the division fair?

Image 6.4.9

10. Donny and Marie have decided to go their separate ways, and each can currently claim joint ownership of a specially designed custom stage set. Using the method of sealed bids, Donny says the set is worth $10,000, while Marie thinks it is worth $12,000. As the higher bidder, Marie gets the set. How much must she pay to Donny to make the division fair?

11. Peter, Edward, and Rose have decided they no longer want to be business partners, and they have agreed to use the method of sealed bids to allow for one of them to buy the business from the others. Peter bids $90,000 for the business, Edward bids $120,000, and Rose says the business is worth $195,000. How much must Rose pay to Peter and Edward to keep the business for herself, and make the division fair?

12. Three brothers will use the method of sealed bids to divide the following items. What will the final distribution be?

Item	David	Ethan	Frank
Car	11,400	13,500	10,200
Boat	9,300	7,500	8,400

13. The semester has ended, and three roommates need to divide two items—an old couch and a fairly new television. They will use the method of sealed bids, and each person puts forth a bid on each item, as follows.

Item	Mickey	Willie	Ted
Couch	90	120	78
TV	330	414	480

What will be the final distribution of these items?

14. A singing quartet has broken up. The four members will use the method of sealed bids to divide their private plane and tour bus, with the bids as indicated below. What will the final distribution be?

Item	Soprano	Alto	Tenor	Bass
Plane	76,000	80,000	68,000	72,000
Bus	52,000	48,000	64,000	68,000

ANSWERS TO SECTION 6.4 EXERCISES

1. They should flip a coin to determine the person who will cut (or break) the cookie. Then, the other person can select either of the two pieces.

2. Brian will get the football and hockey cards.
   Daryl will get the baseball and basketball cards.

3. Daryl will get the football and basketball cards.
   Brian will get the hockey and baseball cards.

4. Alvin will end up with the truck, the boat, and the furniture.
   Simon will end up with the car, the TV, and the computer.

5. Simon will get the truck, the car, and the TV.
   Alvin will get the boat, the computer, and the furniture.

6. 4/5

7. Labor will get 14/15 (about 93%) of the salary they desire. Management will get 1/15 of the salary demands.

8. 62.5%

9. $11,375

10. $5,500

11. Rose pays $50,000 to Peter and $60,000 to Edward.

12. David will get the boat and pay $1,500.
    Ethan will get the car and pay $5,600.
    Frank will receive $7,100.

13. Mickey will get $172.
    Willie will get the couch and receive $90.
    Ted will get the television and pay $262.

14. Soprano will get $36,000.
    Alto will get the plane and pay $44,000.
    Tenor will get $37,000.
    Bass will get the bus and pay $29,000.

6.5 Carving Up the Turkey: Apportionment

Apportionment

Apportionment is the process of dividing something into shares that are proportional to the characteristics of the situation. An example of this is the US House of Representatives. In the House, states with higher populations are given more representatives than states with lower populations.

Solving an apportionment problem should involve an unbiased and repeatable process. A biased process would disproportionately favor one political party or state, and an example of a non-repeatable process would be pulling the results from a hat, as this approach would be unlikely to produce the same results in consecutive attempts. While there are a few different unbiased and repeatable processes that can be used, we will focus our study on a method proposed by the first secretary of the treasury of the United States, Alexander Hamilton.

First, however, we need to establish a few definitions.

Population: The total number of items that need to be represented. In a population apportionment, this is the total population of the group under consideration.

House Size: The number of items that need to be divided. In a population apportionment, this is the number of seats in the House.

Standard Divisor: (Population)/(House Size). In a population apportionment, this is the number of people each member of the House represents.

Quota: (Designated Portion of the Population)/(Standard Divisor). The quota for a designated portion of the population is the number of items from the House that are allocated to that portion. Unless this calculation yields whole numbers for each of the disjoint portions, the decimal values must be considered to ensure all the items in the House are awarded. We cannot, however, award more items than the total number in the House.

Now, let's take a look at an example of an apportionment problem.

EXAMPLE 1:

A 17-member county commission is composed of representatives from four small towns in the county. Representatives are apportioned based upon the number of residents in those towns. Shelby has 800 residents, Cedar Lake has 4000 residents, Lake Dale has 2400 residents, and Lowell has a population of 6400. How many representatives will be allocated to each of the towns?

SOLUTION: First, we need to know the total population in the county. Adding together the populations of the 4 towns, we find that the county has a population of 13,600 people.

The "House size" is simply the 17 members of the county commission.

So here, the standard divisor is $13{,}600/17 = 800$. In other words, there is one commissioner for every 800 people in the county.

Now, we find the quota for each town. The quota for Shelby is $800/800 = 1$. That is, Shelby is apportioned 1 representative.

The quota for Cedar Lake is $4000/800 = 5$, the quota for Lake Dale is $2400/800 = 3$, and the quota for Lowell is $6400/800 = 8$.

We have determined that the final apportionment for the 17-seat county commission includes 1 representative from Shelby, 5 from Cedar Lake, 3 from Lake Dale, and 8 from Lowell.

In the example above, the quotas all worked out to be whole numbers. Unfortunately, that rarely happens. If the calculations for the quotas do not work out to be whole numbers, the decimal portions of the quota calculations must be considered to account for the exact number of items in the "House."

EXAMPLE 2:

The math department at a local college has hired two new faculty members. Together, these new faculty members will teach a total of 10 sections of algebra, calculus, and liberal arts math. The department chair is not sure about the number of sections of each course to assign to these new teachers, so she has gathered some data about student enrollment. A total of 220 students are projected to enroll in those courses in the following manner:

Course	Enrollment
Algebra	103
Calculus	34
Liberal Arts Math	83

Solution: To determine the number of sections of each course that should be offered, we start by calculating the standard divisor.

Standard Divisor = (population)/(house size)

Since the population (number of students) is 220, and the house size (number of sections) is 10, the standard divisor for this example will be 220/10 = 22.

To find the quota for each class, divide the corresponding class population by the standard divisor. Using the numbers from our enrollment data, we have the following:

Course	Quota
Algebra	103/22 = 4.68
Calculus	34/22 = 1.55
Liberal Arts Math	83/22 = 3.77

Since the department chair cannot offer fractions of sections, these quotas will have to be modified to determine the number of sections to offer.

Rounding might seem like a reasonable method for determining the number of sections. However, if we round each quota to the nearest whole number, the department will offer five sections of algebra, two sections of calculus, and four sections of liberal arts math. Unfortunately, this adds up to 11 sections, and the two new instructors cannot cover that many.

For one possible solution, the department chair might decide a calculus class of 34 students is too large and make certain there are two sections of calculus. Then, for the other eight sections, because there are more students enrolled in algebra, she may create five sections of algebra and three sections of liberal arts math.

This may be a reasonable approach, but another person may approach the situation differently. A standard, repeatable process is needed to fairly determine the sections that should be offered.

The Hamilton Method

Alexander Hamilton devised a method of dealing with fractional quotas, which he called the **method of largest fractions**. Using the language associated with the House of Representatives, this process involves three steps:

1. Determine the **quota** for each state by dividing the state's population by the standard divisor. Retain at least two decimal places in each quota.

2. Drop the fractional part of the quota and assign each state the number of seats shown by the whole number. This is referred to as the number of **automatic seats**.

3. If this does not fill all of the seats in the House, then the remaining seats (called **surplus seats**) are given out, one at a time, to the states with the largest fractional parts—by comparing the decimal part of the quotas.

Let's apply the Hamilton Method to Example 2. We will find the quota for each class, and then drop the fractional part (round it down) to determine the number of automatic seats.

Course	Quota	Automatic Seats
Algebra	$103/22 = 4.68$	4
Calculus	$34/22 = 1.55$	1
Liberal Arts Math	$83/22 = 3.77$	3

To begin with, there will be four sections of algebra, one section of calculus, and three sections of liberal arts math. This accounts for 8 of the 10 sections that will be taught by the new instructors. In order to assign the other two sections, we look at the fractional parts of the quotas.

Since it has the highest fractional part (0.77), Liberal Arts Math is given one of the two remaining sections. The next highest fractional part is 0.68 and is associated with Algebra. Thus, the final remaining section will be Algebra.

In this situation, using the Hamilton Method, the final apportionment is:

-   There will be five sections of Algebra.

-   There will be one section of Calculus.

-   There will be four sections of Liberal Arts Math.

When the Hamilton Method is used, every quota in the final apportionment is either equal to the number of automatic seats or is one number larger. The process that follows this condition for apportionment is said to satisfy the **quota rule**.

EXAMPLE 3:

A small country with three states has 40 seats in its Congress. The populations of the states are indicated below. Using the Hamilton Method, how many seats in the Congress will be apportioned to each state?

State	Population
Eastland	2400
Centralia	1950
Westerley	1475

Solution: First, we need to find the total population and the standard divisor. The total population for the country is 5825. Using the formula for the standard divisor, we find:

$$\text{Standard Divisor} = 5825/40 = 145.625$$

Next, we find the quota for each state, and round it down to determine the number of automatic seats for each state.

State	Quota	Automatic Seats
Eastland	$2400/145.625 = 16.48$	16
Centralia	$1950/145.625 = 13.39$	13
Westerley	$1475/145.625 = 10.13$	10

We start by apportioning 16 seats to Eastland, 13 to Centralia, and 10 to Westerley. This accounts for 39 of the 40 seats in Congress, so there is still one seat to be apportioned. It will be given to the state with the quota that has the largest fractional part, which is Eastland.

So, the final apportionment will be:

- Eastland gets 17 seats.

- Centralia gets 13 seats.

- Westerley gets 10 seats.

From a Different Point of View: Using Proportions

It's not a coincidence that the words "apportion" and "proportion" are similar; after all, they share the same root word. The quota calculations in an apportionment problem can be set up using a proportion in which the initial fraction corresponds to the ratio of the portion quota to the house size, and the second ratio is the portion population to the total population. That is:

$$\frac{\text{Portion Quota}}{\text{House Size}} = \frac{\text{Portion Population}}{\text{Total Population}}$$

Keep in mind, though, this is just for the quota calculations. The number of automatic seats is still determined by the whole number parts of the quotas, and the surplus seats get awarded to the states with the highest fractional parts of the quotas.

Revisiting the calculations for the previous example, we can see the house size is 40, Eastland's population is 2400, and the total population is 5825. So, Eastland's quota can be determined by:

$$\frac{\text{Eastland Quota}}{40} = \frac{2400}{5825}$$

Cross-multiplying and solving, we have:

$5825(\text{Eastland Quota}) = 40(2400)$

$\text{Eastland Quota} = 96{,}000/5825 = 16.48$

Similar proportions can be solved to find the quotas for Centralia and Westerly, and then award the surplus seats, as shown in the rest of the example.

Potential Problems

Apportionment procedures, although logical, may unintentionally create problems. One potential problem with Hamilton's method is that it does not guarantee each state will be given representation (for the U.S. House of Representatives, Article 1, Section 2 of the US Constitution does that). It is possible for a state to have a population that is below the standard divisor, and hence, have a quota less than one. Additionally, if it turns out that the fractional portion of that state's quota is not large enough, the state may not get one of the surplus seats remaining after the initial apportionment, and therefore be given no seats. If Hamilton's original method was still being used today, there are four states in the US with populations lower than what would be the standard divisor—Alaska, North Dakota, Vermont, and Wyoming. Each of those states, however, would have a fractional portion large enough to get one of the surplus seats.

Rather than using examples of the US House of Representatives, which would deal with 50 states and 435 seats, we will use examples with smaller numbers to demonstrate some of these problems.

EXAMPLE 4:

Use the Hamilton Method to determine the apportionment of 10 sections of algebra, calculus, and liberal arts math, based on the estimated demand for each course as follows:

COURSE	ENROLLMENT
Algebra	124
Calculus	13
Liberal Arts Math	83

SOLUTION: The total number of students is 220, and there are to be 10 sections. So, the standard divisor is 220/10 = 22.

Finding the quota for each class, and then dropping the fractional part to determine the number of automatic seats, we have:

COURSE	QUOTA	AUTOMATIC SEATS
Algebra	$124/22 = 5.64$	5
Calculus	$13/22 = 0.59$	0
Liberal Arts Math	$83/22 = 3.77$	3

To begin with, there will be five sections of Algebra and three sections of Liberal Arts Math, but no section of Calculus. Since Algebra and Liberal Arts Math have the two highest fractional parts, those courses will each get one of the two remaining sections. No section of Calculus will be offered.

The final apportionment will be:

- Six sections of Algebra
- No sections of Calculus
- Four sections of Liberal Arts Math

In this scenario, there is more demand for extra sections of Algebra and Liberal Arts Math than there is for one section of Calculus.

The Alabama Paradox

A paradox is a situation that seems logistically impossible but can still happen. Based on the results of the 1880 Census, it was discovered that adding a seat to the House of Representatives could actually cause a state (Alabama) to *lose* a seat. Logically, it seems as if the new seat would go to the state with the next highest fractional part. In reality, however, the extra seat changes the standard divisor, which causes the fractional parts of the quotas to change as well. Because this situation involved the State of Alabama, it is called the **Alabama Paradox**.

Image 6.5.1

EXAMPLE 5:

Use the Hamilton Method to apportion 29 seats to four states with the following populations:

STATE	POPULATION
Eastland	150
Centralia	122
Mountania	38
Westerley	109

SOLUTION: First, find the total population and the standard divisor.

$$\text{Total Population/Number of Seats} = 419/29 = 14.448$$

Next, find the quota for each state and round it down to determine the number of automatic seats.

STATE	QUOTA	AUTOMATIC SEATS
Eastland	$150/14.448 = 10.38$	10
Centralia	$122/14.448 = 8.44$	8
Mountania	$38/14.448 = 2.63$	2
Westerley	$109/14.448 = 7.54$	7

Start by apportioning 10 seats to Eastland, 8 to Centralia, 2 to Mountania, and 7 to Westerley. This accounts for 27 of the 29 seats, so there are still two seats to be apportioned. They will be given to the two states with the largest fractional parts, which are Mountania (0.63) and Westerley (0.54).

The final apportionment will be as follows:

- Eastland gets 10 seats.
- Centralia gets 8 seats.
- Mountania gets 3 seats.
- Westerley gets 8 seats.

Now, using the exact same populations, let's see what happens when we add another seat to the House.

EXAMPLE 6:

Use the Hamilton Method to apportion 30 seats to four states with the following populations:

STATE	POPULATION
Eastland	150
Centralia	122
Mountania	38
Westerley	109

SOLUTION: Since there are now 30 seats, the standard divisor has changed:

$$\text{Total Population/Number of Seats} = 419/30 = 13.967$$

Next, find the quota for each state and round it down to determine the number of automatic seats.

STATE	QUOTA	AUTOMATIC SEATS
Eastland	$150/13.967 = 10.74$	10
Centralia	$122/13.967 = 8.74$	8
Mountania	$38/13.967 = 2.72$	2
Westerley	$109/13.967 = 7.80$	7

Start by apportioning 10 seats to Eastland, 8 to Centralia, 2 to Mountania, and 7 to Westerley. This accounts for 27 of the 30 seats, so there are still three seats to be apportioned. The highest fractional parts belong to Westerley (0.80), Eastland (0.74), and Centralia (0.74), so those states will get the three additional seats. This final apportionment will be:

- Eastland gets 11 seats.
- Centralia gets 9 seats.
- Mountania gets 2 seats.
- Westerley gets 8 seats.

Comparing the results of Examples 5 and 6, by adding a seat to the House and without changing the populations, Mountania has actually *lost* a seat. The Alabama Paradox occurs because increasing the number of seats increases the fair share for larger states faster than it does for smaller states.

The Population Paradox

Another curious case that can occur with apportionment is the possibility of a state with an *increasing* population actually losing a seat to a state with a *decreasing* population. This is referred to as the **Population Paradox**.

EXAMPLE 7:

Use the Hamilton Method to apportion 100 seats for the following four states.

STATE	POPULATION
Eastland	34,300
Centralia	20,050
Mountania	1,250
Westerley	19,400

SOLUTION: The standard divisor will be 75,000/100 = 750.

Next, find the quota for each state and round it down to determine the number of automatic seats.

STATE	QUOTA	AUTOMATIC SEATS
Eastland	34,300/750 = 45.73	45
Centralia	20,050/750 = 26.73	26
Mountania	1,250/750 = 1.67	1
Westerley	19,400/750 = 25.87	25

Start by apportioning 45 seats to Eastland, 26 to Centralia, 1 to Mountania, and 25 to Westerley. This accounts for 97 of the 100 seats, so there are still three seats to be apportioned. They will be given to the states with the largest fractional parts, which are Westerley (0.87), Eastland (0.73), and Centralia (0.73).

The final apportionment will be:

- Eastland gets 46 seats.
- Centralia gets 27 seats.
- Mountania gets 1 seat.
- Westerley gets 26 seats.

Over time, the populations of these states change, and a new apportionment is calculated.

EXAMPLE 8:

Use the Hamilton Method to apportion 100 seats for the following four states.

State	Population
Eastland	36,500
Centralia	20,100
Mountania	1,245
Westerley	19,420

Solution: Comparing these numbers with Example 7, we can see that the populations of Eastland, Centralia, and Westerley have increased, while the population of Mountania has decreased.

The new standard divisor is $77,265/100 = 772.65$

Find the quota for each state and round it down to determine the number of automatic seats.

State	Quota	Automatic Seats
Eastland	$36,500/772.65 = 47.24$	47
Centralia	$20,100/772.65 = 26.01$	26
Mountania	$1,245/772.65 = 1.61$	1
Westerley	$19,420/772.65 = 25.13$	25

Start by apportioning 47 seats to Eastland, 26 to Centralia, 1 to Mountania, and 25 to Westerley. This accounts for 99 of the 100 seats, so there is still one seat to be apportioned. Since Mountania has the highest fractional part (0.61), it will be given the remaining seat.

The final apportionment will be as follows:

- Eastland gets 47 seats.
- Centralia gets 26 seats.
- Mountania gets 2 seats.
- Westerley gets 25 seats.

Comparing the results of Examples 7 and 8, even though the populations of Centralia and Westerley are increasing, they have each *lost* a seat. The population of Mountania is actually decreasing, but it has *gained* a seat. Because the total population changed, the standard divisor changed, and this resulted in the fractional parts of the quotas changing as well. Because of this change, the extra seats got distributed differently.

The New State Paradox

A third paradox, the **New State Paradox**, is a bit more complicated. It can occur when new states are added to the House, and a proportional number of seats are added with them. Theoretically, the new states would likely get all of the new seats, and the other apportioned seats would remain the same. However, due to the changes in the divisors and decimal portions of the quotas used, it is possible for an existing state (other than a new one) to *gain* a seat.

EXAMPLE 9:

A homeowner's association (HOA) consists of two neighborhoods: the 296-resident Maplewood Acres and the 105-resident Oakey Oaks. Using Hamilton's Method, how are the 40 seats on the HOA Board apportioned?

Solution: There are a total of 401 residents for 40 seats. So, the standard divisor is $401/40 = 10.025$. The corresponding quota for each neighborhood is:

Neighborhood	Quota	Automatic Seats
Maplewood	$296/10.025 = 29.53$	29
Oakey Oaks	$105/10.025 = 10.47$	10

With the largest fractional portion of the quotas, Maplewood Acres would be given the one extra seat.

- Maplewood Acres gets 30 seats
- Oakey Oaks gets 10 seats

Now, let's look at what can happen when a couple of new neighborhoods are added to the HOA.

EXAMPLE 10:

The HOA from Example 9 invites two new neighborhoods to join: The 52-resident Twin Pines and the 50-resident Ashville. With 102 new residents, the HOA adds 10 more seats to its board. Using the Hamilton Method, what is the new apportionment of the HOA?

Solution: There are now a total of 503 residents for 50 seats. So, the standard divisor is now $503/50 = 10.06$. The corresponding quota for each neighborhood is:

Neighborhood	Quota	Automatic Seats
Maplewood	$296/10.06 = 29.42$	29
Oakey Oaks	$105/10.06 = 10.44$	10
Twin Pines	$52/10.06 = 5.17$	5
Ashville	$50/10.06 = 4.97$	4

With the largest fractional portions of the quotas, Ashville gets one surplus seat and Oakey Oaks gets the other.

- Maplewood Acres gets 29 seats
- Oakey Oaks gets 11 seats
- Twin Pines gets 5 seats
- Ashville gets 5 seats

Comparing the results of Examples 9 and 10, we see that the addition of two neighborhoods to the HOA changed both the overall population and the number of seats. Since each seat on the HOA Board originally represented approximately 10 residents, adding 10 more seats for the 102 new residents is a reasonable proportional increase. Twin Pines and Ashville rightfully got the new seats they deserved, but the extra seat previously given to Maplewood Acres ended up going to Oakey Oaks.

After going through a few different apportionment methods, Congress finally adopted Hamilton's method in 1852. However, since 1940, the United States House of Representatives has used the **Huntington-Hill Method** for apportionment. Although not covered in this book, more information about the Hill-Huntington Method can be found in the vast Wikipedia archives at http://en.wikipedia. org/wiki/Huntington-Hill_method.

As a final note on the topic of apportionment, mathematicians **Michel L. Balinski** and **H. Peyton Young** established **Balinski and Young's Theorem,** which states there is no method of apportionment that satisfies the quota rule and also avoids these paradoxes.

SECTION 6.5 EXERCISES

1. Four brothers, Dave, Dan, Jim, and Ron, have purchased a 90-unit storage building. They have decided to divide the units based on the amounts each of them invested. Dave put up $3000, Dan chipped in $6000, Jim provided $8000, and Ron invested $1000. How many units will each brother get?

2. A small country with three regions has 25 seats in its legislature. The population of each region is as follows:

   - Eastern = 4,680
   - Central = 2,064
   - Western = 1,431

    a. What is the standard divisor? Round your answer to the nearest thousandth.

    b. What is the quota for each region? Round your answer to the nearest hundredth.

    c. Using the Hamilton Method, how many seats in the legislature will be apportioned to each region?

3. A state with 13 seats to be apportioned is to be divided into three districts with the following populations:

- Eastern: 16,280
- Central: 13,490
- Western: 9,560

    a. What is the standard divisor? Round your answer to the nearest thousandth.

    b. What is the quota for each district? Round your answer to the nearest hundredth.

    c. Using the Hamilton Method, how many seats will be apportioned to each district?

4. Three friends have pooled their finances to buy 20 bottles of vintage wine. They decide to divide the bottles using the Hamilton Method, based on the amount of money each person contributed.

Image 6.5.2

- Jerod: $295
- Michael: $205
- Rob: $390

    a. What is the standard divisor? Round your answer to the nearest thousandth.

    b. What is the quota for each person? Round your answer to the nearest hundredth.

    c. How many bottles of wine will be apportioned to each person?

5. A high school government is made up of 50 seats. The populations of the classes are as follows:

- Seniors = 275
- Juniors = 767
- Sophomores = 465
- Freshmen = 383

    a. What is the standard divisor? Round your answer to the nearest thousandth.

    b. What is the quota for each class? Round your answer to the nearest hundredth.

    c. Using the Hamilton Method, how many seats will be apportioned to each class?

6. A country has four territories with the populations listed below, and currently has 315 seats in the legislature.

   - Northalia has a population of 896
   - Southville has a population of 426
   - Eastburgh has a population of 1,166
   - Westonia has a population of 667

   a. Using the Hamilton Method, how will those 315 seats be apportioned?

   b. The legislature is changing, and one new seat will be added. Using the same populations and the Hamilton Method, how will the new 316-seat legislature be apportioned?

   c. Is there a paradox? If so, what type?

7. A country has the following four territories with the populations listed below, and currently has 149 seats in the legislature.

   - Northalia has a population of 896
   - Southville has a population of 426
   - Eastburgh has a population of 1,166
   - Westonia has a population of 667

   a. Using the Hamilton Method, how will those 149 seats be apportioned?

   b. The legislature is changing, and one new seat will be added. Using the same populations and the Hamilton Method, how will the new 150-seat legislature be apportioned?

   c. Is there a paradox? If so, what type?

8. A country has the following four states, and 50 seats in the legislature.

	OLD CENSUS	NEW CENSUS
Northalia	27,200	28,102
Southville	18,600	19,307
Eastburgh	11,400	11,404
Westonia	6,250	6,244

   a. Using the old census data and the Hamilton method, how will the 50 seats be apportioned?

   b. Using the new census data and the Hamilton method, how will the 50 seats be apportioned?

   c. Is there a paradox? If so, what type?

9. A country has the following four states, and 200 seats in the legislature.

	OLD CENSUS	NEW CENSUS
Northalia	93,700	94,502
Southville	35,850	35,853
Eastburgh	56,850	56,859
Westonia	3,450	3,448

    a. Using the old census data and the Hamilton Method, how will the 200 seats be apportioned?

    b. Using the new census data and the Hamilton Method, how will the 200 seats be apportioned?

    c. Is there a paradox? If so, what type?

10. A homeowner's association consists of three neighborhoods, with the following resident counts:

	RESIDENTS
Rosedale	124
Sunnyville	366
Talon	218

    a. Using the Hamilton Method, how will the 20 Board seats be apportioned?

    b. If the association votes to add the 54-resident neighborhood of Underwood and two additional seats on the Board, how will the apportionment change?

    c. Is there a paradox? If so, what type?

11. The United States House of Representatives uses which of the following methods of apportionment?

    a. Randomly assigning the number of seats given to each state.

    b. The Hamilton Method

    c. The Huntington-Hill Method

    d. None of these

ANSWERS TO SECTION 6.5 EXERCISES

1. Dave will get 15 units, Dan will get 30 units, Jim will get 40 units, and Ron will get 5 units.

2. a. 327.000

    b. Eastern = 14.31, Central = 6.31, Western = 4.38

    c. Eastern = 14, Central = 6, Western = 5

3. a. 3,025.385
    b. Eastern = 5.38, Central = 4.46, Western = 3.16
    c. Eastern = 5, Central = 5, Western = 3

4. a. 44.500
    b. Jerod = 6.63, Michael = 4.61, Rob = 8.76
    c. Jerod = 7, Michael = 4, Rob = 9

5. a. 37.800
    b. Seniors = 7.28, Juniors = 20.29, Sophomores = 12.30, Freshmen = 10.13
    c. Seniors = 7, Juniors = 20, Sophomores = 13, Freshmen = 10

6. a. Northalia = 89, Southville = 43, Eastburgh = 116, Westonia = 67
    b. Northalia = 90, Southville = 42, Eastburgh = 117, Westonia = 67
    c. Yes. Alabama Paradox

7. a. Northalia = 42, Southville = 20, Eastburgh = 55, Westonia = 32
    b. Northalia = 43, Southville = 20, Eastburgh = 55, Westonia = 32
    c. There is no paradox.

8. a. Northalia = 21, Southville = 15, Eastburgh = 9, Westonia = 5
    b. Northalia = 21, Southville = 15, Eastburgh = 9, Westonia = 5
    c. There is no paradox.

9. a. Northalia = 99, Southville = 38, Eastburgh = 60, Westonia = 3
    b. Northalia = 99, Southville = 37, Eastburgh = 60, Westonia = 4
    c. Yes. Population Paradox

10. a. Rosedale = 4, Sunnyville = 10, Talon = 6
    b. Rosedale = 4, Sunnyville = 11, Talon = 6, Underwood = 1
    c. Yes. New State Paradox—Sunnyville did nothing and gained a seat.

11. c

CHAPTER 6 CREDITLINES

IMG 6.0.1: Copyright © 2011 Depositphotos/zentilia.

IMG 6.1.1: "HAMILTON, Alexander-Treasury (BEP engraved portrait)," http://commons.wikimedia.org/wiki/File:HAMILTON,_Alexander-Treasury_(BEP_engraved_portrait).jpg. Copyright in the Public Domain.

IMG 6.1.2: "Proposed Electoral College 2012," http://commons.wikimedia.org/wiki/File:Proposed_Electoral_College_2012.svg. Copyright in the Public Domain.

IMG 6.1.3: "Perikles ostracon," http://commons.wikimedia.org/wiki/File:Perikles_ostracon.svg. Copyright in the Public Domain.

IMG 6.2.1: Copyright © 2011 Depositphotos/elenathewise.

IMG 6.2.2: Copyright © 2012 Depositphotos/anastad.

IMG 6.2.3: Copyright © 2015 Depositphotos/103tnn.

IMG 6.2.4: Copyright © 2010 Depositphotos/VisualGeneration.

IMG 6.4.1: Copyright © 2012 Depositphotos/Lusoimages.

IMG 6.4.2: Copyright © 2014 Depositphotos/scanrail.

IMG 6.4.3: Copyright © 2011 Depositphotos/Baloncici.

IMG 6.4.4: Copyright © 2013 Depositphotos/Willard.

IMG 6.4.5: Copyright © 2012 Depositphotos/lifeonwhite.

IMG 6.4.6: Cassius Marcellus Coolidge, "A Friend in Need," http://commons.wikimedia.org/wiki/File:A_Friend_in_Need_1903_C.M.Coolidge.jpg. Copyright in the Public Domain.

IMG 6.4.7: Copyright © 2014 Depositphotos/charmboyz.

IMG 6.4.8: Copyright © 2014 Depositphotos/amstockphoto.

IMG 6.4.9: Copyright © 2012 Depositphotos/ventanamedia.

IMG 6.5.1: Vectorportal, "Alabama Vector Map," http://www.vectorportal.com/subcategory/87/ALABAMA-VECTOR-MAP.eps/ifile/3396/detailtest.asp. Copyright © by VectorPortal. Reprinted with permission.

IMG 6.5.2: Copyright © 2010 Depositphotos/sumners.

INDEX

CPSIA information can be obtained
at www.ICGtesting.com
Printed in the USA
FSHW010034180820
73048FS

9 781516 589739